KT-231-311

Welcome to

HOW IT WORKS

BOOK OF

AMAZING ANIMALS

From their single-celled origins, through the Cambrian explosion and right up to the emergence of recognisable fauna and flora, the organisms that populate our world have continually pushed their limits – adapting and developing organs, limbs and behaviours in response to environmental and social pressures – and demonstrate a tenacity for life that really is sublime. In celebration of the sheer diversity of animals on Earth today, we've gathered together some of the most amazing creatures and gotten right under their skins so we can show you exactly how they work. Creatures of the deep, the land, the air – all are explored and their natural talents explained. Beautifully illustrated diagrams detail everything from the tactics of a lion attack to the anatomy of a crocodile, while high impact photography puts you face to face with living wonders. This second revised edition is packed full of even more facts and tackles some of the greatest animal mysteries, to show you just how amazing the animal kingdom really is.

HOW IT WORKS
BOOK OF
AMAZING ANIMALS

Imagine Publishing Ltd
Richmond House
33 Richmond Hill
Bournemouth
Dorset BH2 6EZ
☎ +44 (0) 1202 586200
Website: www.imagine-publishing.co.uk
Twitter: @Books_Imagine
Facebook: www.facebook.com/ImagineBookazines

Head of Publishing
Aaron Asadi

Head of Design
Ross Andrews

Editor
Jon White

Senior Art Editor
Greg Whittaker

Designer
Abbi Denney

Cover images
Richard Bartz 07, Thinkstock, Ansgar Walk 1996, sxc.hu, DK Images

Printed by
William Gibbons, 26 Planetary Road, Willenhall, West Midlands, WV13 3XT

Distributed in the UK & Eire by
Imagine Publishing Ltd, www.imagineshop.co.uk Tel 01202 586200

Distributed in Australia by
Gordon & Gotch, Equinox Centre, 18 Rodborough Road, Frenchs Forest,
NSW 2086. Tel + 61 2 9972 8800

Distributed in the Rest of the World by
Marketforce, Blue Fin Building, 110 Southwark Street, London, SE1 0SU

Disclaimer
The publisher cannot accept responsibility for any unsolicited material lost or damaged in the
post. All text and layout is the copyright of Imagine Publishing Ltd. Nothing in this bookazine may
be reproduced in whole or part without the written permission of the publisher. All copyrights are
recognised and used specifically for the purpose of criticism and review. Although the bookazine has
endeavoured to ensure all information is correct at time of print, prices and availability may change.
This bookazine is fully independent and not affiliated in any way with the companies mentioned herein.

How It Works Book of Amazing Animals Volume 1 Second Revised Edition
© 2014 Imagine Publishing Ltd

ISBN 978 1909 758 926

Part of the

HOW IT WORKS
bookazine series

IMAGINE
PUBLISHING

HOW IT WORKS BOOK OF AMAZING ANIMALS
CONTENTS

156

152

Mahdi Karim

© Thinkstock

Underwater wonders

© Corbis

Polar bears

The planet's weirdest animals

© Corbis

Micro monsters

© SPL

007

HOW IT WORKS BOOK OF AMAZING ANIMALS
CONTENTS

012
Nature's giants

040
Arctic wonders

068
Coral reefs

050
Sharks

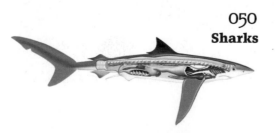

094
Honeybees

116
Life cycle of a frog

108
Crocs

Reptiles & amphibians

Mammals

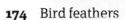

126
Killer whales

Owls
180

Birds

174
Bird feathers

© Thinkstock; DK Images; Alamy; Corbis; Science Photo Library

WONDERS OF THE ANIMAL KINGDOM

022
Komodo dragons

© Corbis

024
Weirdest animals

Armoured animals
032

Swarms
036

© Thinkstock

NATURE'S GIANTS

Taller, heavier, stronger – these are wild animals at large

Bigger is better. That's not just an expression, it's an evolutionary phenomenon called Cope's rule: animals tend to evolve into bigger animals. Over millions of years dinosaurs went from small reptiles into ground-shaking giants. After they went extinct, mammals became the dominant land animals and they too inexorably evolved from mouse-like critters into oversized behemoths such as a six-metre (20-foot) sloth Megatherium and the 12-ton-plus, horse-like Paraceratherium. When the ice ages came, the largest species were wiped out and smaller ones took over and started growing once again. The giant animals that exist today are just the latest swing of a pendulum that has been marking time over geological timescales.

Natural selection drives species to evolve larger bodies for several reasons. Being huge obviously makes it harder for you to be eaten by predators, but this is only part of it. The fiercest rivals most animals face are other members of their own species. The biggest males will be the ones to control the largest territories and have access to breeding females. Darwin thought the giraffe's long neck evolved so that it could reach the leaves on the tallest branches, but recent research has suggested that it may actually be because winning 'necking' contests is how males establish dominance over each other.

Eventually every species will reach a limit to its size. During the Carboniferous period around 300 million years ago, insects and other invertebrates grew to enormous sizes. There were dragonflies with 75-centimetre (30-inch) wingspans and a millipede-like creature called Arthropleura over two metres (6.6 feet) long.

But this was at a time when the oxygen concentration in the atmosphere was above 35 per cent, rather than the 21 per cent it is today. Eventually the oxygen level was so high that forests – and even swamps – caught fire with every lightning strike. As they burned, the oxygen in the air fell to much lower levels. Without sophisticated lungs and circulatory

410kg

WORLD'S BIGGEST BIG CAT

Hercules the liger (a cross between a lion and a tiger) weighs 410 kilograms (904 pounds) and stands 1.4 metres (4.6 feet) at the shoulder. He is 30 per cent bigger than the largest tiger.

DID YOU KNOW? *A single molar tooth from an elephant is the size of a house brick*

Dizzy spells

How do giraffes avoid the blood rushing to their head?

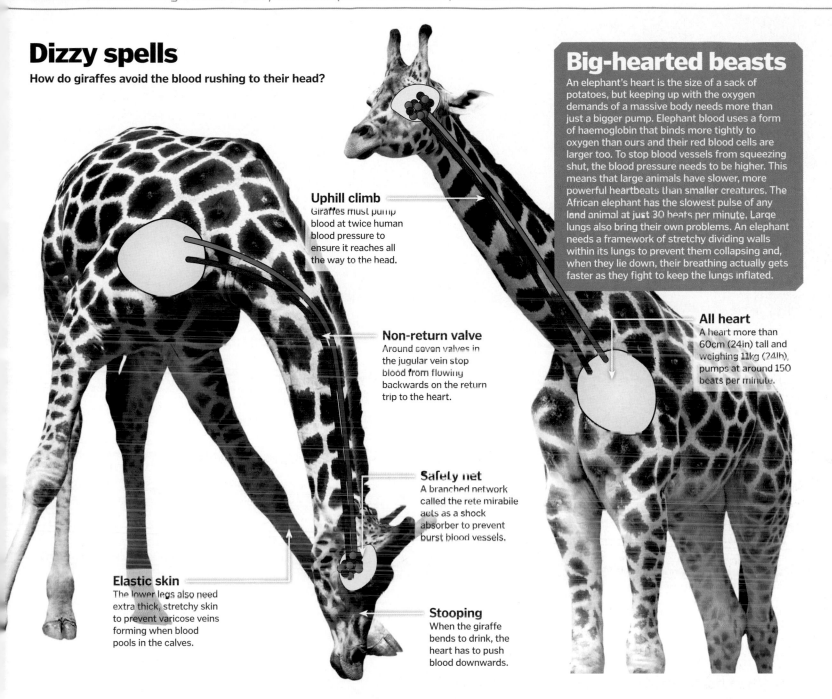

Uphill climb
Giraffes must pump blood at twice human blood pressure to ensure it reaches all the way to the head.

Non-return valve
Around seven valves in the jugular vein stop blood from flowing backwards on the return trip to the heart.

Safety net
A branched network called the rete mirabile acts as a shock absorber to prevent burst blood vessels.

Elastic skin
The lower legs also need extra thick, stretchy skin to prevent varicose veins forming when blood pools in the calves.

Stooping
When the giraffe bends to drink, the heart has to push blood downwards.

Big-hearted beasts

An elephant's heart is the size of a sack of potatoes, but keeping up with the oxygen demands of a massive body needs more than just a bigger pump. Elephant blood uses a form of haemoglobin that binds more tightly to oxygen than ours and their red blood cells are larger too. To stop blood vessels from squeezing shut, the blood pressure needs to be higher. This means that large animals have slower, more powerful heartbeats than smaller creatures. The African elephant has the slowest pulse of any land animal at just 30 beats per minute. Large lungs also bring their own problems. An elephant needs a framework of stretchy dividing walls within its lungs to prevent them collapsing and, when they lie down, their breathing actually gets faster as they fight to keep the lungs inflated.

All heart
A heart more than 60cm (24in) tall and weighing 11kg (24lb), pumps at around 150 beats per minute.

---

systems, these arthropod monsters simply couldn't get enough oxygen to sustain their massive bodies so they died out.

Even without such drastic environmental shifts, there are very real challenges for giant animals. Most predators generally eat animals smaller than themselves. This allows them to hunt abundant prey and achieve an easy kill with minimum risk to themselves. But carnivores heavier than about 21 kilograms (46 pounds) can't catch small animals fast enough to meet their food requirements. Instead they have to hunt quarry much larger than themselves. This is more dangerous and requires a radical shift in tactics. A large

carnivore also has to cope with irregular mealtimes, with long periods of starvation followed by a stomach-stretching blowout.

Herbivores, meanwhile, face challenges of their own. Plants are relatively poor in nutrients, so they need to eat a lot of them. Giant herbivores like elephants and rhinos can quickly overgraze an area if they don't constantly move on, and their large weight can compact the ground to the point where rainwater doesn't soak in properly and seeds find it difficult to become established. Elephants will uproot trees to get at the topmost leaves, turning savanna into grassland. Elephants can't survive on just grass though, so

large populations of elephants can become the agents of their own destruction.

A massive body also creates problems for reproduction. If the young are born too small, they are vulnerable to predators; born too large and the extended gestation period places too much strain on the mother. Elephants spend almost two years pregnant and giraffes must be born with much shorter necks in order to prevent complications during birth.

But if nature has shown us one thing, it's that obstacles are there to be overcome. Around the world in virtually every animal group, colossal creatures have risen to the challenge and stomped on it. Let's meet nature's giants… ✿

Hippos spend the majority of the day in rivers and lakes to escape the Sun, feeding on the banks in the cool of night

The perfect temperature

Large animals have intrinsic protection against the cold. The bigger you are, the more heat is generated by your metabolism. Kodiak brown bears don't hibernate in the winter to avoid the freezing temperatures – they do it because there isn't enough food to support their voracious appetite. Within a given species or genus, the larger variants are normally found in the coldest climates – the Siberian tiger is the largest tiger subspecies, for example.

But in hot climates, being large presents the opposite problem: how to get rid of that excess heat? Hippos spend the day in rivers or lakes and only venture out at night to graze. The southern white rhino spends the hottest part of the day wallowing in a mudhole and even tigers will take a dip in the river to cool off – one of the only large cats that does this. Elephants swim too, but when they are on the open savanna their ears act as natural radiators, pumping hot blood through thin skin to shed heat.

Mighty appetites

An elephant already has to spend between 16 and 18 hours of every day just eating – that's more than 80 per cent of its waking hours! There simply isn't time to eat any more food than that. A big part of the problem is that an elephant's digestion is quite inefficient. In fact, elephant dung still has 50 per cent of the nutrients left in it and so it's a viable food source for hornbills, baboons and dung beetles. Gorillas can't digest plant cellulose either, but they don't have the stomach capacity to just munch indiscriminately. Instead they use their nimble fingers and teeth to strip the edible parts off a plant, like fruit, bark and roots.

For large carnivores, the problem is catching enough food. Tigers are only successful once out of every 10-20 hunting trips. On average they catch just a single deer a week, so they need to be able to eat huge amounts at a single sitting.

POLAR BEAR
Daily food required:
2kg (4.4lb)
....
Single sitting portion:
120kg (265lb)

GREEN ANACONDA
Daily food required:
0.2kg (0.4lb)
....
Single sitting portion:
30kg (66lb)

TIGER
Daily food required:
6kg (13lb)
....
Single sitting portion:
40kg (88lb)

ELEPHANT
Daily food required:
150kg (330lb)
....
Single sitting portion:
212kg (467lb)

GORILLA
Daily food required:
18kg (40lb)
....
Single sitting portion:
6kg (13lb)

GIRAFFE
Daily food required:
34kg (75lb)
....
Single sitting portion:
11kg (24lb)

1. HEAVY

Giant Pacific octopus
Up to five metres (16 feet) across and weighing 50 kilograms (110 pounds), this ocean monster only lives up to five years.

2. HEAVIER

Ocean sunfish
Averaging a ton, this is the largest bony fish on the planet. Females lay 300 million eggs at a time – which is more than any other vertebrate.

3. HEAVIEST

Blue whale
Not just the largest animal alive today, but the largest animal to have ever lived, a blue whale is equivalent to the weight of about 30 elephants, ie 200 tons.

DID YOU KNOW? The giraffe has a prehensile tongue that is 0.5m (1.6ft) long! It's black to protect it from sunburn

Big game hunting

One of the biggest advantages of being large is that it protects you from predators. But if you are a predator yourself, extreme size can often be a disadvantage. The larger you are, the harder it is to sneak up on prey and the less manoeuvrable you are in comparison. Apex predators normally need huge hunting ranges to find enough food; golden eagles, for instance, patrol over 200 square kilometres (77 square miles) of moorland looking for carrion, fish and rodents, etc.

To overcome this, large predators need to be stealthy. Often they prefer to ambush their victims, rather than run them down. Anacondas lie in wait at watering holes, while brown bears will sit patiently in the river at the top of a salmon leap. Others rely on team tactics. Lions are famous for their group hunting techniques, but Philippine eagles also hunt in pairs, with one bird perching to distract a troop of monkeys, while the other swoops in from behind.

GREEN ANACONDA
Tactic: Constriction
Success rate: 1/5

AFRICAN LION
Tactic: Teamwork
Success rate: 4/5

KODIAK BEAR
Tactic: Patience and timing
Success rate: 3/5

TIGER
Tactic: Camouflage
Success rate: 3/5

PHILIPPINE EAGLE
Tactic: Distraction/ambush
Success rate: 2/5

Don't ever race a giraffe!

The legs of a giraffe are two metres (6.6 feet) long but almost half of this is actually the foot. The joint that functions as a knee is anatomically equivalent to a wrist or ankle. The giraffe balances on the tips of its toenails, but to support its weight these toenail hoofs are 30 centimetres (12 inches) across. Giraffes can gallop at 60 kilometres (37 miles) per hour for short periods, while elephants hit the red line at just 25 kilometres (16 miles) per hour.

Because of the way that their legs must be positioned to support the body weight, elephants have very poor leverage and use a single running gait. Long-distance running is a problem for many very large animals. Tigers, for example, can cover as much as 32 kilometres (20 miles) in a single night's hunting, but they do it at an easy walk. To catch prey they must sneak to within 10-20 metres (33-66 feet) of the victim before they are in pouncing range.

Like all ungulate animals (eg deer, goats, cows, etc) giraffes are digitigrade (ie they walk on tiptoes)

Anatomy of a giant

When you weigh between six and seven tons, just standing up is an incredible feat of engineering...

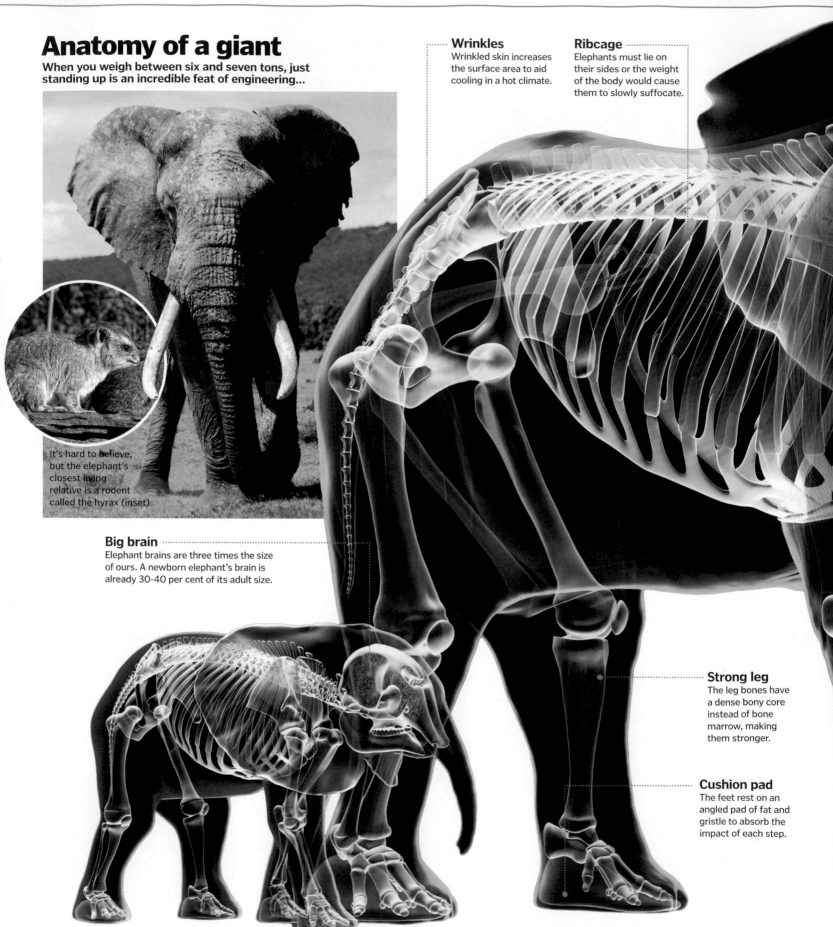

It's hard to believe, but the elephant's closest living relative is a rodent called the hyrax (inset)

Wrinkles
Wrinkled skin increases the surface area to aid cooling in a hot climate.

Ribcage
Elephants must lie on their sides or the weight of the body would cause them to slowly suffocate.

Big brain
Elephant brains are three times the size of ours. A newborn elephant's brain is already 30-40 per cent of its adult size.

Strong leg
The leg bones have a dense bony core instead of bone marrow, making them stronger.

Cushion pad
The feet rest on an angled pad of fat and gristle to absorb the impact of each step.

HEIGHT	3.5m	WATER DRUNK PER DAY (LITRES)	85	MAX SKIN THICKNESS	3.8cm
AVERAGE TOTAL WEIGHT	6 tons	TUSK WEIGHT	65kg	BRAIN WEIGHT	5kg

DID YOU KNOW? The white rhino has the widest nostrils of any land animal, with nasal passages larger than its brain!

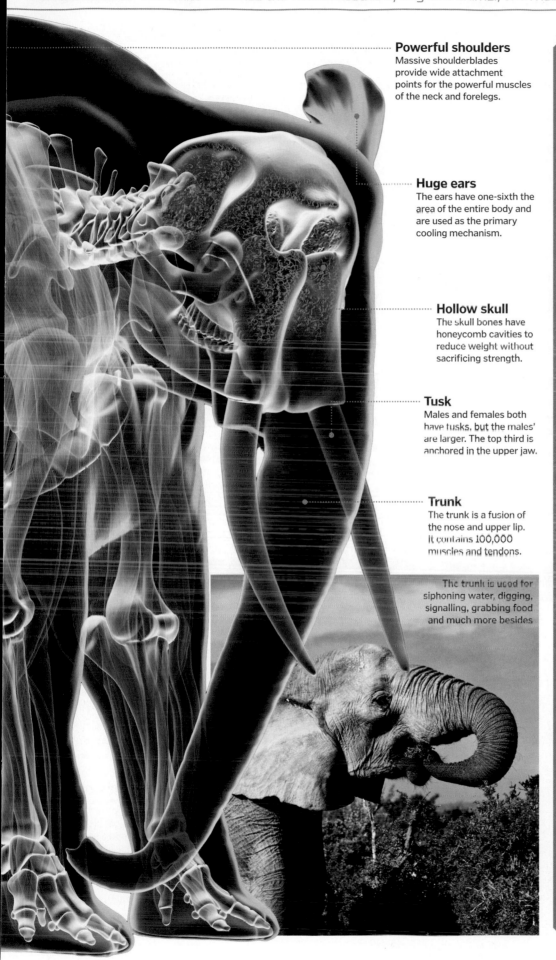

Powerful shoulders
Massive shoulderblades provide wide attachment points for the powerful muscles of the neck and forelegs.

Huge ears
The ears have one-sixth the area of the entire body and are used as the primary cooling mechanism.

Hollow skull
The skull bones have honeycomb cavities to reduce weight without sacrificing strength.

Tusk
Males and females both have tusks, but the males' are larger. The top third is anchored in the upper jaw.

Trunk
The trunk is a fusion of the nose and upper lip. It contains 100,000 muscles and tendons.

The trunk is used for siphoning water, digging, signalling, grabbing food and much more besides

More big beasts!

Hippopotamus
Hippos are more closely related to whales than they are to rhinos or elephants. They can weigh up to three tons and prefer to spend the day in the river, but on land they can easily outrun a human – so be wary!

Mandrill
The largest monkey, adult male mandrills can weigh over 35 kilograms (77 pounds). They eat mainly fruit, but also sometimes catch small animals and even deer, which they kill with a bite from their long canines.

Red kangaroo
The largest marsupial, red kangaroos can be taller than a man and weigh up to 90 kilograms (198 pounds). They are the only large animal that gets around by hopping. At full pelt, they can move at up to 71 kilometres (44 miles) per hour!

Southern elephant seal
They have the largest size difference between males and females of any land-breeding mammal: male elephant seals are six times heavier than females. A large adult male can weigh up to four tons. Their size has evolved because of brutal territorial contests with other males.

Saltwater crocodile
The largest reptile and also the most widely distributed crocodile species around the world. Males can reach over six metres (20 feet) long and weigh over a ton. They have the strongest bite of any animal alive – it's three and a half times stronger than a tiger's.

Chinese giant salamander
Giant salamanders can live for over 30 years and keep growing throughout their lifetime. Large specimens can be 1.5 metres (4.9 feet) long and weigh 50 kilograms (110 pounds). They have tiny eyes, but are very sensitive to vibration, which enables them to catch quick-moving fish and frogs.

Giant golden-crowned flying fox
Although tiny compared to the other animals here, this is the largest bat on Earth. It's under 1.2 kilograms (2.6 pounds), but can have a wingspan of 1.5 metres (4.9 feet). They mainly eat figs.

© DK Images; Thinkstock; Alamy; Corbis; Gregg Yan

Drug lord Pablo Escobar kept pet hippos on his Colombian ranch!

Komodo dragons taste the air to find their prey by flicking their tongues

Jellyfish stings fire with an acceleration of about 40,000 g!

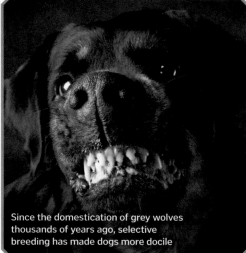

Since the domestication of grey wolves thousands of years ago, selective breeding has made dogs more docile

The planet's deadliest animals

If you go down to the woods today… you may not come out alive!

We don't live in a dog-eat-dog world. It's much more dangerous than that. Dog eat dog suggests an evenly matched fight, but animals in the wild prefer to attack from a position of overwhelming superiority. A snake that has a taste for mice can inject enough venom to kill 125 mice with a single bite, while an animal that relies on physical strength will aim for an instant kill by crushing the skull or slicing the throat.

The prey is fighting for its life and will put up the maximum possible struggle, but the predator is only hunting for its dinner and cannot afford even minor injuries to itself so it must strike hard and kill quickly.

Humans, however, are weak. Almost any animal our size could easily beat us in a fight. We protect ourselves by keeping away from most of

nature and using technology to protect ourselves. Most of the time this works. But you can't spend your whole life in a shark cage and animals carry their weapons with them all the time. So when accidental wild encounters do occur, the fight isn't likely to go our way.

There are lots of ways to rate the deadliness of an animal. The total number of human fatalities every year is one, but it doesn't take into account how rare the animal is, or where it lives. Brown bears kill more people than polar bears do, but that doesn't make the brown bear more deadly per se. It just means that a lot more people go hiking in Alaska than on the sea ice in the Arctic Circle. Official statistics can be misleading too. Shark attack figures tend to exaggerate the deaths from the easily identified species, such as the great white and the tiger shark and those that feed close

to the shore, where there are likely to be lots of witnesses. As you will see, the shark species probably responsible for the most human deaths has almost no confirmed kills to its name, precisely because it never leaves any witnesses…

Where an animal is venomous, rating the deadliness of its venom is very tricky. Venom toxicity is measured using the LD50 rating. This is the dose of venom, in milligrams per kilogram of body weight, required to kill 50 per cent of the mice in a sample. Mice are used because they are a convenient laboratory animal which can stand in for humans. But mice are also common prey for many snakes, scorpions and lizards and so have evolved a high degree of immunity to the venom of several species. The predator adapts to this by injecting ever-larger amounts of venom and this makes them even more dangerous to humans. So

3.4m

LARGEST EVER POLAR BEAR

In 1960 a polar bear was shot in Alaska that weighed over 1,000 kilograms (2,204 pounds)! Rearing up on its hind legs, it was almost twice the average height of a man at 3.4 metres (11.2 feet) tall!

DID YOU KNOW? Mosquitoes can't transmit HIV; the virus is quickly digested and never gets injected back into a host

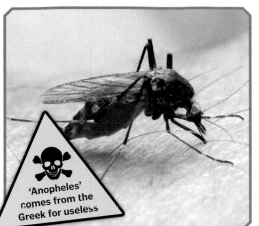

'Anopheles' comes from the Greek for useless

The polar bear is the largest land carnivore and its great size means it can overpower even large prey

75 per cent of attacks occur with cassowaries that have been fed by humans

According to the International Shark Attack Files, records of shark attacks on humans go back to the 16th Century

It takes 70 spider 'milkings' to make just one dose of antivenom

Black mambas are the world's fastest snakes, travelling at up to 19km/h (12mph)!

paradoxically, animals with low venom toxicity as measured by LD50 in mice, can be among the most lethal to humans.

The list we have compiled here contains ten of the very deadliest animals on the planet, covering as wide a range of different habitats and kill tactics as possible. Inevitably, we have had to leave out some very worthy runners-up. The Nile crocodile, for instance, eats about 320 people a year and tigers have killed 373,000 people since the beginning of the 19th century. The cape buffalo is also an extraordinarily aggressive animal that has probably killed more hunters than any other animal in Africa although there are not the records to back this up scientifically. Our list however, is a representative sample of the meanest and most deadly killers from across the whole of Mother Nature's realm. ✿

Hotspots for fatal animal attacks

India
Half of the world's snakebite deaths occur here – 11,000 a year!

Bangladesh
150 people are killed by tigers every year

Venezuela
Rabid vampire bats killed 38 people in 2008

New South Wales
148 severe shark attacks from 1876-2008

South Africa
Cape buffalos kill more hunters than any other big game

Australia
Home of the sea wasp, cassowary and funnel-web spider

SEA WASP JELLYFISH

The sting king

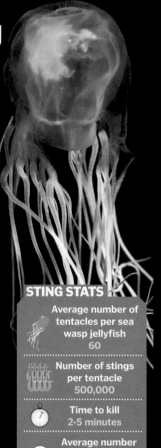

- **Size** 30cm (11.8in) body, 3m (9.8ft) tentacles
- **Habitat** Open water • **Location** Australasia
- **Diet** Prawns, small fish • **Kill tactic** Sting

Commonly known as the sea wasp, Chironex fleckeri is the largest and most deadly of the Cubozoa, or box jellyfish. In fact, it may be the most venomous creature in the world. Found off the northern coast of Australia and throughout the Indio-Pacific oceans, Sea wasps are predators, hunting small fish and shrimp, but their delicate bodies make it essential for them to immobilise their prey immediately. Their venom works on humans by causing red blood cells to leak potassium molecules, which disrupts the electrical signals that allow muscles to contract and so your heart stops beating. This works the same way as the lethal injection used for capital punishment.

Sea wasps can gather in shallow coastal waters in large numbers at certain times of year and their bodies are virtually transparent, making it easy to blunder into one. Treatment is possible but must be rapid. Unfortunately, victims often drown before reaching the shore, or die of heart failure soon after, even after receiving medical treatment.

STING STATS

- Average number of tentacles per sea wasp jellyfish
  60
- Number of stings per tentacle
  500,000
- Time to kill
  2-5 minutes
- Average number of humans killed each year
  40

Microscopic harpoons

Jellyfish tentacles are lined with batteries of stinging cells called nematocysts

1. Loaded
The nematocyst begins as a barbed harpoon pointing downwards, with a coiled tube attached to it.

5. Eject cartridge
Each nematocyst is ripped free and continues to pump venom. A new one grows back after about 48 hours.

2. Trigger
Hairs on each nematocyst, together with chemical sensors on the tentacle, trigger several stings grouped into batteries.

3. Fire
The trapdoor flings open and the coiled tube suddenly swells with water, forcing it to straighten.

4. Bullseye!
The barbed harpoon lodges in the skin, while the hollow tube drives onward to deliver the venom.

ATTACK STATS

- Top speed on land
  40km/h (25mph)
- Bite strength
  350N
- Attack triggers
  Territory encroachment, loud noises, prey behaviours
- Average number of humans killed each year
  100

Dogs kill at least 20 times more people than wolves do

DOG

Friend or foe?

- **Weight** 50kg (110lb) • **Habitat** Our homes • **Location** Worldwide
- **Diet** Commercial dog food • **Kill tactic** Bite to the throat

Dogs have lived alongside humans for 30,000 years. In that time our ancestors have used selective breeding to make them more docile and friendly than their wolf ancestors – or have they? Around 4.7 million people are bitten by dogs and 26 people killed each year in the US alone. Most of these attacks are from the 'Molosser' category of breeds, which includes the boxer, great dane and rottweiler. These are heavy dogs, once bred for guarding, hunting and attacking. The victims are mostly infants who have wandered into a neighbour's garden, babies in their prams and the elderly. Running or snatching your hand away can trigger a predator response that can quickly escalate. But what makes dogs so deadly is that we generally take them for granted; always treat a hound with respect.

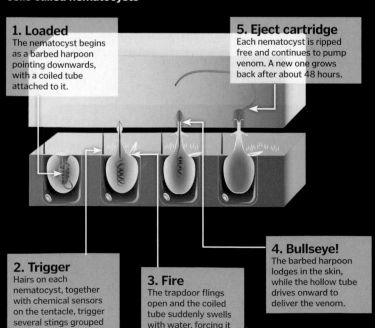

SOUTHERN CASSOWARY

ATTACK STATS

- Top speed on land
  48km/h (30mph)
- Claw size
  12.5cm (4.9in)
- Jump height
  1.5m (4.9ft)
- Confirmed human fatalities
  1

The Queensland slasher

- **Height** 1.7m (4.9ft) • **Habitat** Tropical rainforest • **Location** Indonesia, Australasia
- **Diet** Fruit, insects, fungi • **Kill tactic** Kick/slash

The southern cassowary is the second heaviest bird on Earth, after the ostrich, and is also the only other bird known to have attacked and killed humans. Records of fatalities only exist for Queensland, Australia, and don't include attacks on natives in Indonesia and New Guinea. The southern cassowary is most distinctive for its bright blue neck and a bony crest on its head. The crest is sometimes used to butt victims as the bird charges, but most injuries are caused by its kick. The claw of each inner toe is like a paring knife in sharpness and the cassowary can jump to chest height before slashing. It has been reported that humans have had their throats cut by a single strike from one of these claws and the force of the kick alone is enough to cause internal bleeding.

ANOPHELES MOSQUITO

The silent assassin

- **Length** 15mm (0.6in) • **Habitat** Stagnant water
- **Location** Sub-Saharan Africa, South America, India
- **Diet** Nectar, blood • **Kill tactic** Disease transmission

The mosquito Anopheles gambiae is 12,000 times smaller than a human. Inside its mouth is a protozoan organism that is 12,000 times smaller again. The mosquito itself is not particularly dangerous to humans, and yet between them, they kill almost a million people a year worldwide by transmitting and causing malaria, an often fatal disease which infects the blood and presents in a similar way to flu. Male mosquitoes eat plant nectar and are quite harmless. The female eats nectar too, but some species also bite mammals to supplement their diet with protein from the animal's blood. Although many mosquito species are capable of becoming disease carriers, only a few live in close contact with us. Anopheles gambiae is particularly deadly because it breeds in any available standing water, lives for a long time and prefers to bite humans as opposed to other animals. The Plasmodium parasites that actually cause malaria enter the bloodstream along with the insect saliva and take just minutes to travel to the liver, where they begin to multiply. Malaria appears largely dormant as long as only the liver is infected, but every few weeks or months, the liver cells rupture to release a kind of spore cell that infects red blood cells. This causes fever, vomiting, seizures and anaemia, then the cycle repeats.

Wing
The insect's wings beat roughly 600 times a minute, producing that distinct whining sound.

Abdomen
Can hold up to three times the mosquito's weight in blood. It takes three days to digest.

Salivary glands
Glands inject an anti-clotting agent into the blood, along with the malaria parasite that lives inside the salivary glands.

Antenna
It's the smell of CO2 and octenol from our skin that explains why some people are bitten more than others.

Eye
Mosquitoes use their keen eyesight to locate suitable hosts and to choose their target area.

Mandibles and maxillae
These pierce the skin with a sawing action, driving the proboscis deeper and deeper until it strikes a blood vessel.

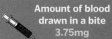

BITE STATS

Duration of average bite	60 seconds
Amount of blood drawn in a bite	3.75mg
Incubation period	10-28 days
Average number of humans killed by malaria each year	930,000

POLAR BEAR

Ice-cold killer

- **Weight** 550kg (1,213lb) • **Habitat** Sea ice
- **Location** Arctic Circle • **Diet** Ringed seals, Bearded seals • **Kill tactic** Skull-crushing bite

An adult male polar bear can rear up over 2.1 metres (seven feet) on its hind legs and weighs twice as much as a silverback gorilla – up to around 700kg or 1500lb. He can outrun and outswim you and a swipe from his paw or a bite from his jaws will be the last thing you see. In the wild, polar bears wait next to holes in the sea ice and, when they smell the breath of a seal, they haul it out of the water with one paw and crush its skull with a single bite of its powerful jaws. Polar bears have been observed taking on one-ton walruses that have metre-long tusks and even beluga whales. Adult polar bears get most of their energy from the fat in blubber. Attacks on humans are rare and mostly occur in autumn when sea ice is gone so they can't hunt. With sea ice melting due to climate change however, bears are forced into towns and attacks have become more of a threat.

Polar bears can swim up to 322km (200mi) from land

ATTACK STATS

Top speed on land	40km/h (25mph)
Bite strength	1,650N
Food consumption	46 seals/year
Average number of humans killed each year	<1

BLACK MAMBA

Fatal fangs

- **Length** 3m (9.8ft) • **Habitat** Savannah, woodland and farmland • **Location** Central and eastern Africa • **Diet** Rats, bush babies, chickens, other snakes • **Kill tactic** Venom

The black mamba is Africa's longest and most venomous snake. It generally keeps away from humans and is responsible for far fewer snakebite cases than the likes of the cobra, viper or krait, but it is very aggressive and has the fastest-acting venom of any serpent on earth. Without antivenom, a bite is invariably lethal to humans. Since the venom spreads so quickly within the body, victims can die within just 20 minutes of being bitten. The black mamba can rear up high and often attacks the body or even the head, striking several times. The venom causes dizziness, paralysis, acute abdominal pain and heart failure. Even if the victim is treated with antivenom within good time, paralysis can often be permanent.

One strike and you're out!

Don't let the tiny teeth fool you – this snake packs an incredibly nasty bite

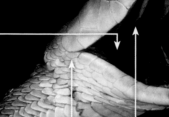

Black mouth
The black mamba is named for the black inside of its mouth, which it gapes to scare off large animals.

Short fang
A black mamba has short fangs which do not fold flat inside the mouth.

Neck muscles
The black mamba can raise the front third of its body off the ground when moving, allowing for powerful forward lunges.

Jaw muscles
Black mambas will bite and release large prey, but mice and rats are gripped firmly until they are dead.

Venom gland
Each bite injects about nine times the lethal dose of venom for humans and they can bite up to 12 times!

BITE STATS
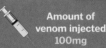

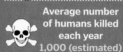

Amount of venom injected
100mg

Fang length
5mm (0.02in)

Time to kill
20 minutes

Average number of humans killed each year
1,000 (estimated)

You're more likely to be bitten by a male Sydney funnel-web

SYDNEY FUNNEL-WEB

The venomous villain

- **Size** 4cm (1.6in) • **Habitat** Under rocks and logs • **Location** Within 100km (62mi) of Sydney, Australia • **Diet** Insects, frogs, lizards • **Kill tactic** Venom

The female Sydney funnel-web spider spends most of her time in a burrow, monitoring the trip wires from her funnel-shaped web. The male, on the other hand, wanders out in warm weather, looking for females. This means you are most likely to be bitten by a male, which is a problem because its venom is six times more powerful than the female's. Sydney funnel-webs are super-aggressive and won't flee if challenged. Instead they will bite multiple times to inject as much venom as possible. The venom contains atracotoxin, which causes muscle twitching, low blood pressure and respiratory failure. Most mammals have a high immunity to Sydney funnel-web venom, but humans are in fact acutely sensitive. The relatively low number of deaths is due to the spider's limited distribution and because a very effective antivenom exists.

BITE STATS

Fang length
6mm (0.2in)

Amount of venom injected
1.7mg

Time to kill
28 minutes

Confirmed human fatalities
14

KOMODO DRAGON

An ambush predator

- **Length** 3m (9.8ft) • **Habitat** Open grassland and forest
- **Location** Indonesia • **Diet** Deer, carrion • **Kill tactic** Bite

There are very few confirmed attacks on humans by Komodo dragons, and even fewer fatalities, but this is mainly because they are very rare. There are fewer than 5,000 in the wild, spread across five remote islands in Indonesia. Komodo dragons are determined predators that normally attack from ambush, but can run at 19 kilometres (12 miles) per hour and even climb trees to reach prey. Their jaws have a bite force that is actually less than a domestic cat's, so they don't kill by crushing. Instead they will hold down prey with their heavy forelimbs and slice chunks out of their victim with incredibly sharp teeth. Komodo teeth also have a layer of living tissue covering them that gets torn as they feed. The mixture of blood, saliva and carrion in their mouths creates a breeding ground for a range of toxic bacteria and, even if prey makes a getaway, bite wounds are very likely to become septic. Komodo dragons also have venom glands that can inhibit blood clotting and induce muscle paralysis.

ATTACK STATS

Smell range
9.5km (5.9mi)

Bite strength
70N

Food consumption
12 meals per year

Confirmed human fatalities
2 in 40 years

Komodos force large prey down their throat by ramming against a tree!

Answer:
The myth that falling coconuts kill more people than sharks is based on a single, widely misquoted research paper. Bee-stings, on the other hand, kill 53 people a year in the United States alone – far more than sharks and coconuts combined.

DID YOU KNOW? *Black mamba venom is at least 20 times more potent than the venom of the European adder*

HIPPOPOTAMUS
The big mouth

- **Length** 4.5m (14.8ft) • **Habitat** Savannah and forest riverbanks • **Location** Sub-Saharan Africa • **Diet** Grass • **Kill tactic** Bite

You may not think it, but the hippopotamus has long had the reputation of Africa's most dangerous animal. Although it only eats grass, the hippo is extremely short-tempered. Their massive canine tusks are razor sharp, half a metre (1.6 feet) long and used purely as weapons. Hippos can open their mouths wider than any other land animal; there are even tales of luckless hunters having their head and shoulders bitten clean off! These animals are very territorial in the water, with males defending their harem and females protecting their calves. Boats are overturned without provocation and the tipped out occupants often killed. On land hippos aren't so territorial, but will still attack safari tours in their vehicles, as well as lions and crocodiles. Fatal attacks have declined in recent years, but only because the hippo itself is growing rarer.

The hippo has the widest mouth on land and equally huge canines ideal for fighting

ATTACK STATS
- **Size of mouth gape** 150° (humans can only open 45°)
- **Bite strength** 8,100N
- **Length of tusk/tooth** 50cm (19.7in)
- **Average number of humans killed each year** 150 (estimated)

OCEANIC WHITETIP SHARK
Deep-sea destroyer

- **Length** 3m (9.8ft) • **Habitat** Deep waters warmer than 18°C (64°F) • **Location** Tropical seas • **Diet** Squid, fish • **Kill tactic** Bite, feeding frenzy transmission

According to the International Shark Attack File, there are only seven recorded unprovoked attacks on humans by oceanic whitetip sharks. On the other hand, the great white shark has 139 unprovoked attacks to its name since 1990, with 29 of them fatal. But what elevates the oceanic whitetip shark to the ranks of the truly deadly is the number of attacks that go unrecorded. This is a deep-water species that rarely comes into contact with swimmers or surfers, but it is believed to be responsible for a large number of deaths among shipwreck victims. In particular, during World War II, the USS Indianapolis and the troop ship Nova Scotia were both torpedoed by submarines in tropical waters. Hundreds of the initial survivors are thought to have been eaten by oceanic whitetip sharks in both cases.

BITE STATS
- **Swim speed** Slow
- **Bite size** 20cm (7.9in) diameter
- **Number of teeth** 54-60
- **Average number of humans killed each year** Unrecorded

Whitetips may have once been the most abundant large predators

© Thinkstock; Alamy; Corbis; Getty; SPL

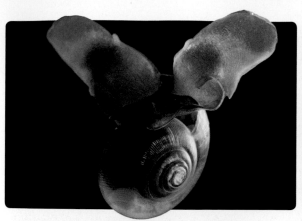

THE WORLD'S WEIRDEST ANIMALS

Meet ten of the world's strangest creatures and find out why they have evolved to be so odd

 You probably think you've seen everything the animal kingdom has to offer. There are a million species of beetle, but they all basically look like beetles, after all. A little bigger here, a different colour there, perhaps some horns, but all quite recognisable. The animals that are most common in the world are those that exploit a wide ecological niche. They are familiar because they are successful, and because their evolution has supplied lots of very minor variations on those themes. But there are other animals that have evolved to exploit very specific niches;

specialists that live in some of the remotest, strangest and harshest environments on Earth. For these animals, the standard body shape and the normal lifestyle strategy just isn't enough. They exist at the extreme edge of the natural selection envelope. Their bodies have distorted to such an extent that their common name often mistakes them for something else entirely: the toad that is really a lizard; the butterfly that's a snail; the mole rat that's neither a mole nor a rat. To us, they are weird. But if you lived where they do, you'd quickly realise there is simply no other way to survive. ⚙

5 TOP FACTS
PREHISTORIC WEIRDOS

Therizinosaurus
1 Although it is thought to have been herbivorous, this five-ton dinosaur had the largest claws ever – three on each hand, each reaching up to a metre (3.2 feet) in length!

Sharovipteryx
2 Unlike pterodactyls, this gliding reptile had its main wing membranes stretched between its hind legs, with a second, smaller pair on the front – possibly for steering.

Opabinia
3 Five eyes and a backwards-pointing mouth that was fed from a single clawed tentacle are the features that qualify the opabinia for a place in this roundup. Was it a crustacean? A sort of worm? No one is really sure.

Argentavis
4 A feathered bird, from around 6 million years ago. It was as tall as a man and had a seven-metre (23-foot) wing span. It's believed to have grabbed prey without landing and swallowed it whole.

Hallucigenia
5 This strange worm from 500 million years ago had spines and tentacles that ended in pincers. Scientists still aren't sure how it fed or even which way up it went!

DID YOU KNOW? Star-nosed moles can smell underwater by blowing out a stream of bubbles and then breathing them back in

Deep-sea gelatinous mass

The blobfish is adapted to live in water 0.8 kilometres (half a mile) deep. At this depth the pressure is 80 times higher than at sea level and a normal gas-filled swim bladder is almost useless. Most creatures at these depths give up trying to swim entirely and simply walk or flop along the seabed. But flopping requires more energy and the blobfish is much too lazy for that. It has traded almost all its muscle mass for a jelly that is just slightly less dense than water. This allows it to coast just above the ocean floor. It doesn't chase its prey, but simply swallows anything that's slow or careless enough to get in the way of its mouth. Unusually for a fish, the female 'sits' on her eggs, instead of just abandoning them after laying. This is probably to protect them from being eaten by other blobfish in the vicinity.

Distribution: Deep water off the coast of mainland Australia and Tasmania

Blobfish

© Caters

Star-nosed mole

"Working in total darkness, the mole can discriminate between an edible larva and a stone or empty shell in 17 milliseconds"

© Getty Images

Distribution: Northern Australia and New Guinea

© Corbis

Distribution: Eastern Canada and north-east USA

22 fingers attached to its nose

The star-nosed mole is the world's fastest-eating mammal. It takes less than a fifth of a second for it to identify if an object is edible and gobble it up. The secret is the ring of 22 tentacles around its nose. These are covered with 25,000 super-sensitive touch receptors, called Eimer's organs. Working in total darkness in a tunnel, or underwater, the mole can discriminate between an edible larva and a stone or empty shell in 17 milliseconds. This is so fast that its brain is working almost at the physical limit of the nerve fibres. Star-nosed moles use this ability to eat very small insects and crustaceans that wouldn't be worth the effort for a slower diner. They are also excellent swimmers and maintain a network of riverbank tunnels up to 270 metres (886 feet) long.

Frill-necked lizard

Wears an Elizabethan collar

Frill-necked lizards are almost a metre (3.3 feet) long with colours ranging from green to dark orange. They are all the same species though; the colour varies to match the local vegetation. Frill-necked lizards have a fan of cartilage spines around their head, supporting a wide flap of skin. The spines are connected to the base of the tongue so, when the lizard gapes its mouth, the frill spreads wide. This is used to scare away predators and also for courtship signalling.

They are also the only lizards that can balance properly on two legs; other lizards can run on their hind legs but they fall forward as soon as they slow down.

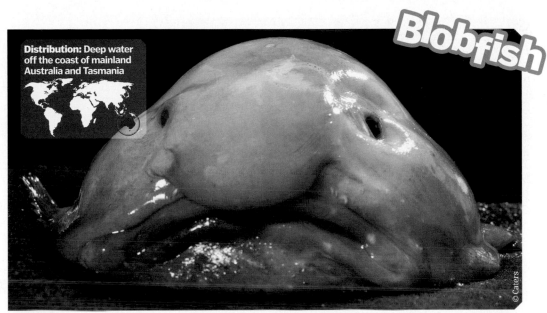

Aye-aye

Distribution:
East coast of Madagascar

© Alamy

Woodpecker fingers

The aye-aye is the largest nocturnal primate. When leaping from tree to tree, it uses its excellent night vision, but when hunting for food it switches to a form of echolocation. Aye-ayes eat insect larvae that burrow in tree trunks. To find them they use their middle finger, which is especially long, as well as thin and bony. By rapidly tapping on the trunk they send vibrations through the wood. After each tap, the fingernail drags lightly along the bark to sense the return echoes and the aye-aye's huge ears enfold the target area to listen for changes in the pitch of the drumming sound. When it finds a hollow channel, the aye-aye uses its forward-slanting teeth to gnaw a hole in the bark and its long finger then does double duty as a specialised winkling tool to extract the juicy grub inside.

Red-lipped batfish

Distribution:
Off the Galapagos Islands

© Corbis

A walking fish with lipstick

This fish lives on the rocky seabed of the Pacific. Because the floor is rough and spiky, it prefers not to swim along the bottom like a flounder – instead it has evolved pectoral fins that work like legs to 'walk' along the seabed. It doesn't use its dorsal fin for swimming either; this has evolved into a spiny projection with a retractable 'fishing rod', which it uses to lure in small fish and shrimp. And the bright red lips? It turns out they really do perform a similar function to lipstick. The batfish uses them to help improve species recognition when searching for a mate.

HoneyPot ant

Distribution:
Western North America

© Alamy

A living larder

Ants of the genus myrmecocystus use specialised workers, called repletes, as living food stores. Their abdomens are inflated to a huge size with a pressurised gas bubble that is gradually displaced by a sugary liquid. To avoid wasting energy, the repletes barely move and spend the rest of their lives clinging to the ceiling of the nest in clusters. When a worker needs food, it strokes a replete with its antennae and it regurgitates a mouthful. If they fall from the ceiling, they can't climb back up and instead are dismembered by the workers. The balloon of food remains on the nest floor for a week or more as the workers gradually transfer its contents to other repletes. A single colony can have 1,500 repletes that hold up to a kilogram (2.2 pounds) of stored food between them.

Distribution:
Southern USA and Mexico

Rodents that live like bees

The nest of a naked mole rat is really not a comfortable place. The network of tunnels under the East African grassland is baking hot by day, freezing at night and almost airless. Life is so harsh that the naked mole rat lives as a hive organism with sterile workers and a single breeding queen. Naked mole rats can run backwards just as fast as forwards and have no sense of pain in their skin. Their metabolism is 30 per cent slower than other mammals of their size. Surprisingly, they have the longest rodent life span (28 years) and never get cancer.

Sea butterfly
Upside-down swimming snail

Thecosomata are sea snails about the size of a lentil, with shells so thin that they are virtually transparent. Rather than sliding on the seabed, their foot has evolved into a pair of thin 'wings' that flap through the water. Sea snails mostly swim upside down because their body and shell is heavier and hangs down from the wings. They are herbivores, feeding on phytoplankton, but they catch their food in webs, like spiders. These webs are made from strands of mucus that can extend as far as five centimetres (two inches) from the sea butterfly. They are preyed on by a kind of swimming sea slug called a sea angel.

Distribution: Throughout Earth's oceans, at depths of up to 100m (328ft)

© Corbis

Honourable mentions

Nature's capacity for weirdness is unlimited. Here are some more that didn't make the top ten

© Alamy

Axolotl
A kind of salamander that's able to regenerate severed limbs.

Butterfly lizard
Endemic to Vietnam, this reptile can clone itself asexually.

Dumbo octopus
This cute sea-critter gets about by flapping its ear-like fins.

Glass frog
A frog so transparent that you can see all its internal organs.

Geoduck clam
A kind of saltwater clam that's able to live for well over 100 years.

Ninja slug
This gastropod injects aphrodisiac darts into potential passing mates.

Pink fairy armadillo
The smallest species of armadillo can 'swim' under desert sand.

Snub-nosed sneezing monkey
Due to its upturned hooter, rain often gets in and makes it sneeze.

Texas horned lizard
The ultimate blood-shot eyes

The horned lizard is camouflaged, spiky and can inflate itself like a pufferfish. But just in case that isn't enough to deter predators, it has one last defence to deploy. By closing off certain blood vessels, the horned lizard abruptly increases the blood pressure in its head. This ruptures capillaries near the corners of its eyes and a jet of blood squirts from each, as far as 1.5 metres (five feet). In a single squirt, the lizard can lose a third of its total blood. Texas horned lizards eat Maricopa harvester ants, which have the most toxic venom of any insect. But far from poisoning the horned lizard, these toxins are stored and injected by special glands into the liquid projectile to cause a nasty burn.

© Alamy

Hairy frog
Wolverine of the amphibian world

This 11-centimetre (4.3-inch) frog appears to have tufts of hair on its sides and thighs, but they are actually dermal papillae – fleshy outgrowths that contain arteries. They act to massively increase the skin surface area, which allows the hairy frog to absorb more oxygen when sitting underwater. But it's not just its 'sideburns' that make the hairy frog resemble X-Men's Wolverine, it can also extrude sharp claws by intentionally forcing them through its skin. The spines are normally held in place with a ligament but, when threatened, the frog clenches its fist so forcefully that the ligaments snap and pierce its skin. Unlike Wolverine, the spines can't be actively retracted; they just ease back over time and the skin regrows over them.

Naked mole rat

Distribution: Eastern Africa, especially Ethiopia, Kenya and Somalia

Distribution: Central Africa

Animal camouflage

The sneaky secrets of the most amazing animals you've never seen

 Almost every animal has a good reason to hide. Going undetected makes it easier to catch food – and easier to avoid becoming someone else's. In any species, the individuals that stand out the most will be the first to be eaten and the last to catch their own dinner, and so natural selection picks the ones with the best camouflage.

There are several different kinds of camouflage. The most basic is to hide under a rock, or in sand or leaves. This is sometimes called 'crypsis', and some animals will incorporate bits of their environment on their bodies to improve the effect. Three-toed sloths have algae growing in their fur, which gives them a dark green hue that helps them hide among the trees. Coral crabs deliberately attach young polyps to their shells so they resemble part of the reef.

The next step is to change your own body colouration. Mammals have a colour pallet restricted to white, black, brown and yellow, but fish, amphibians, reptiles and birds can all produce a vivid array of greens and bright reds. Red might not seem like a great colour for camouflage, but lots of seaweed and corals are red, and in fact many sea creatures obtain the red pigment for their bodies by eating the corals and seaweed that they hide among.

Camouflage is a show, performed for a few specific observers. Most mammals see in black and white, or only two colours. Primates see three primary colours, while birds see four. Insects can see well into the ultraviolet part of the spectrum and many snakes can sense infrared. Choosing the right camouflage is about exploiting the weaknesses in your target's visual system. Even if your colour is a very close match to your surroundings, your outline can still give you away. One of the earliest parts of the brain to evolve was concerned with recognising the edges of things, and most animals still have a dedicated outline recognition brain region. Good camouflage uses contrasting patterns of light and dark, or different colours. These trick the outline recognition system so that it mentally carves up your shape into smaller, irregular blocks. In some environments, there is so little to hide behind that this

5 TOP FACTS
MASTERS OF DISGUISE

Pink soft coral crab
1 This crab attaches coral polyps to its own shell as a sort of marine ghillie suit. With matching shell colouration from eating coral, it becomes a walking coral reef.

Sea dragon
2 The leaf-like protrusions on this relative of the seahorse make fast swimming impossible, but they do provide excellent camouflage.

Ghanaian praying mantis
3 Normally green, the Ghanaian praying mantis will moult its skin and change to a black colour after a forest fire, in order to retain its camouflage.

Leaf insect
4 The wide flattened body of the leaf insect looks just like a leaf, and the legs are disguised either as smaller leaves or as bite marks from the main leaf depending on the species.

Gaboon viper
5 A 1.5m snake that's as thick as your arm sounds hard to miss, but the incredibly disruptive pattern perfectly matches the jumble of dried leaves on the African forest floor.

DID YOU KNOW? Tigers are well camouflaged in the jungle because most of the animals they hunt are green/orange colour blind

A broadclub cuttlefish

How the cuttlefish gets its spots

Cephalopods – particularly the octopus and the cuttlefish – are the undisputed masters of the quick change. Their skin is packed with specialised cells called 'chromatophores' that change the colour or reflectivity of the skin. Each chromatophore has its own activating muscle and nerve fibre, and these are connected to a part of the brain dedicated to coordinating the complex patterns. Although the chromatophores only contain red, yellow and brown pigments, cuttlefish can create almost any colour by combining different layers of coloured and reflecting cells. Green, for example, is achieved by using an iridescent layer deep in the skin to scatter light back through yellow pigments, which act as a filter. All the layers are controlled independently and simultaneously, so a cuttlefish can change its entire skin colour in less than a second. Chameleons use a similar arrangement of skin cells but the chromatophores are controlled using hormones, rather than nerve impulses, so the change occurs more slowly.

Harmless hoverflies can mimic wasps

What's brown and sticky? A stick!

Camouflage is usually about blending anonymously into the background, but there are times when it is better to disguise yourself as something specific. Mimics copy the shape, colouring, movement and sometimes even the smell of another species to fool prey or predators. This is an evolutionary arms race; as predators evolve more and more acute senses to see through the subterfuge, so the mimics must constantly refine their disguise. One of the most common forms of mimicry, known as 'Batesian mimicry', is where a harmless species pretends to be a dangerous one, such as the many species of hoverfly that mimic stinging wasps. But poisonous species can mimic each other, too. Monarch and viceroy butterflies show this kind of 'Müllerian mimicry' – both are toxic, but they have evolved to mimic each other so that bird predators only have to learn one wing pattern to avoid, rather than two.

Under the skin

Chromatophore
When the cell is relaxed, the pigment forms an inconspicuous dot in the centre. By pulling the radial muscles, the chromatophore is stretched into a larger disc and the colour is visible.

- Orange-yellow
- Red-orange
- Black-brown

Pigment
Radial muscle fibres

Iridophore
Iridophores generate iridescent colours using stacked crystals of translucent guanine proteins as tiny prisms. By altering the angle of the iridophore, the colour changes.

Iridosomal platelet

- Pinks
- Yellows
- Greens
- Blues
- Silver

Nucleus

Leucophore
Leucophores use the same proteins as iridophores, but instead of stacking them in plates, the crystals are arranged on the surface of the cell. Squeezing or flattening the cell controls how much light is reflected.

Nucleus
Cell body
Transparent refractive granule

Top layer
Stacked layers of chromatophores contain the three basic pigments. Reds, yellows, browns and black colours are all produced here.

Middle layer
The iridophores create interference patterns to generate shimmering, metallic patterns, and are also used to create blue and green colours.

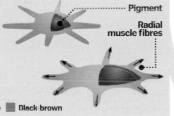

Mirror granules
The guanine crystals are actually transparent, but by arranging them in tiny beads they act like crushed glass and form a white base.

Base layer
Leucophores are white. White is used as a danger signal by many octopuses, but this layer is also used as a 'base coat' to modify the colours of the chromatophores above.

'dazzle' camouflage is all you have. The Royal Navy used this technique in World War I, to make it hard to judge the speed and heading of battleships on the featureless ocean. But the orca, or killer whale, beat them to it by several million years. The bright patches of white on a black body disrupt its outline so that it is not immediately recognised as a threat. Zebras use the same technique, but this time the entire herd merges into one huge zebra that is much more intimidating and confusing to lions and cheetahs.

Sometimes, a purely visual camouflage isn't enough. Procrypsis is the technique of camouflaging your movement. Predators are acutely sensitive to movement, but a typical forest is a whirl of activity and they must quickly tune out the background motions of wind, water and all the non-food animals if they are not to be overwhelmed. Chameleons, leaf insects and preying mantises can exploit this by moving with a rocking motion that mimics the swaying of branches in the wind. Some Pacific octopuses will curl up like a rock, but still manage to move along the seabed by synchronising movement with the back-and-forth patterns of shadow cast by sunlight through the waves.

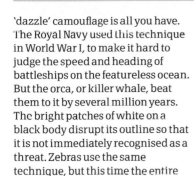
A monarch butterfly mimics to ward off predators

Jungle illusionists

An impressive game of hide and seek takes place among the trees

Jackson's chameleon

Technique: Colour and movement
Reason: Hunting

In the lush, high-altitude forests of Kenya and Tanzania, the bright green skin of the Jackson's chameleon blends with the mosaic of thick waxy leaves. Their skin is mottled to break up the animal's outline and has very rough scales to create a thorny, irregular texture. When they perch, their long tail is coiled into a tight circle to help the chameleon look more like a leaf, and they move with a swaying motion to mimic the effect of the breeze through the branches.

Tawny frogmouth

Technique: Disruptive colour pattern
Reason: Defensive

This distant relative of the owl and cuckoo lives in Australia and New Guinea. It eats insects and small frogs by sitting still until food comes within range, and then pouncing. It feeds at night, so the camouflage is to protect it during the day. Perched motionless in the crook of a tree branch or on a dead log, the pattern of its feathers mimics the texture of tree bark.

Bird dropping spider

Technique: Mimicry
Reason: Defensive

This Australian spider catches moths at night by luring them with their own sex pheromones, but during the day it is vulnerable to being eaten by birds. So it disguises itself as the least appetising thing for a bird: their own droppings! The creamy-coloured abdomen with brown stippled patches closely resembles the guano of a bird that feeds on insects.

Jaguar

Technique: Disruptive pattern
Reason: Hunting

Hiding 100kg of big cat in the dense forests of south America isn't easy, but if you are an ambush predator, it's vital that you succeed. Jaguars use a similar rosette pattern on their fur to the African leopard but the rosettes are larger, darker and have a small spot in the middle. The effect is similar to the dappled shade cast by the thick jungle foliage on the forest floor. This makes it very hard to trace the outline of the jaguar, until it moves. And by then, it's too late.

Lying low on the land

The land is home to many sly creatures, so watch your step

Human vision

Lion vision

A lone zebra is easier for lions and other predators to see, compared to when they're huddled together

Israeli sand gecko

Technique: Colour and counter-shading
Reason: Protection and hunting

Sand geckos use the huge surface area on their finger pads to cling to the walls or roofs of rock crevices in the desert. The mottled sandy colour that covers all of their upper surface, including their eyelids, blends against the gritty sandstone rocks. When they are the right way up, hunting insects on the desert floor, their white belly appears to neutralise the shadow cast by their upper body.

Chameleon changes

The word 'chameleon' is a by-word for invisibility and camouflage, but most chameleons don't change colour to match their surroundings. Their default colour is already an excellent camouflage and colour changes are used to signal their mood to other chameleons.

© Richard

Zebra
Technique: Dazzle pattern
Reason: Confusing predators
The African savannah is a difficult place to hide, but the bright stripes of the zebra work in a different way. Instead of making the animal blend into its surroundings, they make it blend into the herd. When threatened, zebras huddle together and the stripes make it difficult to tell where one starts and another ends. Lions and other predators rely on splitting one target away from the herd. The visual clump created by the stripes confuses and acts as a survival technique for the zebra.

Mackerel
Technique: Stripes and counter-shading
Reason: Defensive
Mackerel swim in huge schools. Seen from above, the distinctive striped pattern resembles the rippling pattern of shadow seen in shallow seas. At close range the effect may be similar to the zebra's stripes and make it hard for predators to lock on to any single fish. The counter-shaded belly is common to most fish, making them harder to spot from below against the lighter surface.

Invisible mysteries of the deep
Below the surface of the water lurk a talented band of beasts

Cuttlefish
Technique: Colour changing
Reason: Signalling, hunting and protection
Cuttlefish have the most advanced colour changing system of any animal. Not only can they change their colour in less than a second, but they can also move from static camouflage patterns to rapidly pulsing displays to hypnotise prey or communicate with other cuttlefish. Their skin can also change the polarisation of the light reflecting off it, important because many marine animals are sensitive to the polarisation angle of light.

© Silke Baron

Snowshoe hare
Technique: Seasonal colour
Reason: Defensive
During the short Alaskan spring and summer, the snowshoe hare has fur that is standard 'rabbit brown' to blend against the leaves and heather. But this hare doesn't hibernate and a brown animal wouldn't last long on a carpet of snow with lynx and great horned owls patrolling. So it moults to a winter coat, which is pure white except for a black tip on each ear.

Indonesian mimic octopus
Technique: Colour changing and behavioural mimicry
Reason: Protection and hunting
The mimic octopus is an active predator and can't afford to spend long periods sitting on the seabed pretending to be a rock. But it does have lots of predators of its own, so uses its camouflage abilities to imitate more than 15 other animal species. As well as changing the colour and patterning of its skin, it can also radically alter its texture from smooth to spiny and contort its arms and body to change shape.

Egyptian nightjar
Technique: Colour and pattern
Reason: Protecting its eggs
Birds normally defend themselves against predators by flying away, but the Egyptian nightjar lives in the desert, where there are no trees for roosting. It also eats moths, which means it is active by night. In the day it rests on the sandy ground, but its mottled brown, rather scruffy-looking plumage is almost impossible to spot. The nightjar just looks like a stone or a piece of dried wood. Egyptian nightjars don't even build nests, hiding their eggs beneath their own camouflage.

Stonefish
Technique: Colour and spines
Reason: Ambush
The stonefish catches small fish and shrimp by lying still on the seabed and resembling a stone. When food swims close, it pounces and then goes back to being a stone. To defend itself from its own predators, the stonefish has 13 poisonous spines. Whereas most poisonous animals are brightly coloured as a warning, the stonefish's camouflage means that it's often trodden on by accident, killing a human in two hours.

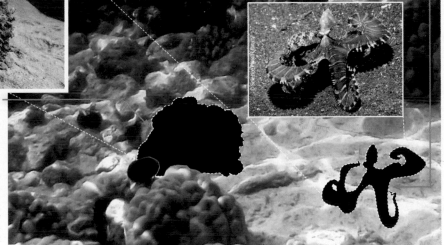

Armoured animals

It takes more than sticks and stones to hurt these well-protected beasts...

Animals have used armour to protect themselves from predators for as long as there have been predators. There are heavily armoured trilobites in the fossil record from as far back as 540 million years ago, and natural selection drove the prey to evolve a tough skin. It's logical evolution. When something tried to bite them, the better-armoured ones were more likely to survive.

In a marine environment, weight is much less critical than on land so most invertebrates reinforce their exoskeletons with calcium carbonate extracted from the seawater, to make them literally harder. On land this would make movement almost impossible, so terrestrial armour plating needs to use lighter materials such as keratin and chitin, and assemble them in complex layered or honeycomb structures to keep them strong but flexible.

All armour is a trade-off between protection and restriction. Some armour can be put to more than one use; eg the devil lizard uses the tiny cracks between its armoured scales to wick up water from the desert dew. But the best kind of shield is the one that you can raise and lower at will. The blowfish is covered with sharp spines that would massively increase its drag when swimming if they stuck out all the time. So it keeps them folded back most of the time and, when danger threatens, it takes a deep breath of water to inflate its body and push out the spines. Most animals don't have armour over their entire body either; it's easier to just protect the

How do armadillos normally cross a river?

A By swimming **B** By walking **C** By crocodile

Answer:
The armadillo's heavy shell means it normally sinks in water. But armadillos can hold their breath for up to six minutes, so they just walk along the bottom. For larger rivers they swallow air to inflate their stomach and float across.

DID YOU KNOW? After moulting, a lobster will eat its own shell in order to regain lost calcium

Natural plate mail

All reptiles have scaly skin, but crocodiles and their relatives have reinforced this with bony plates under the skin, called osteoderms, to provide extra protection along the back. Turtles and tortoises have taken this a step further by fusing the osteoderms into a rigid shell. A shell provides excellent protection from predators but it's very slow and heavy. When mammals evolved, they swapped scales for fur and lost their armour plating. But two strange animals – the armadillo and the pangolin – have since re-evolved their own version. Pangolins (pictured below) have overlapping scales like a pine cone. The scales are made of keratin and are a bit like a coat made of fingernails. Pangolins have scales running right down to the tip of their tail and when threatened, they will roll into a ball like a hedgehog. Armadillos have armour made of bone, with a layer of smaller keratin scales on top. The head, shoulders and rear each have a single fused piece of armour, but the middle has a concertina of armoured rings that allow the armadillo some flexibility. The three-banded armadillo is the only one able to roll completely up into a ball. The other species rely on a combination of armour and speed to escape.

exposed areas. For example, the cassowary bird has just a single bony plate on its head, to act as a crash helmet as it charges through its forest home's thick undergrowth.

Evolution is a natural arms race. Whatever defences one animal comes up with, there will be a predator that evolves a way around it. However, in order to pass your genes on to the next generation, you don't need to be completely invulnerable. You just need to be harder to eat than the guy next to you. ✿

Spine power

Spines are a specialised form of hair. They are made from hollow tubes of keratin protein that taper into a thin point. Hedgehogs and porcupines both use spines as armour but the animals are not related. Hedgehog spines are short and firmly attached to the skin. The hedgehog simply rolls into a ball when threatened and hopes a predator will give up trying to find a way in. Porcupines are much more aggressive, with up to 30,000 spines that can be 10-20 centimetres (four to eight inches) long. They will actively charge at predators or swipe with their tails. The spines dislodge on contact and the tip expands with the body heat of the victim, trapping it there. North American porcupine spines even have barbs that will ratchet their way deeper into the body – moving several millimetres a day! Predators can die from the stab wound or starve to death because a mouthful of spines stops them eating.

A focus on quill anatomy

How porcupines control the release of their spiky self-defence

❶ Quill shaft
A porcupine quill is hollow and much thicker than the root that anchors it to the skin, helping its release.

❷ Skin
The root doesn't sit under the porcupine's skin; the skin surrounds it like a cup.

❸ Guard spool
A ring of connective tissue stops the quill from being driven back into the porcupine's body.

❹ Transverse muscle
When the porcupine is alert, this muscle tenses to 'arm' the spine.

❺ Piloerector muscle
The same muscles that raise the hairs on your arm when you're cold lift the porcupine's spines when threatened.

❻ Safety on
With the transverse muscle relaxed, the guard spools can move up and down and the spines stay attached.

❼ Fire!
As the muscle grips the spool, the spine tears the quill at the root, releasing it from the skin.

❽ Retinaculum
Anchoring tissue holds the skin in place as the quill is pulled free.

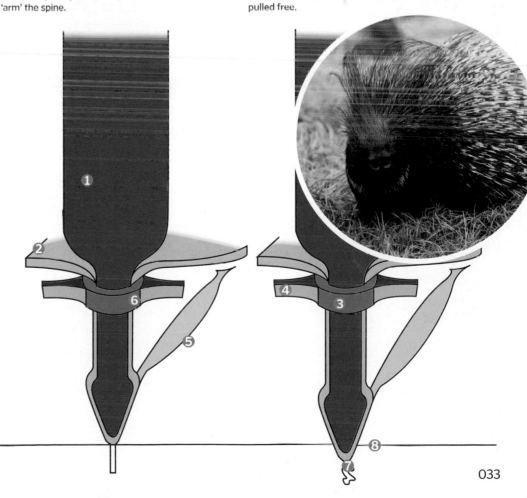

Thick skin

Elephants are pachyderms. The name means 'thick skin' and elephants can have up to three-centimetre (1.2-inch)-thick skin on their back and around their trunk and legs. But the skin around an elephant's ears and chest can be as thin as paper so elephants are actually quite vulnerable to sunburn in certain areas.

The real champions of skin armour are whales and sharks. Sperm whales have a layer of blubber that can be 35 centimetres (13.8 inches) thick – the thickest skin of any animal. Blubber is a mixture of fat reinforced with collagen fibres and densely supplied with blood vessels. Its primary purpose is to provide insulation and buoyancy, but sperm whales hunt giant squid and the whale's blubber protects it from the squid's tentacles armed with hundreds of suction cups with saw-tooth cutting edges. Sharks, meanwhile, have skin covered in overlapping scales called dermal denticles that are constructed like teeth, complete with enamel and serrated cutting edges. This makes their skin almost bulletproof!

Like their thick-skinned relations, rhinos are pachyderms along with elephants and hippos

Colourful jewel beetle shells serve the dual purpose of protection and attracting mates

Extraordinary exoskeletons

An exoskeleton is more than just a piece of armour. It also provides the attachment points for the muscles, to give them something to pull against. Both insects and crustaceans use chitin as the main building material of their exoskeleton. Chitin is a polysaccharide, like starch or cellulose, but it performs the same role as the keratin protein in vertebrates. By itself, chitin is soft and pliable, but the chains are very strong and hard to snap. By arranging it into sheets with the fibres running in different directions, chitin forms a tough, tear-proof layer. That's plenty for small creatures like insects, but crustaceans take this process a step further by impregnating the weave of this chitin cloth with calcium carbonate. The result is a carapace as strong as stone but much less brittle. The biggest disadvantage of all exoskeletons is that they can't grow with the animal, so they must be shed periodically.

Temporary shelter

Hermit crabs don't have shells of their own but their soft abdomen is curved in a spiral that makes it a snug fit for the shells of gastropod molluscs, like sea snails. They have to regularly upgrade to a larger shell as they grow but they save themselves the considerable metabolic cost of hardening their own exoskeleton. Some of the borrowed shells gain an extra layer of protection in the form of sea anemones that attach to the outside. The anemone feeds on scraps dropped by the crab and in return, its stinging tentacles keep predatory fish away. One species of hermit crab even uses colonies of encrusting coral-like bryozoans to extend the size of its shell. This clever subcontracting arrangement gives the crab the advantages of a living shell, without the expense of building it

Attack is the best defence

1 Golden poison frog
The most poisonous of the poison dart frogs and possibly the most poisonous animal of all. The alkaloid toxins on the skin of a single frog would be enough to kill you ten times over, if you ate one.

2 Giant squid
Rather than producing a cloud of ink as a smoke screen, the giant squid squirts a long thin blob that resembles the squid itself. Then it jets away, leaving the confused predator chasing shadows.

3 Skunk
Skunks secrete a foul-smelling mixture of thiols and thioacetates from their anal glands. If they are running away, they spray a mist that predators must run through, but can also shoot a directed stream from 3m (10ft) away.

4 Texas horned lizard
When threatened by coyotes, horned lizards raise the blood pressure around their eyes until they squirt a jet of blood mixed with irritating chemicals. The lizards can fire up to a third of their total blood volume this way.

5 Bombardier beetle
The bombardier beetle possesses the ultimate squirt defence, combining hydrogen peroxide and hydroquinone in a combustion chamber in its abdomen. Exploding on contact, they eject hot gas that can kill attacking insects and deter larger predators.

Why are lobster shells so strong?

See the components that make up a crustacean's armour, right down to the atomic level

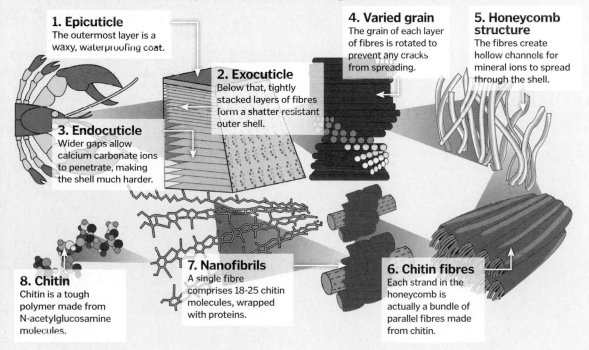

1. Epicuticle
The outermost layer is a waxy, waterproofing coat.

2. Exocuticle
Below that, tightly stacked layers of fibres form a shatter resistant outer shell.

3. Endocuticle
Wider gaps allow calcium carbonate ions to penetrate, making the shell much harder.

4. Varied grain
The grain of each layer of fibres is rotated to prevent any cracks from spreading.

5. Honeycomb structure
The fibres create hollow channels for mineral ions to spread through the shell.

6. Chitin fibres
Each strand in the honeycomb is actually a bundle of parallel fibres made from chitin.

7. Nanofibrils
A single fibre comprises 18-25 chitin molecules, wrapped with proteins.

8. Chitin
Chitin is a tough polymer made from N-acetylglucosamine molecules.

© Alamy; The Children's Museum of Indianapolis; Thinkstock

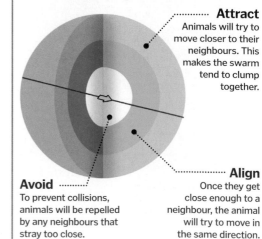

Swarms

From bees to bison, animals all over
the world find safety in numbers –
mind-bogglingly huge numbers...

Birds of a feather flock together. But why exactly? It's not just birds – mammals, reptiles, amphibians, fish, insects and even bacteria all do it. Virtually every corner of the animal kingdom has found that banding together is a great tactic for surviving in the wild. As with everything else in nature, it boils down to two things: finding enough food and avoiding becoming food for something else. Swarming can help with both.

Herring, for example, feed on copepods. These tiny crustaceans, one or two millimetres (0.04-0.08 inches) long can shoot suddenly sideways to evade an approaching fish. Herring aren't agile enough swimmers to react to this jump, so instead they swim in large schools with the gap between fish synchronised to the jump distance of the copepod. This increases each fish's chance of a meal because if a copepod leaps out of the path of one fish, it lands directly in front of another.

At the other end of the food chain, another marine crustacean – the krill – swarms to avoid predation. A large swarm of randomly swirling krill makes it much harder for fish to pick out any single target. Ironically, krill swarms are so huge that it has become viable for a much larger kind of animal – the baleen whales – to evolve the specialised apparatus for straining out several tons of krill in a single gulp. Ironically the very behaviour that protects them from small fish and penguins makes them vulnerable to the biggest creatures of them all.

Swarming also helps because it increases the number of eyes and ears on the alert for danger. A herd of wildebeest or a flock of seagulls allows each member to borrow the senses of the other animals as a sort of long-range radar. There's no need for direct communication; simply keeping up with the rest of their neighbours means that when one end of the group spots danger, the whole swarm wheels away from the threat as if it were a single organism. In fact, it's possible that multicellular life itself began as nothing more than swarming behaviour. Dictyostelid amoebae (a form of slime mould) live the ordinary, solitary life of a single-celled organism when food is ▶

Modelling the swarm

When all the individual members of a group adopt one particular combination of the attract, align and avoid rules below, a convincing swarm is simulated

Attract
Animals will try to move closer to their neighbours. This makes the swarm tend to clump together.

Avoid
To prevent collisions, animals will be repelled by any neighbours that stray too close.

Align
Once they get close enough to a neighbour, the animal will try to move in the same direction.

STRANGE BUT TRUE
IN FOR THE KRILL

On average how long do krill live for?
A 9 months **B** 10 years **C** 7 days

Answer:
For such a small animal, krill have a surprisingly long life span of up to a decade. Females can lay 10,000 eggs – sometimes several times a year. This explains how krill are able to form such huge swarms, despite the mighty appetites of whales.

DID YOU KNOW? In 1958, one of the largest locust swarms ever recorded ate 167,000 tons of crops in Ethiopia

Collective consciousness in focus

Each of your brain cells has no intelligence by itself. But connected together in sufficient numbers, they display remarkable new properties. In a similar way, a swarm of animals exhibits behaviours that go far beyond the reasoning abilities of individuals. Honeybee swarms will invariably choose the best site for a new hive, even though each bee will have personally visited, at most, one of the potential sites and so can't compare it with any others. Decisions are made by means of a positive feedback loop, with more of the returning bees 'voting' enthusiastically for the better sites through their special dance.

The way a swarm moves together as a coherent unit might seem like it involves a high degree of communication and leadership. But there is actually no centralised control. Ants, for instance, will follow a pheromone trail laid on the forest floor. But as they walk they also lay down a trail of their own. This makes the scent trail more powerful and the path becomes more popular. Like a stream cutting an ever-deeper valley as it flows downhill, the ant colony reinforces the popular routes and the swarm sticks together without any individual ant actually marshalling their movement.

Even the more complex animals such as birds form swarms on the basis of surprisingly simple rules. Starlings, for example, simply try to fly in the same direction as their closest six or seven neighbours. But the result is a swirling cloud of birds that appears as if to have a collective mind of its own.

A perfect swarm

Animal: Bee
Swarm technique: Swarm

Honeybees swarm when the colony grows too big for its current hive. The queen and up to 60 per cent of the worker bees leave the hive and settle on a tree branch a few metres away. Other workers scout out possible new nest sites over the course of a few days and then the swarm flies together to establish a new colony.

Animal: Locust
Swarm technique: Swarm

Locusts are the final adult stage of certain grasshopper species. In crowded conditions, the grasshoppers will change into a ravenous, fast-breeding form. The population quickly explodes into swarms of billions and each locust will eat its own body weight in plant matter every day. Large locust swarms can cover an area the size of Greater London.

Animal: Starling
Swarm technique: Flock

Starlings are highly social birds and will often congregate in large flocks of up to a million birds. This reduces the risk of predation from birds of prey as they move between roosting sites and feeding grounds, because the swirling mass makes it hard to pinpoint a single target. Flocks will often contain individuals from several different species of starling.

Cloud
Modelling a swarm with just 'attract' and 'avoid' zones creates a swirling cloud that's similar to a chaotic swarm of gnats.

Whirlpool
Adding in the 'align' zone can lead to swirling circles. Some fish behave in this way to confuse predators.

Flock
By increasing the width of the 'align' zone, coherent flocking behaviour emerges naturally in the simulation.

© Corbis; Getty; Thinkstock

▶abundant. But when it runs out, they secrete a chemical signal called cyclic adenosine monophosphate (cAMP) that attracts other nearby Dictyostelids. At a certain critical mass, the amoebae form into a multicellular 'slug' up to four millimetres (0.16 inches) long and move off in search of new food. The 'slug' has a definite front and back end and moves towards heat, light and humidity. It acts like a simple multicellular animal, but it's actually just an amoeba swarm.

Although they can be beneficial to the animal, swarms also have a dark side to them. Because the swarm moves and acts as one, it can quickly become unstable and out of control. At low population densities, locusts move about randomly or in small groups. This is controlled by the level of serotonin in each locust, which increases in response to stress. As the density rises they become more and more co-ordinated until, at about 74 locusts per square metre, they stop changing direction altogether and march like an army for hours at a time. Locust swarms begin in response to overcrowding, but because they all travel together, they just make the overcrowding worse, sweeping across farmland like a wildfire and destroying all plant life in their path such as crops on farms. It is precisely the co-ordination and synchronisation that can make the swarm so destructive. ✿

It's a stampede!
What happens when the herding instinct turns nasty?

Cattle and wilderbeast stampedes can be started by the slightest sound

The power of the swarm

While individual swarm members do relatively little damage, en masse they have the power to consume everything in their path

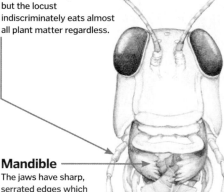

Not all swarms are destructive. A swarm of honeybees is essentially peaceful, unless the queen is in some way threatened by a potential predator. In a similarly harmless way, krill drift in the open ocean so the most they can do is eat a lot of already abundant plankton.

However, swarms feeding on land can quickly strip an area bare of all plant life,

simply by virtue of their immense population density.

Locust swarms, for example, can reach into the billions – with some 380 million insects per square kilometre. Resembling a uniform blanket of locusts, there's no amount of vegetation that can withstand that many mouths for long.

Even when overfeeding isn't a problem, swarms can still cause enormous damage. An animal that might be perfectly innocuous by itself can cause a lot of trouble in large enough numbers. Large flocks of starlings can leave a carpet of droppings up to 30 centimetres (11.8 inches) deep under the trees where they roost. The ammonia compounds in their droppings can quickly reach toxic levels, poisoning grass and other plants or even water systems as the toxins are washed into streams and rivers if the flock doesn't move on within a few days.

Jaws of destruction
Swarms wreak havoc in many different ways. A billion locusts, for example, can chew through the countryside

Maxillary palp
These are sensitive to taste but the locust indiscriminately eats almost all plant matter regardless.

Labial palp
These palps hold the ball of food in place while the mandibles grind it.

Mandible
The jaws have sharp, serrated edges which can rasp tough plant fibres into shreds.

1. Tinderbox
Cattle, wildebeest and even elephants can become easily startled, particularly at night when they can't see to reassure themselves there are no predators or dangers lurking nearby.

2. Alarm
The panic is infectious; each animal is running because the herd is. They don't wait to verify the danger for themselves and suddenly thousands of animals are moving madly.

3. Riot
Without intervention, a stampede will run until the creatures are exhausted. This can drive animals off cliffs or through human settlements, trampling everything in their path.

4. Head them off
Experienced cowboys will outflank a stampede and bend it in on itself so that the leaders circle round to the tail-enders. This enables the stampede to safely run itself out of steam.

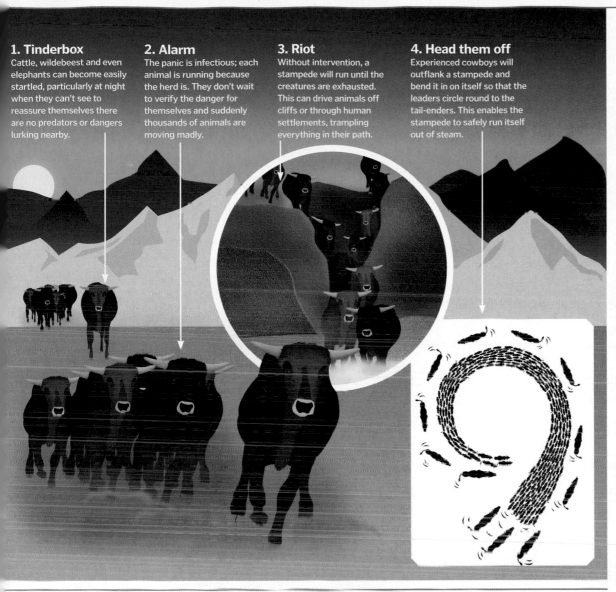

A perfect swarm

Animal: Sardine
Swarm technique: Shoal

Every year, young sardines swim from the tip of South Africa, where they spawned, up the coast of Mozambique and into the Indian Ocean. It is thought that cold-water currents trigger this migration. The school can cover an area of 7.1 x 1.5 kilometres (4.4 x 0.9 miles) and 30 metres (98 feet) deep, containing billions of sardines. Up to 18,000 dolphins tag along to feed.

Animal: Krill
Swarm technique: Shoal

Krill are a shrimp-like crustacean. Antarctic krill have a total biomass twice that of all the humans in the world. Half of this is eaten every year and, to protect themselves, they band together in huge shoals that drift up and down in the water column every day.

Animal: Wildebeest
Swarm technique: Herd

Wildebeest migrate annually across the Serengeti to follow the rainfall and most nutritious grass available to them. Herds of 1.4 million travel 2,900 kilometres (1,800 miles) per year in a clockwise circle around eastern Africa. Wildebeest are powerful and aggressive, but they still need the additional security of the herd to protect them from powerful predators such as hyenas and lions.

Wasteful
Locusts can't digest cellulose, which makes them very inefficient grazers so they have to eat voraciously.

Swarming humans

When large crowds gather, the limited communication between people causes them to fall back on simple rules: keep moving in the same direction as everyone else; try not to get too squashed; don't get left behind. If there's a bottleneck or something triggers a panic, the crowd can suddenly become dangerous. In 2005, almost a thousand people died during a stampede in Iraq, when pilgrims marching to the Al-Kadhimiya Mosque in Baghdad became panicked by fears of a suicide bomber. But the science of swarming can also be useful to humans. The simplicity of the rules that control a swarm makes them ideal for robots and simulations. Airports use swarming behaviours adapted from ant colonies to model the flow of passengers through the terminal and to determine the best departure gate for each flight. Elsewhere hovering drones have already been successfully programmed to fly in formation and navigate around obstacles without a human to steer them.

© Thinkstock/Getty

ARCTIC WONDERS

Explore a strange frozen world and meet the wide variety of life that calls it home

 The Arctic is about as alien an environment as any non-native human will encounter on Earth. At the North Pole, days and nights last for six months at a time, temperatures can plunge to below -50 degrees Celsius (-58 degrees Fahrenheit) and there's no land for hundreds of miles. Instead, it's sheer white as far as the eye can see as a 14-million-square-kilometre (9.3-million-square-mile) sheet of thick ice stops you from getting your feet wet in a perpetually ice-capped Arctic Ocean that's never warmer than -2 degrees Celsius (28.4 degrees Fahrenheit). The skies often ripple and literally hum with the iridescence of the aurora borealis – surreal waves of light caused by high-energy particles colliding with our atmosphere, sun haloes and mirages. Meanwhile, even weirder acoustic phenomena can be caused by the cold, dense air and hard ice, allowing conversations or ▶

RECORD BREAKERS
HOT 'N' COLD

-109.8°c

BIGGEST TEMPERATURE RANGE

The village of Verkhoyansk, Siberia, recorded an Arctic record low of -69.8 degrees Celsius (-93.6 degrees Fahrenheit) in 1892 and hit a high of 40 degrees Celsius (104 degrees Fahrenheit) in July 1982.

DID YOU KNOW? Incredibly, when lemming populations boom, even large herbivores like reindeer will eat them

What is permafrost?

Much of the subsurface soil of Greenland, Svalbard and the northerly regions of Scandinavia, Russia, Alaska and Canada has been frozen since the last ice age. Continuous freezing and thawing, known as cryoturbation, allows meltwater to circulate and keep the soil relatively fertile. But lower layers than this remain permanently a few degrees below freezing, which can dramatically affect the landscape. Here, drainage is very poor, resulting in boggy ground dominated by mosses, small hills (pingos) pushed up by the ice and deep cracks where water can collect and freeze. Arctic areas with little permafrost are host to thick shrub tundra, willows, dwarf birch and other such hardy plants.

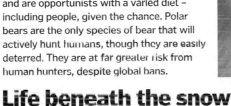

Danger: man-eater

The polar bear is the world's biggest land carnivore (along with the kodiak bear) and can weigh up to 680 kilograms (1,500 pounds). They're an intelligent species with an appetite for meat that's only rivalled by their insatiable curiosity. They have a highly developed sense of smell (capable of detecting a seal's breath from beneath ice) and are opportunists with a varied diet – including people, given the chance. Polar bears are the only species of bear that will actively hunt humans, though they are easily deterred. They are at far greater risk from human hunters, despite global bans.

An Arctic fox during winter and, inset, in summer

Seasonal wear

It's not just the landscape that sees a dramatic change between seasons. A range of creatures react to the melting snow by shedding their thick white coats and adopting black, brown or dappled coats that can make them look like an entirely different species, let alone a different animal. Roebuck deer turn from a ruddy fox colour in the summer to grey with white on their hindquarters, in order to lose potential predators in the snow. Arctic foxes and weasels have adopted this strategy too, as much as an aid to hunting their own quarry as to protecting themselves. Experiments have shown that the shedding of an old coat and growing a thicker one is triggered by temperature change, rather than the seasons, so the animal can change coats at the perfect time.

Life beneath the snow

How It Works digs deep to reveal the critters who set up home underground to escape the white-out

Arctic hare
This species will forage for sprouts and berries in the summer, but can resort to eating meat if necessary.

Lemming
Lemmings multiply exponentially when food is abundant, providing food for dozens of carnivores.

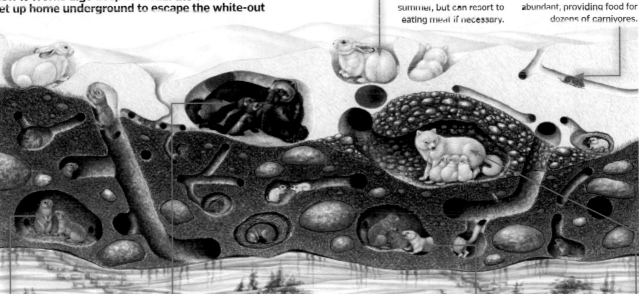

Arctic ground squirrel
One of the few Arctic species to hibernate, it gorges during autumn and then retreats underground in winter.

Wolverine
The biggest member of the weasel family is notoriously ferocious, tackling prey like deer and sheep, and even seeing off wolves and polar bears.

Least weasel
This small and successful carnivore has a huge range that covers large parts of North America, Europe, Russia, parts of Asia and even Morocco.

Arctic fox
Like Arctic wolves, Arctic foxes have extreme northerly territories and can have as many as 25 kits in a single litter.

© Corbis; Getty

A long-exposure shot showing the movement of the Sun across the North Pole

Land of the midnight Sun

The Arctic Circle region experiences one of its most famous phenomena over a period during the summer months: the midnight Sun. The number of days the Sun can be seen in the sky at its lowest point after 12am increases the closer to the North Pole you get. At the pole itself, the Sun can light up the sky for six months of the year, dipping behind the horizon for another six months, plunging the land into perpetual darkness in the winter. On the Arctic Circle itself, 66 degrees latitude, midnight Sun occurs from 12 June to 1 July. This phenomenon happens because the Earth tilting on its axis according to the seasons sees the poles shift into the dark or the light on either side of the planet. The South Pole experiences this as well, though there are no permanent human settlements south of the Antarctic Circle, unlike the Arctic.

---

otherwise inaudible sounds to be heard up to three kilometres (1.9 miles) away.

But along the continental landmasses that nudge above the geographical Arctic Circle and across the sea ice, a huge variety of highly specialised plants and animals still call this harsh region of the world home. They thrive here in a carefully balanced, interdependent ecosystem where the classic food chain hierarchy isn't as transparent as it seems.

At the apex is the polar bear, whose blubbery prey in the form of seals, walruses and even whales become trickier to catch in the summer when the ice retreats. In this lean season, everything edible becomes fair game for the world's largest land meat-eater, including birds, berries and seaweed. Filling out the predator niches below the polar bear are smaller carnivores like the Arctic fox, snowy owl and wolverine, which will all scavenge on leftovers as well as hunt their own food. In fact, despite running the risk of becoming an entrée itself, the crafty Arctic fox will often follow polar bears in the hope of a free meal.

Lemmings are incredibly important to the whole ecosystem. Their population fluctuates in a boom and bust system from low to enormously high in a regular cycle: at their peak, as well as directly feeding the upper echelons of predators in the food chain (which time the rearing of larger broods of young to this abundance of food), they strip the summer tundra of seeds and grasses. The proliferation of their faeces is devoured by invertebrates, bacteria and fungi as well as fertilising the soil for the next generation of flora. As a result, summer brings swarms of insect prey for insectivores like larks and waders, which in turn feed owls, falcons and other avian predators. Then, when the lemmings can no longer sustain their numbers, the population crashes as predation and disease take over, and the land can recover.

The climate is typically cold and dark, with long, freezing winters and short, cool summers. The range of temperatures in the Arctic Circle is huge compared to elsewhere in the world, from bitter winters that average -40 degrees Celsius (-40 degrees Fahrenheit) to hot summer highs of 30 degrees Celsius (86 degrees Fahrenheit) plus in some places. It is getting warmer though: summer 2012 saw unprecedented melting of the Arctic ice cap, with less than 50 per cent of the average summer ice coverage from 1979-2000. Some scientists predict that by 2050, the Arctic ice will melt completely in the summer months. The repercussions this could have go without saying, although we shouldn't jump the gun: these records only go as far back as 1979, so any doomsday predictions should definitely be put on ice for the time being.

Arctic wildlife

Get to know some of the resourceful creatures who have found a way to live in this bitter terrain

Dall sheep
These hardy animals inhabit the mountains in the northern Alaska and Canada, and are staple food for wolves, bears and coyotes.

Snowy owl
Snowy owls are nomadic, moving from their Arctic Circle habitat thousands of miles south according to prey and breeding season.

Caribou
Also known as reindeer, caribou are a species of deer that thrive in the North American and Eurasian tundra.

Musk oxen
These large, shaggy bovines graze the northern coast of Canada and Greenland. Their young and sick sometimes fall victim to wolves.

Arctic wolves
A subspecies of the grey wolf, the Arctic wolf isn't threatened by humans because its habitat is so far north.

Rock ptarmigan
This is a game species that lives in mountainous and Arctic regions. It too turns completely white in winter, except for its tail feathers.

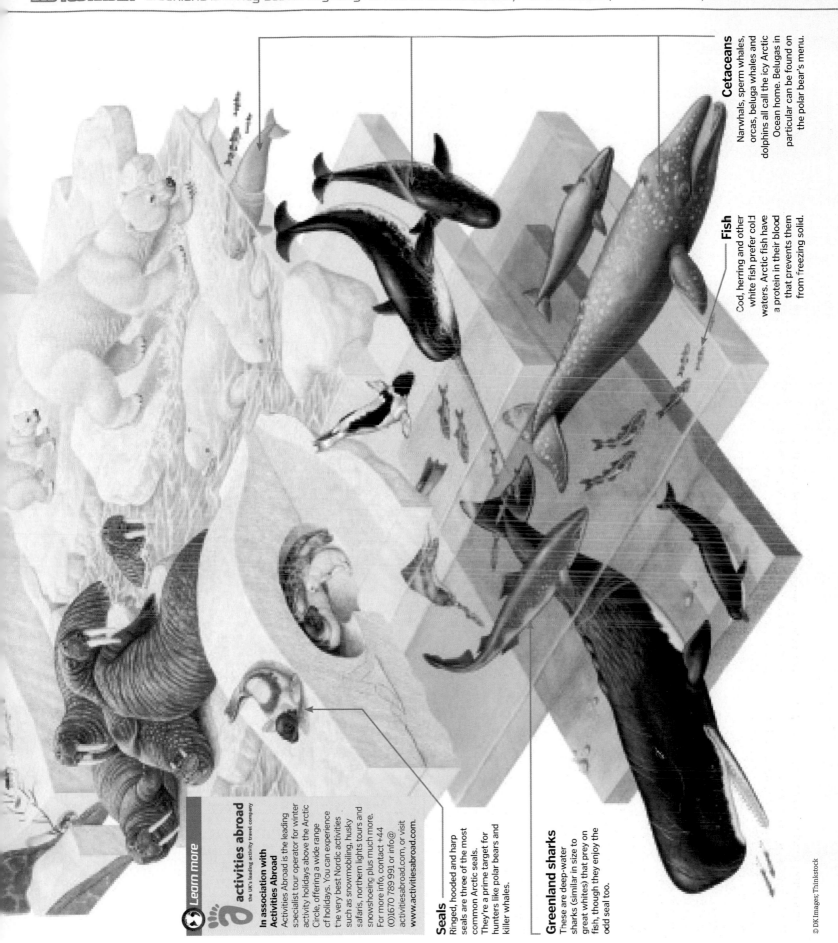

Cetaceans

Narwhals, sperm whales, orcas, beluga whales and dolphins all call the icy Arctic Ocean home. Belugas in particular can be found on the polar bear's menu.

Fish

Cod, herring and other white fish prefer cold waters. Arctic fish have a protein in their blood that prevents them from freezing solid.

⊙ Learn more

activities abroad
the UK's leading activity travel company

In association with Activities Abroad

Activities Abroad is the leading specialist tour operator for winter activity holidays above the Arctic Circle, offering a wide range of holidays. You can experience the very best Nordic activities such as snowmobiling, husky safaris, northern lights tours and snowshoeing plus much more. For more info, contact +44 (0)1670 789 991 or info@ activitiesabroad.com, or visit www.activitiesabroad.com.

Seals

Ringed, hooded and harp seals are three of the most common Arctic seals. They're a prime target for hunters like polar bears and killer whales.

Greenland sharks

These are deep-water sharks (similar in size to great whites) that prey on fish, though they enjoy the odd seal too.

© DK Images; Thinkstock

SEA LIFE

Sharks
050

Creatures of the coral reefs
072

Coral reefs
068

060
Pufferfish

044

© Corbis

© Thinkstock

© DK Images

© Jonathan Sun, 2005

© Corbis

UNDERWATER WONDERS

Real-life sea monsters so gigantic they dwarf the dinosaurs

 The open ocean is an extremely dangerous place to live. There are no trees to hide in, no burrows you can dig. Death surrounds you in three dimensions and everything larger than you is a predator. To survive, you have to think big. For some species, this means living as part of a large school of fish. For others, it means actually becoming genuinely, truly enormous. Tiny fish are eaten by small fish. Small fish are eaten by larger fish and so on. In every size bracket, natural selection favours the larger animal over the smaller one. Over millions of years, animal species tend to grow gradually larger and larger until they are too big to fit in anyone's mouth.

Being big is easier in the sea than on land because the buoyancy of water supports an animal evenly around its body, instead of just through the soles of its feet. An African elephant, for instance, can't grow much larger than ten tons without fracturing its own legs. A blue whale, meanwhile, will weigh this much before it's three months old.

Sea giants can get by with much smaller skeletons and their bones don't need to be so strong as they aren't subject to so much shock loading. But the density of water also presents some challenges. It's much harder to move through water than air, so streamlining is essential. A blue whale is 60 times longer than it is wide, compared with only 3.5 times for a hippo. The rear third of the whale's body provides the muscle to drive the 7.5-metre (25-foot) tail fluke up and down. Why does an animal with no natural predators need to cruise at 32 kilometres (20 miles) per hour? One reason is that it makes it much harder for barnacles to attach. It's ironic that an animal as large as a whale should

be threatened by something as small as a barnacle, but if enough take hold, the extra drag drastically increases the energy required to swim.

Food is the limiting factor for all large sea creatures. Light doesn't penetrate far in water so there are no grassy plains for large herbivores to graze. Instead the ocean is a thin soup, with the occasional chunk of meat bobbing in it. You can chase after the chunks, but catching them requires more energy, which means you need more food.

The largest animals in the sea have found it is more lucrative to swallow the 'soup' instead. This is a mixture of unicellular organisms, fish larvae and shrimp, ie plankton. They are too small to swim against the current, so it's just a matter of straining them from the water. The lion's mane jellyfish can do this while expending virtually no energy. It swims slowly up by pulsing its bell and then

1. BIG

Oarfish
15m (49ft) long and eel-like in appearance. Rare sightings of these normally deepwater fish may have given rise to legends of sea serpents.

2. BIGGER

Whale shark
The largest verified specimen was 12.7m (41.5ft) long, but there are unconfirmed reports of whale sharks that reach a staggering 18m (59ft)!

© Zac Wolf

3. BIGGEST

Leedsichthys problematicus
Fossils of this fish from 155 million years ago show it was 22m (72ft) long, making it the largest known fish ever to live.

© Dmitry Bogdanov

DID YOU KNOW? In 2010 in New Hampshire, 150 people were stung by a single dead lion's mane jellyfish which had disintegrated

The largest animal ever to have lived

Binomial name: Balaenoptera musculus

Type: Mammal

Diet: Filter feeder, eg krill, copepods

Average life span in the wild: 80 years

Weight: 180,000kg (396,832lb)

Size: 30m (98ft)

Worldwide distribution: Throughout the world's oceans, in five to seven main populations

Amazing fact: A newborn blue whale is the same size as a full-grown adult hippo at 2.7 tons. They drink 400l (700 pints) of milk every day and put on 90kg (198lb) of weight on a daily basis for the first seven months.

1 blue whale = 36 African elephants

Blue whale

Japanese spider crab

Claws that can straddle a car

Binomial name: Macrocheira kaempferi

Type: Crustacean

Diet: Carnivore, eg shellfish and carrion

Average life span in the wild: 80 years

Weight: 19kg (42lb)

Size: 3.8m (12.4ft) claw to claw

Worldwide distribution: Southern coast of Japan

Amazing fact: Those huge legs are quite fragile; indeed, almost three-quarters of Japanese spider crabs have a leg missing. This isn't a problem because they can survive with up to three legs missing and the walking legs can grow back when the crab moults to a new carapace.

1 Japanese spider crab = 1 child

Lion's mane jellyfish

A tangled cloud of floating stingers

Binomial name: Cyanea capillata

Type: Scyphozoan

Diet: Carnivore, eg plankton, small fish

Average life span in the wild: 1 year

Weight: 25kg (55lb)

Size: 2.5m (8.2ft)-diameter bell; 30m (90ft) long tentacles

Worldwide distribution: Arctic, north Atlantic and north Pacific

Amazing fact: The largest lion's mane jellyfish ever found washed up in Massachusetts Bay, USA, back in 1870. Its tentacles were 36m (118ft) long, making it longer than a blue whale and possibly the longest animal ever recorded.

1 lion's mane jellyfish = 1 child

relaxes to drift down again like a parachute. As it does, its tentacles billow out like hair to cover a wide area and prey gets speared by its stinger cells. Most large whales, along with the whale shark and the manta rays, adopt a slightly more active strategy by either swimming at speed into a dense cloud of plankton or taking huge gulps to suck them in, and then filtering them through a mesh of fibres made from modified teeth or gill bars. Different animals have different sized filter meshes that trap a particular size of plankton. Whales and whale sharks trap only the relatively large krill (a kind of shrimp) and crab larvae. A ton of krill contains about 450 thousand calories – which is about a tenth as much as a ton of chocolate – and an adult blue whale needs 3.5 tons of krill a day.

Very large animals need to protect their young to give them time to grow big enough to fend off predators. Whales are mammals so the embryo develops inside its mother to protect it. Great white sharks and manta rays have abandoned the usual fishy strategy of laying eggs on the seabed and copied mammals; the eggs are retained inside the female and hatch as live 'pups'. The mating and birthing of the whale shark has never been studied, but they are believed to use the same technique. Even the giant Pacific octopus will guard her nest of eggs until they hatch. Her month-long vigil is the last thing she does though because the exertion kills her.

Huge fish have other tricks normally reserved for mammals too. Large sharks and manta rays have a low surface area compared to their body size so they don't lose as much heat. This makes them effectively warm-blooded and allows them to maintain a more active lifestyle even in colder seas.

The best-studied ocean giants are those that live in fairly shallow water – above 200 metres (656 feet) – where most of the plankton is. But there are very large animals including squid that live in the perpetual blackness beyond. If you are an air-breathing mammal like a sperm whale that feeds on these squid, you face a unique challenge. To feed you need to dive to depths of up to three kilometres (1.9 miles), but to breathe you need to return to the surface. The pressure change in a round-trip is almost 300 atmospheres! Sperm whales have three times more myoglobin in their muscles to store more oxygen and their ribcage is flexible so that the lungs collapse under pressure and reduce the amount of nitrogen that dissolves into the blood. Despite this, the skeletons of older whales show pitting from the decompression effects of repeated dives. ❁

Supersized diets

Large animals have big appetites. Exactly how big depends on how fast you burn energy. At the bottom of the scale are the invertebrates. Jellyfish can grow to be huge, but their body is about 95 per cent water and they move very slowly. Eating just 0.04 per cent of their body weight is enough to sustain them. Blue whales, at the other end of the scale, have a warm-blooded body to support as well as a complex brain. But the hungriest creatures in the ocean are the killer whales. Their extremely active, predatory lifestyle means they need 3.7 per cent of their body weight each day to survive; when your body weighs six tons, that's a lot of fish!

How the largest animal eats the smallest prey

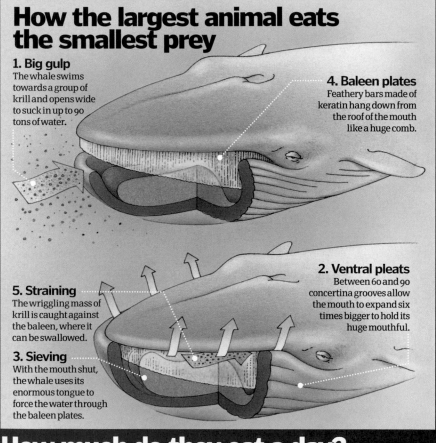

1. Big gulp
The whale swims towards a group of krill and opens wide to suck in up to 90 tons of water.

4. Baleen plates
Feathery bars made of keratin hang down from the roof of the mouth like a huge comb.

5. Straining
The wriggling mass of krill is caught against the baleen, where it can be swallowed.

3. Sieving
With the mouth shut, the whale uses its enormous tongue to force the water through the baleen plates.

2. Ventral pleats
Between 60 and 90 concertina grooves allow the mouth to expand six times bigger to hold its huge mouthful.

How much do they eat a day?
...and how many cheeseburgers would that equate to?

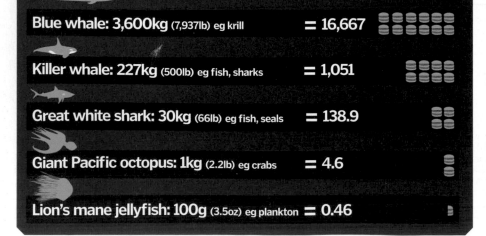

Blue whale: 3,600kg (7,937lb) eg krill **= 16,667**

Killer whale: 227kg (500lb) eg fish, sharks **= 1,051**

Great white shark: 30kg (66lb) eg fish, seals **= 138.9**

Giant Pacific octopus: 1kg (2.2lb) eg crabs **= 4.6**

Lion's mane jellyfish: 100g (3.5oz) eg plankton **= 0.46**

The shark with the biggest bite

Binomial name: Carcharodon carcharias

Type: Elasmobranch fish

Diet: Carnivore, eg tuna, dolphins

Average life span in the wild: 30 years

Weight: 1,900kg (4,189lb)

Size: 6m (19.7ft)

Worldwide distribution: Tropical and temperate seas, eg off South Africa, Australia and USA

1 great white shark = 27 men

Each arm is as long as you are

Giant Pacific octopus

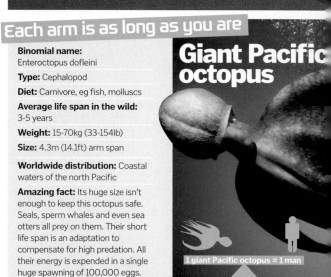

Binomial name: Enteroctopus dofleini

Type: Cephalopod

Diet: Carnivore, eg fish, molluscs

Average life span in the wild: 3-5 years

Weight: 15-70kg (33-154lb)

Size: 4.3m (14.1ft) arm span

Worldwide distribution: Coastal waters of the north Pacific

Amazing fact: Its huge size isn't enough to keep this octopus safe. Seals, sperm whales and even sea otters all prey on them. Their short life span is an adaptation to compensate for high predation. All their energy is expended in a single huge spawning of 100,000 eggs.

1 giant Pacific octopus = 1 man

Super-smart king of the gliders

Giant oceanic manta ray

Binomial name: Manta birostris

Type: Elasmobranch fish

Diet: Filter feeder, eg plankton, shrimp

Average life span in the wild: 27 years

Weight: 1,300kg (2,866lb)

Size: 6.7m (22ft)

Worldwide distribution: Shallow water of the western Pacific and Indian Ocean

Amazing fact: Manta rays may be the most intelligent of the sharks, rays and skates, as their brain-to-body ratio is much higher than other fish. A network of blood vessels called the rete helps to keep their brain warm.

1 giant oceanic manta ray = 18 men

900KG

HEAVIEST TURTLE
The largest turtle ever found was a leatherback that washed up on a beach in Wales in 1988. It was 2.75 metres (nine feet) long and at least 100 years old when it died.

DID YOU KNOW? *Lobsters don't seem to age and grow almost indefinitely. The biggest ever caught was over 1m (3.2ft) long!*

Great white shark

Amazing fact: Great white sharks have two stomach compartments and can store food in one compartment for days or weeks without digesting it. Great whites have been found with shoes, wigs, newspapers, licence plates and even cannon balls in their stomachs.

Whale shark
The world's largest fish

Binomial name:
Rhincodon typus

Type: Elasmobranch fish

Diet: Filter feeder, eg krill, crab larvae

Average life span in the wild:
80 years

Weight: 9,000kg (19,842lb)

Size: 9.7m (32ft)

Worldwide distribution:
Tropical seas worldwide

Amazing fact: According to the Whale Shark & Oceanic Research Center, there are several reports of whale sharks three or four times bigger than the norm. Indeed, in 1994 a shark caught off the coast of Taiwan allegedly weighed almost 36 tons!

1 whale shark = 1.8 African elephants

Ones that got away!
Meet a few more behemoths of the deep

Seven-arm octopus
Heavier than the giant Pacific octopus, but with shorter tentacles. It actually has eight arms altogether but keeps one coiled up out of the way, except when it's mating.

Colossal squid
Thought to grow up to 14m (45.9ft) long, an adult specimen has never been found. It has the largest eyes in the animal kingdom.

Sperm whale
This 40-ton cetacean has the largest brain of any animal ever to have lived and has teeth that weigh 1kg (2.2lb) each. Its diet includes the colossal squid.

Giant clam
The biggest bivalve mollusc. They can weigh up to 200kg (441lb) and live on a combination of filter feeding and photosynthesis from symbiotic algae.

Brisingid starfish
Midgardia xandaros is the biggest starfish. Its slender arms can be up to 1.4m (4.6ft) long. Most starfish have five arms while some, like the one pictured, have 12 or more!

Giant isopod
Bathynomus giganticus might look like a garden woodlouse, but this relative can weigh up to 1.7kg (3.7lb) and reach 76cm (29.9in) long; that's the size of a newborn baby!

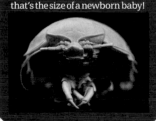

What does it take to sustain a whale shark?

© Emily S Damstra

Mouth
When a whale shark is feeding, its mouth can gape 1.5m (4.9ft) wide. This creates tremendous suction that makes it impossible for small animals to swim out of the way. Whale sharks have over 300 rows of teeth but each tooth is quite small and they don't appear to serve any purpose.

Gills
The real business of feeding occurs at the gills. As well as extracting oxygen from the water, the gills have ten filter pads (see picture) that sieve out anything over 2-3mm (0.08-0.12in). Although efficient, sometimes the pads can become blocked and the shark must 'cough' to clear them.

Brain
Whale sharks have quite small brains compared to other sharks. Brain tissue requires a lot of energy, so big brains must earn their keep. These sharks don't actively hunt, and their huge size keeps them safe from most predators, so they don't need the same cunning as other shark species.

Skeleton
Sharks have cartilage rather than bone, and no ribcage. Whale sharks beached in shallow water are quickly crushed to death by their own body weight. In the open sea, though, a cartilage skeleton saves weight because it has half the density of bone. This makes the whale shark a much more efficient swimmer.

Skin
10cm (3.9in) thick skin provides a rigid covering that maintains the shark's streamlined shape; when we swim, the water causes our skin to ripple, which leads to drag. Shark skin is also covered with tiny placoid scales. Each one is structured like a tooth, with enamel, dentine and a pulp cavity; the scales reduce microturbulence.

Liver
Instead of a swim bladder, sharks use an oil called squalene to maintain buoyancy. This is stored in the liver and, since oil isn't as light as gas, the whale shark needs lots of it – indeed, the liver can weigh up to two tons! Fishermen in Kenya hunt whale sharks for their liver and the oil from a single shark can last them for years.

© Corbis; Thinkstock; DK Images; Getty

SHARKS!

50 INCREDIBLE FACTS ABOUT THE PLANET'S MOST EXTREME UNDERWATER PREDATOR

MOST CELEBRATED

1. Jaws
After a gigantic great white shark goes on a killing spree, a police chief, marine scientist and experienced fisherman set sail to stop it, with explosive and gory results.

MOST DERIDED

2. Shark Attack 3
Despite being extinct for over 24 million years, megalodon returns in this widely condemned B-movie to wreak gory havoc. Can no one stop its reign of terror?

MOST STUPID

3. Mega Shark vs Giant Octopus
When a colossal shark and octopus have a royal rumble off the coast of California, only scientist Emma MacNeil can save the Earth.

DID YOU KNOW? You are roughly twice as likely to die from a coconut falling on your head than a shark bite

Nearly every stereotype of the shark is wrong. They aren't primitive animals, they aren't mindless killing machines and they don't prey on humans. Sharks are elasmobranchs, meaning that they are fish that have cartilage skeletons instead of bones. Far from being an evolutionary leftover, however, this evolved to save weight so that large sharks could still be fast and agile swimmers. Cartilage also lets sharks conserve calcium and phosphorous, which is important because they need both for making teeth. And they get through a *lot* of those. Sharks treat their teeth as disposable weapons and can lose a couple with every bite. In fact, sharks get through so many teeth in their lifetime that the availability of the mineral phosphorous was historically the biggest constraint on their spread around the world.

Sharks haven't always been objects of fear. Victorian sailors regarded them as entirely benign – like dolphins. Then in 1916, along the coast of New Jersey, four people were killed and one badly injured in a spate of unprovoked attacks by sharks. This sparked a media frenzy that inspired the 1974 novel *Jaws* by Peter Benchley, and sharks have been the villains of the sea ever since. Despite the fact that you are roughly twice as likely to die from a coconut landing on your head than a shark bite, we still have a grossly inflated sense of the threat these creatures pose. Sharks are apex predators and very well adapted for hunting in the sea, but the fact remains that for every human eaten by a shark, 20 million sharks are eaten by humans. ✿

Sharks were once regarded as benign by sailors

© Thinkstock

SHARK ANATOMY

1 What's inside a shark?

Cloaca
Combined opening for excretion, defecation and reproduction. Males have clasper fins instead of a penis.

Second dorsal fin

Upper lobe

Caudal fin

Lower lobe

Epigonal
Unique to sharks. It is thought to help with making red blood cells, since sharks have no bone marrow.

Spine
Made of cartilage rather than bone. It extends into the top tail fin, for extra power.

First dorsal fin

Spine

Pelvic fin

Corkscrew valve
Slows down food through the very short intestine, to give enough time to digest it.

Stomach
Very large compared to the intestine and can stretch to cope with large meals.

Pectoral fin

Nostrils
Used for smelling, not breathing. Some sharks have protrusions called nasal barbels that act as smelling probes.

Heart
Sharks have much lower blood pressure than us. Swimming muscles assist the weak heart.

Liver
Full of dense squalene oil, the liver can comprise up to 30 per cent of the shark's mass and take up as much as 90 per cent of the space in the body.

© DK Images

2 Why do sharks have so many fins?

They don't really have many more fins than other fish, it's just that they are larger and more conspicuous. Sharks use their wide pectoral fins to generate lift, like the wings of a plane. The tail, or caudal fin, has a larger upper lobe because the spine extends into it. This generates thrust and the notches reduce turbulence. The dorsal and anal fins reduce the amount of side-to-side motion as the tail beats. The second dorsal fin is the only one missing from other fish and it offsets the movement of the large upper caudal lobe.

"Sharks treat their teeth as disposable weapons and can lose a couple with every bite"

SHARK BITES

6 DO SHARKS HAVE TONGUES AND A SENSE OF TASTE?

The basihyal looks a bit like a tongue, but it is really just a protrusion of cartilage on the floor of the mouth. Sharks have tastebuds on the rest of their mouth, though, and often give prey a test bite to check the flavour.

7 HOW CAN YOU TELL A SHARK'S GENDER?

Male sharks have a pair of protrusions called claspers on their belly, between the pelvic fins. These are used like a penis to insert into the female's cloaca.

© Jlenden

8 HOW DO SHARKS HEAR?

A small opening on each side of the head leads to the inner ear. Sharks have very good hearing that is tuned to lower frequencies than our ears. They can hear fish struggling from several miles away.

9 HOW DO YOU TELL THE AGE OF A SHARK?

It's not easy. Because they shed their teeth so often, you can't measure the growth rings in them to determine age. The vertebrae have growth rings too, but they aren't added at a uniform rate, so researchers inject marker chemicals to captured sharks to provide reference samples.

3 If a shark stops swimming does it drown?

Yes. It's essential that sharks keep moving in order to get enough water across their gills to breathe. Find out more about shark respiration below…

2. Gill slits
It passes over the gill bars and exits through the gill slits.

4. Spiracle
Bottom-dwelling sharks have an opening behind the eye that can pump water over the gills when the shark isn't moving.

1. Inhale
Water enters through the mouth, driven by the forward motion of the shark.

Gill septum
Capillaries
Gill arch
Oxygen-depleted water
Gill filaments
Oxygen-rich water

5. Gulping
Some species also use the mouth to actively gulp water across the gills.

Gill arches
Ventral aorta

Heart

3. Passive ventilation
Open-water species need to keep swimming anyway or they will sink, so this system works fine.

4 How many teeth does a shark get through in a lifetime? Why is this number so high?

Shark teeth aren't embedded in the jaw, but are attached to the skin. They are designed to be disposable and are continually replaced like a conveyor belt from the back of the mouth. A great white shark can get through up to 50,000 teeth in its lifetime.

Growth
Layers of razor-sharp, serrated teeth roll forward to replace broken or missing ones.

© DK Images

The huge jaws of a prehistoric shark, the megalodon

"A great white shark can get through up to 50,000 teeth in its life"

© Thinkstock

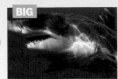

BIG

1. Great white shark
The great white shark (carcharodon carcharias) is actually not the largest. The largest example found to date measured 7.9m (26ft).

BIGGER

2. Basking shark
The basking shark (cetorhinus maximus) is rather large, weighing in at up to 19 tons despite being a harmless filter feeder.

BIGGEST

3. Whale shark
Measuring in at over 12.8m (42ft) in exceptional cases, the whale shark (rhincodon typus) is the largest on the planet; they can live for up to 70 years.

DID YOU KNOW? Open-water species have to keep swimming or they will sink

5

How do sharks give birth, and what are 'mermaid's purses'?

Most sharks retain their eggs inside the female and give birth to live young. A few species, including the horn shark and Port Jackson shark lay eggs inside a leathery egg case. Empty egg cases that wash up on the shore are called mermaid's purses.

© Alice Wiegand

(Above) Some sharks lay eggs inside a case; (Below) Shark skin scales resemble tiny teeth

10 DO SHARKS HAVE BONES?
No. Sharks belong to the elasmobranch group of fish that have lighter, more flexible cartilage in their skeleton, instead of bone. Their muscles are anchored directly to the inside of their tough skin.

11 HOW DO SHARKS STAY BUOYANT?
Sharks don't have a swim bladder like other fish, so they use their liver instead. The amount of squalene oil stored there is adjusted to leave the shark slightly heavier than water. The extra buoyancy is supplied by dynamic lift from the shark's fins as it swims.

12 HOW GOOD IS A SHARK'S EYESIGHT?
Sharks have good night vision and can contract and dilate their pupils, which bony fish cannot do. Sharks are either colour-blind or can see only shades of grey and green.

13 DOES A SHARK'S SKIN HELP IT SWIM FASTER?
Shark skin is covered with scales like other fish, but shark scales are made from dentine and actually resemble tiny teeth more than scales. These 'dermal denticles' generate tiny vortices on their trailing edges as the shark swims and this vastly reduces the shark's drag through the water.

© Science Photo Library

SPECIES

Megalodon

Great white

Size
Megalodon was probably 12-20m (39-66ft) long. That's larger than a modern whale shark.

Bones
Although megalodon didn't have true bones, its skeleton was much more calcified than modern sharks.

Snout
Megalodon ate whales, so its snout was shorter to let it bite into large prey.

Teeth
18cm (7in) long and very robust. Edges were lined with very fine serrations.

Jaw
Calculations suggest that megalodon had a bite five times more powerful than that of a tyrannosaurus rex.

© Science Photo Library

14

Was megalodon a true shark?

Megalodon is an extinct species that lived between 28 and 1.5 million years ago. Only teeth fossils and a handful of isolated vertebrae have ever been found, so most of what we know about this animal is extrapolated from comparisons with living sharks. It does seem to have been a true shark – probably related to the great white and mako sharks. But it was much bigger – between 2.5 and 3 times the size of a great white.

15

How many shark species are there?

True sharks are classified in the superorder selachimorpha and there are more than 440 species alive today. A new species of shark, skate or ray is identified approximately every two weeks.

SHARK BITES

21 HOW LONG DO SHARKS LIVE?

Most species live for between 20 and 30 years. But the whale shark is estimated to live for up to 100 years.

22 WHAT'S THE SMALLEST SPECIES OF SHARK?

A kind of deepwater dogfish shark called etmopterus perryi. It lives in the Caribbean Sea and grows no larger than 20cm (7.8in).

23 DO ANY SHARKS GLOW IN THE DARK?

Yes, a few species use bioluminescence to lure prey. The brightest is the cookie cutter shark, which glows over its entire stomach, except for a dark band round its neck. This makes it look like a much smaller fish silhouetted against the sky.

24 IS IT TRUE THAT SHARKS DON'T GET CANCER?

Sharks definitely do get cancer, but there's some evidence that a compound called angiogenin, an inhibitor in shark cartilage, reduces the ability of tumours to grow.

25 WHAT'S THE MOST ENDANGERED SPECIES OF SHARK?

Both the large sawfish and the common sawfish are listed as critically endangered by the International Union for Conservation of Nature. Their saw snouts become very easily entangled in fishing nets.

26 WHICH IS THE FASTEST SHARK EVER?

The shortfin mako shark. An open-water hunter that chases fast fish such as tuna, it can reach up to 32km/h (20mph).

16 How does a hammerhead shark know which way it's going?

Despite their oddly shaped heads, hammerhead sharks can see forwards at least as well as other sharks, and possibly better. All fish have their eyes set on the sides of their head, but the hammer or cephalofoil on a hammerhead shark is right at the front so they have much less snout to get in the way of forward vision than other sharks. The wide separation also allows better directionality of the special electrical sense of sharks. Hammerheads eat stingrays and their electrical sense helps them find rays buried under the sand on the seabed.

Big bodied
The whale shark. As well as being the largest shark, this is also the largest fish. Only true whales are larger. Adults can be over 20m (66ft).

© Science Photo Library

18 What's the biggest shark?

17 Which ones don't look like sharks?

Stingray

Electric ray

Sawfish

Skate

Frilled shark

Manta ray

Carpet shark

19

© Thinkstock

What is the deadliest shark?

The International Shark Attack File keeps records going back to the 16th century and shows that the tiger, bull and great white between them account for 99 per cent of shark attacks on humans. Of these, the great white tops the list with 249 unprovoked attacks and 65 fatalities.

20 What's the oldest shark on record?

Modern sharks date back around 100 million years, but there were primitive sharks as long ago as 420 million years. One of the earliest was cladoselache, which lived around 370 million years ago. Very well preserved fossils show skin, muscles and even some internal organs. Apart from a few around the mouth and the fins, cladoselache had no scales. Its teeth were smooth and it swallowed its prey whole.

BEHAVIOUR

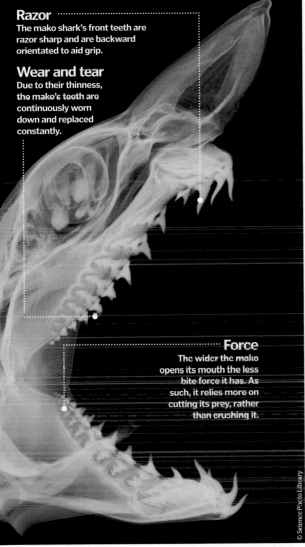

Razor
The mako shark's front teeth are razor sharp and are backward orientated to aid grip.

Wear and tear
Due to their thinness, the mako's teeth are continuously worn down and replaced constantly.

Force
The wider the mako opens its mouth the less bite force it has. As such, it relies more on cutting its prey, rather than crushing it.

© Science Photo Library

27 How powerful are shark jaws?

A six-metre shark, such as a great white, can exert more than 18,000 newtons of force with a bite. That's a huge force – twice as much as the largest alligators, which have the strongest bite of any land animal, and more even than current estimates of the bite of the T-rex. But it doesn't end there. An alligator only exerts maximum bite force when its jaws are almost shut. The wider it opens its mouth, the less leverage is available for the jaw muscles and the weaker the bite becomes. Great white sharks have a unique arrangement of muscles in their jaw that enables them to exert maximum bite force, regardless of how wide their mouth is opened.

28 How smart are sharks?

Sharks have a similar ratio of brain to body mass as that in most mammals and birds. They certainly aren't mindless killing machines. Seven great white sharks were observed in 1987 off the coast of South Africa, co-operating to refloat a dead, beached whale so that they could eat it. When great whites hunt dolphins, they approach from above and behind, to prevent the dolphin using its echolocation sense to detect the shark.

29 What are the weirdest items found in a shark?

- Ladies' pyjamas
- A rubber tyre
- A roll of chicken wire
- Tar paper
- A bag of potatoes
- Odd shoes
- A dog
- A can of Spam
- A sack of coal
- The head and forequarters of a crocodile

(All found in the stomachs of tiger sharks, which are the most indiscriminate feeders.)

31 DO SHARKS SLEEP?

Not properly. Some species rest on the seabed, but their eyes will still follow nearby swimmers. Others may rest one half of their brain at a time, like dolphins do. The spiny dogfish uses its spine to co-ordinate swimming, so that it can rest its entire brain without stopping.

32 ARE SHARKS SOLITARY OR DO THEY LIVE IN GROUPS?

Many species are highly social. Scalloped hammerheads can form schools of up to 100 sharks, for example. Even the normally solitary hunting species can congregate in groups around a rich food source or to breed.

33 DO SHARKS EVER ATTACK/PREY ON OTHER SHARK SPECIES?

Most shark species have fairly specific diets – blue sharks mainly eat squid, for example. But great whites, tiger sharks and mako sharks will eat tuna, seals, sea lions, dolphins and even smaller shark species. Hammerhead sharks dine almost exclusively on rays, which are closely related to sharks.

34 DOES ANY OTHER ANIMAL PREY ON SHARKS?

Orca (killer whales) have been known to attack and kill great white sharks, and sperm whales are also occasionally believed to kill sharks. These are exceptions, though. Most of the time, sharks sit firmly at the top of the food chain.

30 Do sharks use electricity to sense their prey?

Ampullae of Lorenzini
These jelly-filled sacs in the head help the shark locate prey.

Sharks have an arrangement of jelly-filled pores, concentrated around the head. These are called ampullae of Lorenzini and they allow the shark to detect electromagnetic fields. As well as giving sharks an internal compass, this lets them detect the minute electrical fields produced by the muscle contractions of all living animals. A few fish and other animals can also sense electrical fields, but sharks have by far the most sensitive version of this sixth sense.

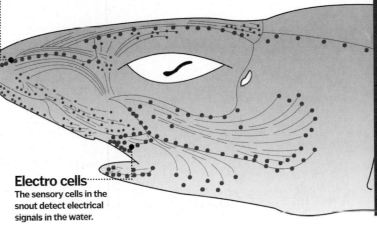

Electro cells
The sensory cells in the snout detect electrical signals in the water.

35

Can sharks smell blood from miles away, and if so how?

The open-water species can detect blood at concentrations as low as one part per million, but they are even more attracted to the smell of fish guts. By comparing the timing of the scent's arrival at each nostril, they can tell its direction and quickly home in on distant prey.

Eyelid
The eyes roll back in their sockets before the shark strikes.

36

How do sharks attack?

Only a few species of shark are solitary ambush predators – many are filter feeders or eat small fish and crustaceans on the seabed. The aggressive hunters – tiger shark, bull shark and great white – usually patrol close to the surface. They attack at dawn or dusk, when light is poor, and from above so their light-coloured bellies make them hard to spot against the sky. Some species of shark have an extra transparent eyelid (called a nictitating membrane) that can shield their eyes, but the great white does not, so it rolls its eyes back in their sockets just before its strike connects, to protect them. Very often sharks will pursue a hit-and-run technique, taking a single bite out of their prey and then retreating to allow it to bleed to death.

Great white sharks roll their eyes when they attack

37 HOW MANY PEOPLE ARE KILLED/ATTACKED BY SHARKS A YEAR?

In the last ten years, the number of fatalities caused by sharks averages out at less than five per year, worldwide.

38 HOW MANY SHARKS ARE KILLED/ATTACKED BY PEOPLE A YEAR?

About 100 million sharks are killed every year by humans. Some of this is recreational fishing, but most is commercial. Sharks are killed for their fins for shark fin soup, and in the Australian state of Victoria, shark is the most commonly used fish in fish and chip shops.

39 IF YOU TURN A SHARK UPSIDE DOWN DOES IT GO INTO A TRANCE?

This is called 'tonic immobility' and it doesn't work with all species, but yes, lemon, nurse and bull sharks and even great whites will suddenly become paralysed when flipped on their back. This may have evolved as part of mating, to protect females from aggressive males.

40 HOW FAST CAN A SHARK SWIM?

Sharks contract the muscles on their left and right sides alternately to drive their large tails sideways. This makes the head move side to side. Their rigid skin and drag-reducing dermal denticles allow them to reach speeds of up to 32km/h (20mph).

41 Statistically, what are the most deadly places on Earth with regard to shark attacks?

Between 1580 and 2010 there have been 2,320 recorded shark attacks worldwide. Here is a statistical breakdown of the most dangerous areas in the world.

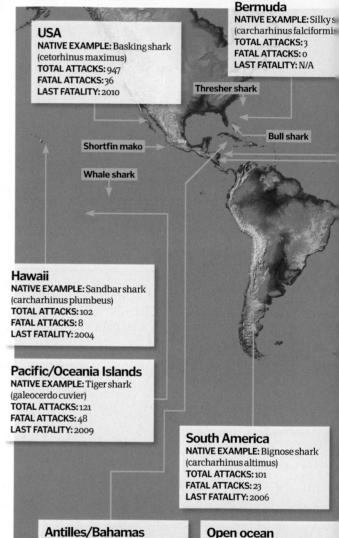

USA
NATIVE EXAMPLE: Basking shark (cetorhinus maximus)
TOTAL ATTACKS: 947
FATAL ATTACKS: 36
LAST FATALITY: 2010

Bermuda
NATIVE EXAMPLE: Silky s (carcharhinus falciformi
TOTAL ATTACKS: 3
FATAL ATTACKS: 0
LAST FATALITY: N/A

Thresher shark

Bull shark

Shortfin mako

Whale shark

Hawaii
NATIVE EXAMPLE: Sandbar shark (carcharhinus plumbeus)
TOTAL ATTACKS: 102
FATAL ATTACKS: 8
LAST FATALITY: 2004

Pacific/Oceania Islands
NATIVE EXAMPLE: Tiger shark (galeocerdo cuvier)
TOTAL ATTACKS: 121
FATAL ATTACKS: 48
LAST FATALITY: 2009

South America
NATIVE EXAMPLE: Bignose shark (carcharhinus altimus)
TOTAL ATTACKS: 101
FATAL ATTACKS: 23
LAST FATALITY: 2006

Antilles/Bahamas
NATIVE EXAMPLE: Blacktip shark (carcharhinus limbatus)
TOTAL ATTACKS: 61
FATAL ATTACKS: 15
LAST FATALITY: 1972

Open ocean
NATIVE EXAMPLE: Dusky shark (carcharhinus obscurus)
TOTAL ATTACKS: 17
FATAL ATTACKS: 5
LAST FATALITY: 2006

42 Are there sharks living in every ocean on the planet?

Yes. Sharks can cope with a wide range of ocean temperatures, even within the same species. Some sharks migrate thousands of miles each year.

THE STATS
GREAT WHITE SHARK

LIFE SPAN	25 years	LENGTH	4.6 metres	WEIGHT	5,000lbs
BITE FORCE	4,000lbs	NUMBER OF TEETH	3,000	TOOTH SIZE	>3 inches

DID YOU KNOW? There are over 30 species of shark native to British waters

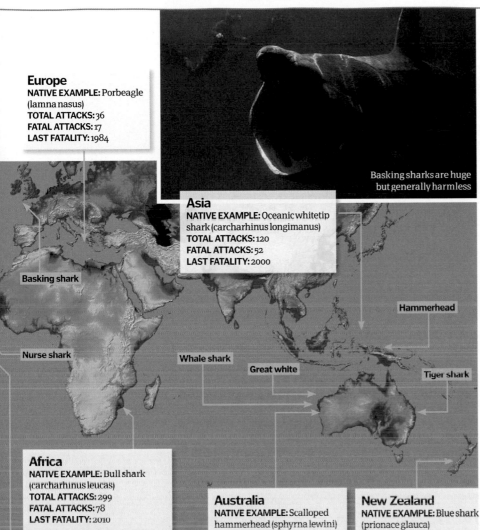

Basking sharks are huge but generally harmless

Europe
NATIVE EXAMPLE: Porbeagle (lamna nasus)
TOTAL ATTACKS: 36
FATAL ATTACKS: 17
LAST FATALITY: 1984

Asia
NATIVE EXAMPLE: Oceanic whitetip shark (carcharhinus longimanus)
TOTAL ATTACKS: 120
FATAL ATTACKS: 52
LAST FATALITY: 2000

Basking shark

Nurse shark

Whale shark

Great white

Hammerhead

Tiger shark

Africa
NATIVE EXAMPLE: Bull shark (carcharhinus leucas)
TOTAL ATTACKS: 299
FATAL ATTACKS: 78
LAST FATALITY: 2010

Australia
NATIVE EXAMPLE: Scalloped hammerhead (sphyrna lewini)
TOTAL ATTACKS: 417
FATAL ATTACKS: 131
LAST FATALITY: 2010

New Zealand
NATIVE EXAMPLE: Blue shark (prionace glauca)
TOTAL ATTACKS: 44
FATAL ATTACKS: 8
LAST FATALITY: 1968

Central America
NATIVE EXAMPLE: Great white shark (carcharodon carcharias)
TOTAL ATTACKS: 52
FATAL ATTACKS: 26
LAST FATALITY: 2008

43 What's the most common shark in British waters?

Most of the small shark species seen off the British coast are referred to collectively as dogfish. This includes the spotted dogfish and the spiny dogfish. They can reach 1-1.5m (3.3-4.9ft) in length.

44 Is there such a thing as a freshwater shark?

No shark species spends all its time in fresh water, but both the river shark and the bull shark have specially adapted kidneys that allow them to cope with fresh water for extended periods. They can swim hundreds of miles up large rivers in search of prey.

45 Where can I find sharks?

BASKING SHARK: temperate waters, both coastal and offshore
BULL SHARK: shallow tropical coastal waters, estuaries and large rivers
GREAT WHITE: coastal and offshore temperate waters worldwide
HAMMERHEAD: temperate and subtropical waters on the continental shelf
NURSE SHARK: shallow tropical reefs off the coast of West Africa and Central America
SHORTFIN MAKO: offshore tropical and temperate waters worldwide
TIGER SHARK: tropical and subtropical deep water around reefs
THRESHER SHARK: tropical and temperate waters on the continental shelf of North America and Asia
WHALE SHARK: offshore tropical and subtropical water, especially the west coast of Australia

INTERVIEW
Richard Peirce

Richard Peirce, chairman of the Shark Trust, answers a few questions about sharks, their behaviour around humans and how many species are becoming increasingly endangered.

46 What kinds of activities does the Shark Trust undertake?

The Shark Trust was founded in 1997 and it was set up to advance the profile of all families of sharks through awareness, education, legislation and policy. In recent years we have become accepted as the first stop for government departments wanting to take a look at fisheries legislation.

47 Which sharks are native to the UK's waters and are media claims of danger overblown?

My book, Sharks In British Seas, lists the 30 or so species that inhabit our native waters. There are many top-of-the-range and iconic species close to home. For example, the hammerhead is a British species, the same can be said for threshers, makos and blue sharks. A favourite of mine is also native: the porbeagle, which is a genuine mini great white... and is quite often mistaken as one.

On the area of danger to the public... there has never been a single recorded shark attack in British waters in the conventional sense. There have been shark-caused deaths and accidental incidents, but there has been nothing like we have tragically seen in the Seychelles recently, despite us having some sharks that certain people would consider dangerous to man.

48 Does a shark's behaviour differ in the presence of humans?

It differs mainly from species to species and between circumstances. If you are a diver on air and just chilling out, diving along a reef, that is completely different from being with a shark in a baited situation where its feeding senses have been stimulated. So if you are chumming for sharks – a process where you put an attractant into the water to generate a scent corridor – and in a cage then they will be behaving completely differently.

49 What is cage diving all about?

Cage diving is a fantastic way to see sharks... The cage has a hinged top that rests on the surface of the water. So the human jumps over the side of the boat and into the cage... They then proceed to move to the bottom of the cage, which is commonly about nine feet in depth. So the top of their head is usually only about three feet below the surface of the water... There is a rope out with some bait on it and the shark is drawn to that. The bait line is then drawn towards the cage and the shark will follow it. The boat's operator will then say something like 'coming in from the left', and the cage's occupant will then take a big draw of breath and submerge themselves for ten seconds or so, viewing the shark as it passes.

50 Where is the best place in the world to go cage diving?

I would say South Africa. It isn't necessarily the place with the clearest waters, but it is affordable and it is pretty commercialised, with companies running multiple dives a day. You can do it off Britain, though, and I myself helped set up Atlantic Divers in Newquay, Cornwall.

The life cycle of a sockeye salmon

Discover the epic journey a salmon undertakes from birth to death

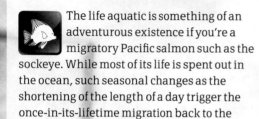

The life aquatic is something of an adventurous existence if you're a migratory Pacific salmon such as the sockeye. While most of its life is spent out in the ocean, such seasonal changes as the shortening of the length of a day trigger the once-in-its-lifetime migration back to the freshwater rivers of its youth.

The annual salmon run performed by the adult fish takes place usually in late-spring to summer. This instinctive behaviour, written in the genes, sees the salmon battle its way from the ocean back along estuaries, past fishermen's hooks, up treacherous bear-lined rapids and on to the gravel beds of the stream where it was born. For some varieties of salmon runs can cover staggering distances of up to 3,200 kilometres (2,000 miles) up the Yukon River. It's unknown quite how the salmon knows where it's heading, but it's thought it could be following its nose and tracking a certain familiar scent.

The death-defying voyage is exhausting for the adult salmon and, once it arrives at the spawning ground and lays/fertilises its eggs, it will die. The new eggs develop into the next generation of salmon that will embark on precisely the same cycle of life.

Around six to nine weeks after the eggs have been laid and fertilised in the gravel, the young will begin to hatch in the freshwater where they will remain developing for up to three years. First hatching as alevins they develop from defenceless small fry through to well-camouflaged parrs, then smolts and eventually to adults. After that they will migrate to the ocean for their first taste of saltwater where they will continue their growth into maturity. ✿

Ladders for fish

When salmon make their way back upstream to spawn, they can encounter a number of manmade barriers, such as dams and locks. To ensure the fish can progress, humans have built stepped channels that go over or around the obstructions. Known as fish ladders these help the salmon overcome otherwise impassable obstacles and carry on the rest of their perilous journey. The most common type of fish ladder looks like a long staircase of mini waterfalls up which the fish can leap, but other varieties include elevators, pools-and-weirs and baffles.

The Bonneville Dam on the Columbia River is a major salmon thoroughfare from the Pacific to freshwater spawning areas between Oregon and Washington. Hundreds of thousands of salmon take this route every year so the addition of the Bonneville fish ladder means these aquatic commuters can get where they need to go.

Where do sockeye salmon live?

1 Columbia River, USA
2 Ten Mile River, USA
3 North Hokkaido, Japan
4 Bathurst Inlet, Canada
5 Anadyr River, Siberia

Life stages of a salmon

A sockeye goes through a number of dramatic physical – not to mention geographical – changes in its lifetime...

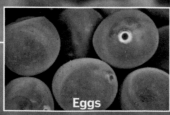

Eggs

The tiny translucent eggs spawned in the gravel beds of freshwater rivers and streams are a pinkish-orange colour. Each male salmon fertilises over 2,000 eggs, which hatch after a few weeks.

Alevin

An alevin hatches out of the soft eggshell but remains hidden in the gravel for another month. It will feed on a nutrient-rich yolk sac that remains attached to the small alevin's body, until it is absorbed.

Fry

The salmon is now starting to look like a fish. At five to ten weeks old, it leaves the gravel nest and learns to swim and feed on minuscule aquatic insects. At this point the salmon are very vulnerable.

5 TOP FACTS
GREAT MIGRATIONS

Arctic terns
1 The Arctic tern's annual round trip from the Arctic Circle down to the Antarctic Circle in the south sees this little seabird travel at least 32,000 kilometres (20,000 miles).

Monarch butterflies
2 Like the sockeye salmon, the monarch butterfly also embarks on a one-off migration travelling vast distances of up to 4,800 kilometres (3,000 miles).

Wildebeest
3 Fuelled by hunger, 1.5 million wildebeest migrate in a giant 2,900-kilometre (1,800-mile) loop in eastern Africa every year. They are following the rains that replenish the grass.

Red land crabs
4 Millions of the red land crabs native to Christmas Island crawl out of the forests before the monsoon season and march sideways for up to a week towards the shore.

Sperm whales
5 Groups of adult sperm whale bachelors embark upon journeys that stretch into thousands of miles before reuniting with the female whales.

DID YOU KNOW? A fish has the same number of scales all its life; as the fish grows so too does each scale

Gill cover
Also called the operculum, this hard but flexible outer lining shields the gills. When the fish gulps in water, it seals off its mouth and throat to allow the water to pass over its gills, which absorb oxygen.

Lateral line
This is a series of fluid-filled canals (similar to what we have in our ears), which sense vibrations through the water and help the fish hear, or distinguish movements in the water and the direction in which it is flowing.

Scales
These overlapping plates provide flexible protective body armour against predators. Scales grow in at the fry stage of life. As they develop, they form rings like you see in tree trunks. If a scale falls out a new one grows but without the inner growth rings.

Dorsal fin
Like the salmon's other fins, the large dorsal fin features a fan of bony spines covered with a thick skin. Acting as a rudder, this fin keeps the fish steady and travelling upright through the water.

Pectoral fin
A pair of pectoral fins below the gill covers helps with balance and manoeuvrability. Fins are embedded into muscle, not other bones as with human limbs, so they're highly flexible. Pectorals help to maintain the correct depth in strong currents.

Pelvic fin
Like the pectoral fins, the paired pelvic fins assist the salmon with balance, steering, stopping and hovering.

Anal fin
The balancing anal fin helps to keep the fish upright in the water.

Caudal fin
The largest and most powerful fin is the caudal fin, or tailfin. This waves water from side to side to propel the fish forward, often against strong currents.

Adipose fin
This has seemingly no function.

The statistics...

Sockeye salmon
Binomial: Oncorhynchus nerka
Type: Fish
Diet: Omnivore (eg krill, zooplankton)
Average life span in the wild: 3-5 years
Weight: 2-7kg (5-15lb)
Length: 84cm (33in)

Parr
After a few months, when the fish is about 15cm (6in), the fry becomes a parr. It's still vulnerable and so develops dark vertical stripes on its sides for camouflage. It will remain at this stage for up to three years.

Smolt
By the time the salmon is one to three years old, it no longer bears any stripes but appears silver. Smolts head for the sea, and in the estuary undergo smoltification as they adjust to the saltwater.

Adult
Once it gets to the ocean, the adult quickly reaches maturity. The skin is silvery blue with black speckles while it lives at sea, but when it returns to freshwater to spawn it turns red with a greenish head.

Spawning adult
The adults then make the perilous trek from ocean to stream. The spawning female digs a nest called a redd into which she lays her eggs for a male to fertilise. Within about two weeks the fish will have died.

© Alamy; Corbis

The deadly pufferfish

A look at why, despite its size and timid appearance, one type of fish can be extremely deadly when it comes to defending itself

The pufferfish is a group of over 100 species that are so-named for their unique line in defence. When cornered, a puffer's last gasp is to draw in water (or sometimes air) and pump it to the stomach, expanding to three times its normal size; deterring potential predators and when possible, affording it the vital seconds necessary to escape.

To achieve this with the required efficiency and speed, once the puffer has taken on water its gills clamp shut and a powerful bow-door-like valve closes over the inside of the mouth. Once the mouth's cavity is compressed, this forces the water into its stomach.

Despite its resulting comic appearance, the tissues and organs of many a puffer are no joke, laced with the potent poison tetrodotoxin – a single pinhead of which could kill a grown man. This makes it ten times more deadly than the black widow spider. The poison is produced as part of a mutually beneficial relationship by common bacteria where nutrients are exchanged as payment for the ultimate deterrent.

Some species such as the porcupine puffer are more sporting than others, covered with spines that offer added protection and ample warning to any would-be attackers. Each spine is attached to the skin by an ingenious tripod-shaped bony base. When the skin stretches, one of the legs is pushed forward and two are pulled back to snap the spine outwards... a point well made in more ways than one. ✿

Fact File
Pufferfish

Type: Fish
Diet: Omnivore: algae, molluscs, invertebrates and crustaceans
Average life span: 4-8 years
Power: Pressurised water reactor, fuelled for life
Weight: 150g-30lbs
Size: 1in-3ft
Habitat: Tropical/sub-tropical, saltwater, brackish, freshwater

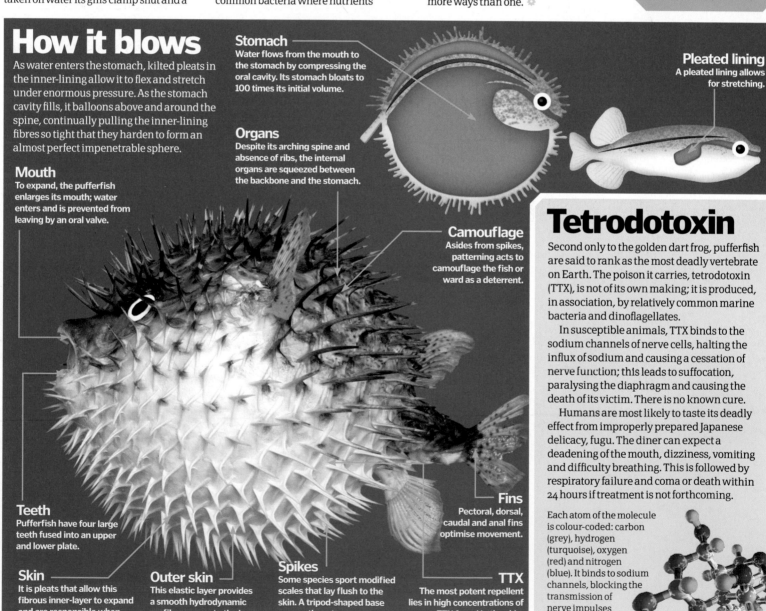

How it blows

As water enters the stomach, kilted pleats in the inner-lining allow it to flex and stretch under enormous pressure. As the stomach cavity fills, it balloons above and around the spine, continually pulling the inner-lining fibres so tight that they harden to form an almost perfect impenetrable sphere.

Mouth
To expand, the pufferfish enlarges its mouth; water enters and is prevented from leaving by an oral valve.

Stomach
Water flows from the mouth to the stomach by compressing the oral cavity. Its stomach bloats to 100 times its initial volume.

Organs
Despite its arching spine and absence of ribs, the internal organs are squeezed between the backbone and the stomach.

Pleated lining
A pleated lining allows for stretching.

Camouflage
Asides from spikes, patterning acts to camouflage the fish or ward as a deterrent.

Teeth
Pufferfish have four large teeth fused into an upper and lower plate.

Skin
It is pleats that allow this fibrous inner-layer to expand and are responsible when stretched for its rigid form.

Outer skin
This elastic layer provides a smooth hydrodynamic profile as cover to the inner pleated layer.

Spikes
Some species sport modified scales that lay flush to the skin. A tripod-shaped base causes them to snap up when the fish is puffed.

Fins
Pectoral, dorsal, caudal and anal fins optimise movement.

TTX
The most potent repellent lies in high concentrations of TTX found in the skin, gonads, liver and intestines.

Tetrodotoxin

Second only to the golden dart frog, pufferfish are said to rank as the most deadly vertebrate on Earth. The poison it carries, tetrodotoxin (TTX), is not of its own making; it is produced, in association, by relatively common marine bacteria and dinoflagellates.

In susceptible animals, TTX binds to the sodium channels of nerve cells, halting the influx of sodium and causing a cessation of nerve function; this leads to suffocation, paralysing the diaphragm and causing the death of its victim. There is no known cure.

Humans are most likely to taste its deadly effect from improperly prepared Japanese delicacy, fugu. The diner can expect a deadening of the mouth, dizziness, vomiting and difficulty breathing. This is followed by respiratory failure and coma or death within 24 hours if treatment is not forthcoming.

Each atom of the molecule is colour-coded: carbon (grey), hydrogen (turquoise), oxygen (red) and nitrogen (blue). It binds to sodium channels, blocking the transmission of nerve impulses and poisoning the nervous system.

How do anglerfish hunt?

Discover how these menacing fish use bioluminescence to search for prey

Anglerfish are usually found in deep and temperate tropical seas, around 1,000m (3,300ft) below sea level. Protruding from their head is a long and thin growth made of flesh, used like the lure of a fishing rod to attract prey. Some species have luminescent bacteria in the tip to more easily search for and attract prey in the darkness of the deep ocean.

The light produced is blue-green in colour, as most marine animals are sensitive to blue light, and it also travels best in water. The tip of an anglerfish's growth, the photophore, contains the light-producing chemicals that cause bioluminescence. A compound known as 'luciferin' is oxidised by an enzyme known as 'luciferase', which produces the cold light and attracts prey. ✿

"An anglerfish's photophore contains the chemicals that cause bioluminescence"

The most venomous fish in the world

Almost invisible among the coral reefs, the stonefish is a real-life killer

The stonefish is the world's most venomous fish thanks to its ability to inject deadly neurotoxins from the spines on its dorsal fin into its target. The stonefish's neurotoxins work by attacking the nerve cells of whatever it is injected into, causing severe pain, sickness, nausea, paralysis and, depending on the depth of spine penetration into

skin, death within three hours (humans can be killed just two hours after being poisoned).

Unlike most other poisonous fish who dwell in the dark depths of the ocean - leaving little chance of human contact – stonefish dwell in shallow waters and are likely to be found anywhere between just a few inches beneath the surface down to a depth of three metres. ✿

"The stonefish's neurotoxins work by attacking nerve cells"

If it doesn't want to be stepped on, why evolve to look like a stone!

061

The life of manatees

Why do we call these unusual aquatic mammals 'cows of the ocean'?

 Also called sea cows, manatees might not immediately resemble your average land-based bovine, but they do share a number of their characteristics. They are bulky, generally peaceful creatures and spend a large proportion of their time grazing on plants; in fact, they're the only marine mammal with an exclusively vegetarian diet.

Surprisingly graceful in the water, they use their powerful flippers and tails to navigate tropical coastal regions and river networks. Their average speed is just eight kilometres (five miles) per hour, but they are able to reach 24 kilometres (15 miles) per hour for short spurts.

Although they never venture onto land (like whales and dolphins they're even born in the water) they're actually more closely related to elephants than other water-based animals. They also need a ready supply of air; the longest they can go submerged is about 15 minutes.

Due to their slow movement and typical habitat coinciding with highly populated areas, manatees were extensively hunted in previous centuries. They remain vulnerable to extinction to this day because their tendency to swim near the surface means they often fall victim to motorboat propellers and fishing nets. ✿

Sea cow distribution
Where do manatees live around the world?

US east coast
Concentrated in marshy regions like the Florida Everglades during winter, but in the summer the range extends as far north as Rhode Island.

Amazon
This manatee species lives exclusively in the freshwater areas of the Amazon rainforest and often has white or pink patches on its chest.

West Africa
The least researched of all three subspecies, the West African manatee's range is huge, including bays, canals, rivers and lakes.

The statistics...

Manatee

Family:	Trichechidae
Type:	Mammal
Diet:	Herbivore (eg leaves, algae)
Length:	Up to 4m (13.1ft)
Weight:	Up to 600kg (1,300lb)
Life span in wild:	40-60 years

Stunning biology
The unique anatomy of the electric ray enables it to capture prey with ease

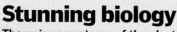

Electric organ
Kidney-shaped organs either side of the ray's head can produce up to 1kW of power.

Muscle
Rays use strong muscles to wrap their prey inside their pectoral fins, delivering repeated electric shocks.

Tail
Unlike other rays, electric rays do not use their fins to swim, and instead rely largely on their tails.

Electroreceptor
Electric rays have a sixth sense and can detect changes in the electric fields in the water around them.

Pectoral fins
Rays have a flattened body and enlarged pectoral fins, giving them a disc-like appearance – perfect for enveloping their victims.

A torpedo ray is smaller than the Pacific electric ray but can still generate 220v

Electric rays
The shocking mechanism used for defence and attack

The Pacific electric ray, which grows up to 1.5 metres long, uses its electrical ability to ambush prey. When a fish comes within range, the ray wraps its huge fin disc around it, delivering rapid pulses of electricity. Once the fish is stunned, the ray will swallow it whole. Due to its size the Pacific electric ray has few predators, but smaller rays use their electrical organs only in self-defence. Electric rays are also able to detect electricity. They have electroreceptors in jelly-filled pores on their heads, capable of picking up changes in the electrical fields in the water. When another fish swims past, the contraction of its muscles generates electricity, which the ray can sense. ✿

© Corbis; A/B Larsen; Thinkstock; Alamy

RECORD BREAKERS
R-EEL-LY DEEP

8,370m

DEEPEST RECORDED FISH
A basketweave cusk-eel was discovered at a depth of 8,370 metres (27,460 feet) – that's 8.4 kilometres (5.2 miles) down – in the abyssal zone of the Puerto Rico Trench, making it officially the deepest living fish known.

DID YOU KNOW? Moray eel jaws are strong enough to bite off a human finger!

How moray eels feed

Find out why catching a fish dinner is a doddle when you've got two mouths

The moray eel is a slender, reef-dwelling fish native to the nooks and crannies of subtropical and temperate seas. While they are voracious eaters, they are not great swimmers due to their lack of a pectoral fin. Instead they lurk almost motionless in rocky crevices, often with just their heads peeking out, waiting for a meal to swim by.

Most other bony fish have developed a method of slurping up prey by very rapidly opening their mouths to create an area of negative pressure directly in front of them. This quickly draws water – and any unsuspecting victim – back into the mouth cavity. While fish that bite also use suction to get food from their mouths into their throats, the moray eel doesn't. In fact, few fish consume their food in as impressive – or terrifying – a manner as the moray eel.

Because they live in tight crevices, the suction method wouldn't work for a moray because the head has no space to expand into. And besides, the eel's prey is generally too large to really be affected by the suction technique. Instead, morays are the only known species of vertebrate to possess two pairs of jaws. It sounds like some kind of special-effects monster from the movies, but the moray eel has a second set of raptorial jaws in its pharynx: the pharyngeal jaws. These gnashers located behind the eel's skull lurch forward after the fish has taken the initial bite and grab at the victim, drawing it back down into the throat so the eel can swallow it.

It's widely thought that this set of movable second jaws is a result of years of adaptation to better suit the small, confined spaces that these fish tend to inhabit in various reef environments. ✿

Off the menu
Moray eels are high up the food chain, which leaves them more susceptible to the accumulation of toxins. Ciguatoxin, for instance, is a nasty organic compound made by a specific type of dinoflagellate (a single-celled organism). At first the ciguatoxin may be consumed by a snail, which may then be eaten by a crab; the crab might become dinner for a larger fish and so on until, finally, the moray eel eats something contaminated. Essentially, the higher up the food chain, the greater the toxin concentration. Cooking does not destroy ciguatoxin so it's safest simply to avoid eating moray eels.

Jaw-dropping anatomy
Get the lowdown on this opportunistic reef hunter

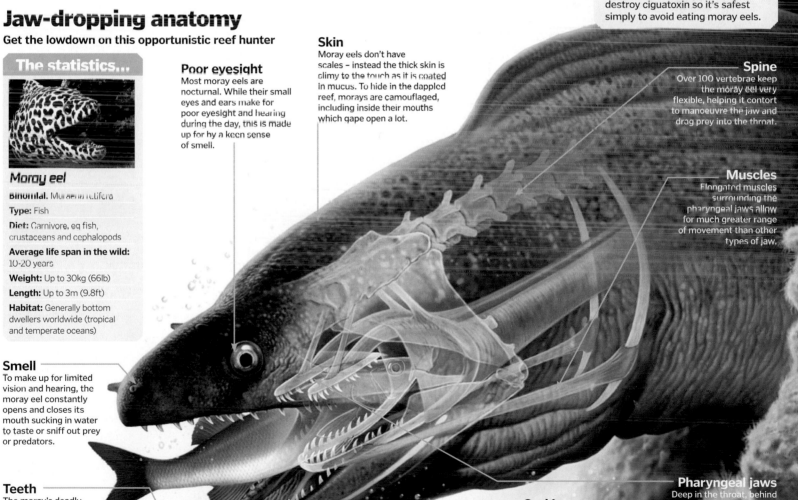

The statistics...

Moray eel

Binomial: Muraena retifera

Type: Fish

Diet: Carnivore, eg fish, crustaceans and cephalopods

Average life span in the wild: 10-20 years

Weight: Up to 30kg (66lb)

Length: Up to 3m (9.8ft)

Habitat: Generally bottom dwellers worldwide (tropical and temperate oceans)

Poor eyesight
Most moray eels are nocturnal. While their small eyes and ears make for poor eyesight and hearing during the day, this is made up for by a keen sense of smell.

Skin
Moray eels don't have scales – instead the thick skin is slimy to the touch as it is coated in mucus. To hide in the dappled reef, morays are camouflaged, including inside their mouths which gape open a lot.

Spine
Over 100 vertebrae keep the moray eel very flexible, helping it contort to manoeuvre the jaw and drag prey into the throat.

Muscles
Elongated muscles surrounding the pharyngeal jaws allow for much greater range of movement than other types of jaw.

Smell
To make up for limited vision and hearing, the moray eel constantly opens and closes its mouth sucking in water to taste or sniff out prey or predators.

Teeth
The moray's deadly looking mouthful of incredibly sharp teeth curve inwards slightly to prevent their meal wriggling back out.

Oral jaws
The lengthy lower mandible of the first oral jaw enables the fish to snap its mouth shut very quickly and powerfully grip its victim as if in a vice.

Pharyngeal jaws
Deep in the throat, behind the eel's skull, is a second set of ballistic jaws shaped a bit like forceps and used to grab prey and drag it into the oesophagus.

© Corbis; Thinkstock

The statistics...

Octopus

Class: Cephalopod

Diet: Carnivore

Average life span in the wild:
6 months–5 years

Weight: 0.1-200kg

Size: 3cm–9m

Octopuses

The incredible abilities of this eight-legged wonder of the natural world, exposed

 Octopuses are the superheroes of the animal kingdom, with so many amazing abilities and adaptations that it begins to look greedy. They can solve mazes, open screw-top jars and use tools. They can walk, they can swim and they can even jet propel themselves at high speed. They can change colour, imitate other animals, squirt ink, inject poison and jettison their own legs. When you can do all that, who cares if you can predict football results or not?

Although they are molluscs, octopuses don't have a shell or bones and the only hard part of their body is a small beak, made of keratin. This allows them to squeeze through extremely small gaps – an octopus a metre across can pass through a tube the size of a 50 pence coin. Octopuses mainly eat crabs and small fish that they winkle out of crevices in rocks and coral reefs, but they can also tackle small sharks by enveloping the shark's gill openings and suffocating them.

Octopus blood uses a greenish-blue copper pigment called haemocyanin, instead of the iron-based haemoglobin in our own blood. Haemocyanin can't carry as much oxygen as haemoglobin, but it is actually more efficient at low oxygen concentrations and in cold water. Despite this, octopuses have poor circulation and quickly run out of energy. This may be one of the reasons for their intelligence – they don't have the stamina for a prolonged chase and must instead rely on their cunning to survive.

Male octopuses die almost immediately after mating. The females are even bigger martyrs. They guard their 20,000 eggs for a month and rather than leave the nest to hunt, they will eat some of their own legs. After that, the female dies and the eggs hatch into babies approximately the size of a walnut. ✿

Eye
This looks much like our own, with a lens and an iris but it evolved in a different way. Octopuses don't have a blind spot where the optic nerve passes through, because the retina is positioned differently.

Poison glands
These evolved from salivary glands, and as well as paralysing prey they also soften up the flesh, making it easier to eat.

Chromatophores
The colour-changing cells in the skin are funnel-shaped. By squeezing ink into the funnel from a bulb at the base, the octopus can control the size of the coloured dot.

Colouration
This blue-ringed octopus can change colour to match the sea bed or suddenly flash the bright blue rings to startle predators.

Suckers
Twin rows run the length of the tentacles to allow the octopus to grip and to taste anything it touches.

Jet-propelled

Octopuses normally swim by pulsing their tentacles, like the bell of a jellyfish. This is quite energy efficient but it lacks acceleration, so when an octopus needs a sudden turn of speed it switches to jet propulsion. To do this, they suck water into the mantle cavity and then squirt it at high pressure out of their siphon tube. This is the same way that they circulate water over their gills, so the octopus is really taking a deep breath and then blowing out hard. The siphon is positioned on the side of the octopus's body but it can be steered like the engines of a Harrier jet. Sometimes they use it as a boost when walking as well.

The way forward when the octopus needs a quick burst of speed

Great for gripping...

SMART

1. Mimic Octopus
To scare predators and fool prey, this octopus changes shape and colour to impersonate snakes, jellyfish and even crabs.

© Steve Childs

SMARTER

2. Common octopus
Several octopuses in zoos have figured out how to undo screw-top jars to get at food inside.

© Beckmannjan

SMARTEST

3. Coconut octopus
The only invertebrate to demonstrate tool use, the coconut octopus carries around two halves of a coconut shell and climbs inside when threatened.

© Nhobgood

DID YOU KNOW? Octopuses have three hearts. Two pump blood through the gills, the third serves the rest of the body

Octopus anatomy

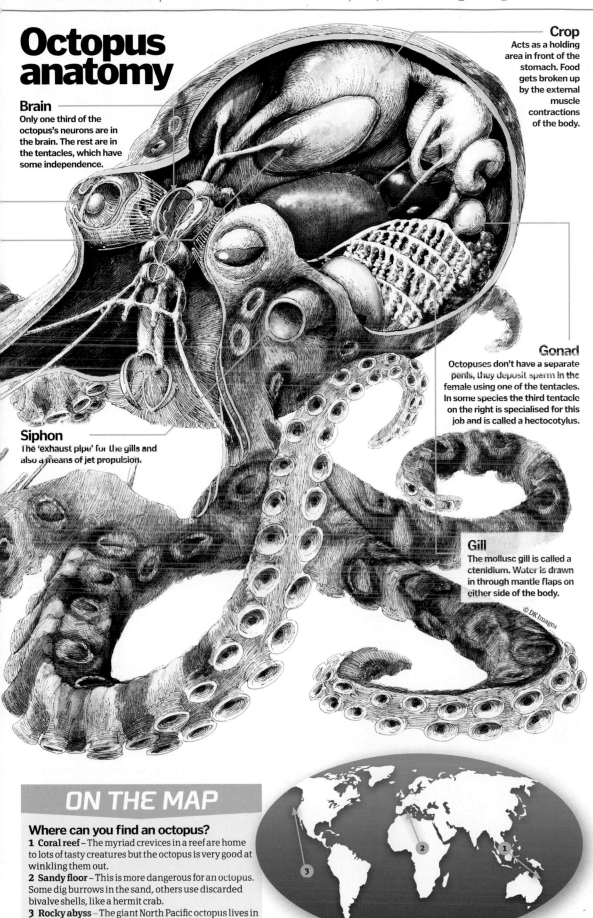

Brain
Only one third of the octopus's neurons are in the brain. The rest are in the tentacles, which have some independence.

Crop
Acts as a holding area in front of the stomach. Food gets broken up by the external muscle contractions of the body.

Gonad
Octopuses don't have a separate penis, they deposit sperm in the female using one of the tentacles. In some species the third tentacle on the right is specialised for this job and is called a hectocotylus.

Siphon
The 'exhaust pipe' for the gills and also a means of jet propulsion.

Gill
The mollusc gill is called a ctenidium. Water is drawn in through mantle flaps on either side of the body.

© DK Images

ON THE MAP

Where can you find an octopus?
1 Coral reef – The myriad crevices in a reef are home to lots of tasty creatures but the octopus is very good at winkling them out.
2 Sandy floor – This is more dangerous for an octopus. Some dig burrows in the sand, others use discarded bivalve shells, like a hermit crab.
3 Rocky abyss – The giant North Pacific octopus lives in the deep, freezing depths of the Pacific seabed.

Defences

All octopuses inject a paralysing poison through their beak to subdue prey. The smaller the octopus, the more deadly the poison and the 10cm blue-ringed octopus can kill a human.

Octopuses have lots of predators of their own though, and most of their adaptations are to evade capture. Colour-changing skin cells, called chromatophores, can be used for camouflage or to flash alarming colours to scare predators. Many species also have tiny muscles under the skin to change their texture to resemble spiky coral or fringed seaweed. The mimic octopus will even hold its legs and swim in such a way as to look like a flounder, sea snake or a poisonous lionfish.

If that doesn't work, the octopus can squirt a cloud of melanin dye. This provides a smoke screen and also interferes with the sense of smell that most sharks use to locate prey.

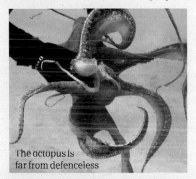

The octopus is far from defenceless

Intelligent legs

With the ability to twist in every direction, and suckers that can grip and release individually, octopus legs are too complicated to be controlled from a central brain. Instead they operate semi-autonomously. An octopus is like a man holding a bunch of trained snakes; he issues instructions and trusts that they will be carried out, occasionally he has a look to make sure. This means that an octopus doesn't have a very good idea of where its legs actually are at any moment and can't work out the shape of something by feeling it, like we can.

Octopuses can taste through their suckers and, if they need to escape, detach a leg and regenerate a new one. One species, the Paper Nautilus, use a leg to deliver sperm. It detaches and swims over to the female by itself.

Do giant squid exist?

Yes they do. A species of squid can reach up to half a ton!

Fiction is commonly built upon myth, however in the year 2007 the tales of maritime folklore were revealed to be true. Exciting the zoological world, a half-ton Architeuthis, or giant squid, was discovered by fishermen in Antarctic waters south of New Zealand. This female measured 33 feet in length and weighed exactly 1,089lbs.

This discovery was significant, as scientists determined the species lives up to 3,000 feet below the surface, descending deeper to 6,500 feet to aggressively hunt prey, with eyes 11-inches wide – useful at depths where light is scarce. Anatomically, this species is found to be a keen predator, with each of its tentacles containing swivelling hooks. Further up these limbs are three razor points, all helping it to attach to prey, including deep-sea fish and other squid species.

Amazingly, after comparing this sea creature's beak with specimens found in the stomachs of sperm whales, researchers believe that Architeuthis can reach up to 46 feet in length. ✿

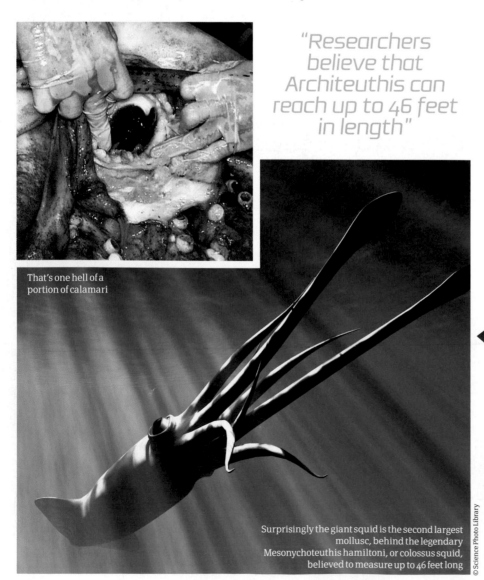

That's one hell of a portion of calamari

"Researchers believe that Architeuthis can reach up to 46 feet in length"

Surprisingly the giant squid is the second largest mollusc, behind the legendary Mesonychoteuthis hamiltoni, or colossus squid, believed to measure up to 46 feet long

© Science Photo Library

How do squid swim?

The jet propulsion system that powers squid though water

To move itself through water a squid will emit constant, steady bursts of fluid to provide the necessary acceleration. Squid are able to take water into their mantle and expel it at a high rate, reaching speeds of up to 24mph (40kmh) after expelling 94 per cent of their fluid.

Shaped like a torpedo, the rear body of a squid lets it travel almost like a rocket. By quickly compressing the mantle, a jet of water shoots out behind the squid. The force of this jet moves the squid forwards, allowing it to drift until it comes to a stop, when the process is repeated. To refill the cavity, elastic tissue in the mantle works in tandem with radial muscles to bring in water, in addition to the pressure of incident water as the squid moves. During feeding, the squid swims in the other direction using its arms, allowing it to easily grab prey.

To quickly evade predators, squid can hyperinflate their mantle cavities, expanding them beyond their normal size. This allows for a quick and sudden intake of water that can be rapidly expelled for a fast getaway. ✿

Method of propulsion

Mantle
As the squid prepares to propel itself, the walls of the mantle expand to bring in water, filling the mantle cavity inside.

Cavity
Powerful muscles in the walls of the mantle contract and pressurise the water in the cavity.

Steering
To change its direction it uses two fins at its tail end, in addition to altering the direction of the jet.

Funnel
A one-way valve known as the funnel allows water to be stored for jettison at a later period.

Expel
The water is spurted out near the squid's head, propelling it backwards through the water.

These jet-propelled swimmers can reach speeds of 25mph

© Dan Hershman

The most venomous creature on Earth

Over 5,500 deaths have been recorded due to box jellyfish stings since 1954, but why is it so deadly to humans?

The box jellyfish is so named due to its box or bell like shape. It has four distinct sides and can have up to 15 tentacles, each one of these stretching up to three metres long with thousands of stinging cells, called nematocysts, on each one. The primary purpose for these nematocysts is to stun and paralyse their prey, ensuring that damage is not sustained to the creature's delicate tentacles. When the venom enters the bloodstream of the stung animal, it quickly targets the nervous system and heart, paralysing them. In humans, cardiac arrest often occurs and the individual will die before they receive aid. Even if they do survive the stings, massive scarring is left where the nematocysts attached.

Very few creatures, such as sea turtles – which actually consume box jellyfish – are seemingly immune to the venom, but most other creatures are known to react in the same way as humans. ✿

Box jellyfish anatomy

1. Unactivated nematocyst
When dormant, nematocysts contain a coiled shaft. There are up to 5,000 of these cells on each box jellyfish tentacle.

2. Activated nematocyst
When a chemical stimulus is sensed by the nematocyst, the spine-covered shaft shoots out and embeds itself into the prey's skin.

5. Prey
Each shaft not only serves to release venom into the prey, but also to attach the jellyfish to their prey. This is crucial as this is how they hunt, as well as defend themselves.

4. Tentacle
This is where most nematocysts are situated, but some species of jellyfish also have nematocysts on their main body.

3. Fully extended nematocyst
The tip of the shaft is like a hypodermic needle, which then releases venom straight into the bloodstream of the prey from the bulb of the nematocyst.

© DK Images

© DK Images

The jellyfish life cycle

How do these predatory invertebrates develop?

Medusa
The ephyrae continue to grow and develop a distinctive large bell. It spends the rest of its life independent from the polyp colony. At the medusa stage it's capable of reproduction.

Planula
Once the eggs have begun embryonic development, they become tiny free-swimming larvae called planulae. They grow tiny hairs called cilia to propel themselves around.

Growth stage
As the polyp grows, it produces clones of itself – a process called asexual budding. This new 'colony' of polyps starts to propagate on the stem of the main polyp, linked by feeding tubes. This can go on for years before the baby jellyfish (or ephyrae) detach and swim off independently.

Polyp
The planula stage is extremely short and before long it will have attached itself to a hard surface on the floor of a coastal reef. Here the planula grows a stalk with which to anchor itself to something solid like a rock. At the top of the polyp a mouth and tentacles develop for feeding and growing.

How jellyfish sting
Some jellyfish and other cnidaria have stinging cells called cnidocytes in their tentacles, used for hunting and self-defence. Each cell features a poison-tipped stinging thread coiled inside. On the outside is a trigger that discharges the stinger, firing it towards the victim. The venom includes a paralysing neurotoxin.

Egg
Depending on the species, the female's eggs are fertilised either by being released into the water where they encounter the sperm, or by the adult female collecting the sperm in special brooding folds.

Sperm
Both male and female jellyfish sex cells are made in reproductive organs called gonads. The male adult jellyfish produces sperm, which it releases via its mouth.

© SPL

The secret to understanding how coral reefs work is that they flourish in tropical waters that contain hardly any food. They are often described as the rainforests of the ocean but it is more accurate to think of them as oases in a saltwater desert. Warm water doesn't dissolve nutrients very well so it doesn't support the soup of plankton that exists in colder waters. But this means that the water is also very clear, which makes it ideal for photosynthesis. By striking up a symbiotic allegiance with photosynthetic zooxanthella bacteria, the corals can harness the sunlight to provide them with most of their food, while at the same time retaining their animal ability to capture small prey and gather essential nitrogen.

The limestone skeleton that corals produce to protect themselves also dramatically affects the ocean environment. It absorbs and deflects wave energy, creating sheltered lagoons in its lee and provides innumerable crevices and attachment points for other animals. A reef is a complex ecosystem with each species contributing to the stability of the whole. Algae help cement the reef together, sea urchins keep the algae under control, molluscs stop the sea urchins from overgrazing, and so on.

Over geological timescales, coral reefs grow so as to regulate the depth of the water above them, even during times of rising sea level. This prevents the ecosystem from simply 'drowning' in the increasing gloom and makes coral reefs some of the most long-lived biological structures on the planet. Some coral atolls are 30 million years old. ✿

Coral reefs

Incredible biological richness in the most nutrient-poor waters in the world? The paradox of the coral reef is explained...

Colourful soft corals, anthias, moray eel and other fish species

© Thinkstock

5 TOP FACTS
REEF DWELLERS

Dwarf seahorse
1 The slowest fish in the world. Never straying far from the safety of its nest crevice, this fish swims at just five feet per hour, that's an incredibly slow 0.0004m/s.

Seven-figure pygmy goby
2 The high risk of predation on the reef encourages this fish to live fast and die young. It is the shortest-lived vertebrate with a natural life span of just 59 days.

Yellowfin goatfish
3 At night, this bottom feeder trawls the sands for worms and crustaceans. But by day it changes colour and hides among shoals of bluestriped snapper.

Crown-of-thorns
4 This starfish grows up to 40cm across and each one can eat up to six square metres of living coral a year. It is the second largest sea star in the world.

Giant triton
5 A giant sea snail and one of the only predators of the crown-of-thorns. The triton is in decline because of overfishing for its huge 50 centimetre shell.

DID YOU KNOW? *60 per cent of the world's coral reefs are at risk of destruction – ten per cent are already dead*

Types of coral reef

Reefs form in shallow waters close to the shore. At the end of the last ice age, 10,000 years ago, the sea level began to rise. In order to keep close enough to the surface for photosynthesis, the coral reefs grew upward. They also grew outwards but because the sheltered conditions on the shoreward side of the reef are less favourable, they grew more slowly there. This, combined with the shrinking shoreline as the sea level rises, causes the reef to separate from the shore.

With enough time, erosion and rising seas may remove the central island altogether and all that is left is a coral atoll.

1. Volcano
An undersea volcanic eruption erupts enough lava to create an island that juts above the surface.

2. Fringing reef
The shallow seas near the shoreline and the turbulence from the wave action encourages the formation of a fringing reef.

3. Rising sea
Over time, the sea level rises, shrinking the portion of the extinct volcano that juts above the water.

4. Barrier reef
The coral grows upward, to stay close to the surface. A sheltered lagoon now begins to form between the coral and the shore.

5. Atoll
Eventually the volcano may become completely submerged, leaving a ring or partial ring of coral around a shallow lagoon.

6. Plant life
Broken coral and animal shells form sand that collects in the gaps between the coral. Plants take root, stabilising and raising the ground level.

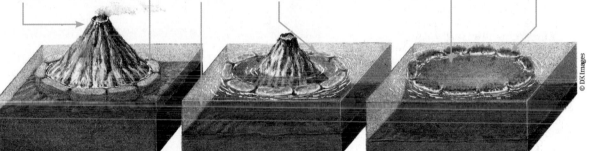

© DK Images

What's inside coral?

Coral looks and behaves rather like a plant but it is actually a colony of animals, related to sea anemones, called polyps. Each polyp anchors itself to the existing reef and builds a calcium carbonate skeleton to protect its body. Successive generations of polyps build on the dead skeletons of the one before as the reef grows.

8. Rough surface
Coral skeletons are deliberately rough to encourage turbulence, which helps circulate nutrients and prevents stagnant water layers from suffocating the polyps.

1. Tentacles
Reef building corals have tentacles in multiples of six arranged in a ring.

3. Mouth
Polyps only have one opening to their stomach cavity. This serves as both mouth and anus.

6. Zooxanthellae
Photosynthetic bacteria called zooxanthellae live within the polyp's tissues. These trap sunlight and provide 90 per cent of the energy requirements of the coral. In return, the polyp supplies nitrogen and carbon dioxide.

2. Nematocysts
Stinging cells in the tentacles, called nematocysts, are used to catch zooplankton that drift by. Each nematocyst can fire only once and then must be replaced.

7. Living tissue
A 'head' of coral consists of a colony of genetically identical cloned polyps. These are connected together by a surface layer of living tissue that allows metabolic products to be exchanged between polyps.

4. Basal plate
The polyp is glued to the reef by a calcified ring. Muscular ridges protrude from this into the polyp and can retract it quickly if threatened.

5. Skeleton
As the coral grows, the calcified skeleton builds around it. Eventually, a new basal plate forms higher up and the lower section becomes fully calcified.

DID YOU KNOW?

Most corals are hermaphrodite. They reproduce by 'broadcast spawning', which is where the entire reef releases sperm and eggs in a synchronised wave to increase the chances of successful fertilisation.

Great Barrier Reef

It's a big one down under...

 The Great Barrier Reef is the largest structure in the world made by living organisms and covers 344,400 square kilometres. Coral reefs have existed off the north coast of Australia for at least 18 million years, but the formation of the modern reef began about 20,000 years ago. As sea levels rose by 120m over the next 14,000 years, the corals formed reefs around the flooded coastal hills, which became islands and eventually disappeared completely. The Great Barrier Reef is home to whales, dolphins, dugongs, sharks, turtles and giant clams. Fishing and tourism together account for around £1.2 billion each year. It is known as one of the seven natural wonders. ✿

© Science Photo Library

Where is it?
The reef has risen on the shallow shelf fringing the Australian continent, in warm waters that have enabled the corals to flourish.

Sum of the parts
The reef actually consists of some 2,100 individual reefs and some 800 fringing reefs. formed around islands or bordering coastlines.

© Thinkstock

The reef was declared a Marine Park in 1975, to provide long term protection for the many species that live there

BIG

1. East Rennell Island
At 86km by 15km, this is the largest raised coral atoll in the world. Its lagoon is also the largest in all the Pacific islands.

BIGGER

2. Belize Barrier Reef
The largest barrier reef in the northern hemisphere. The reef system includes hundreds of sand cays (low islands) and lagoons.

BIGGEST

3. Great Barrier Reef
The largest reef in the world. It is 2,600km long, incorporates 940 islands and is visible from outer space.

DID YOU KNOW? *Two-thirds of the global population of the Layson Albatross (1.5 million birds) nest on the Midway Atoll*

This coral is suffering from a process called bleaching

©Thinkstock

How big?
It extends in roughly a northwest-southeast direction for more than 1,250 miles (2,000km).

Offshore
The reef is at an offshore distance ranging from ten to 100 miles (16 to 160km).

Threats to the coral reef

Corals are very sensitive to changes in sea temperature and water quality. When stressed, corals will eject their symbiotic zooxanthella bacteria in an attempt to conserve energy – a process known as coral bleaching. If the unfavourable conditions do not improve within a few months, the coral will not acquire new symbionts and will die. Global climate change is raising ocean temperatures; increasing the frequency of bleaching events. Rising carbon dioxide levels also make the seawater more acidic, which inhibits the formation of calcium carbonate skeletons. Corals are also threatened by fertiliser run-off from farms, and destructive fishing practices such as dynamiting.

© Jon Hanson, 2005

Plant life of the coral reef

There are three main kinds of coral plants. The familiar seaweeds (or macroalgae) are found in the shallowest waters, usually on the top of the reef. Turf algae are short filaments that form carpets usually less than one centimetre high. These are an important food source for reef herbivores because they grow very quickly.

The crustose coralline algae don't look like plants, they appear as red or pink splashes of paint, coating the surface of the coral. These thin sheets of plant life have cells reinforced with calcium carbonate, just like the corals. They favour the outer face of a reef, where the wave action is most aggressive and are important in cementing the reef together.

Creatures of the coral reef

Coral reefs support an amazing array of animals and creatures

Coral reefs cover just one per cent of the ocean's surface area, but they account for 25 per cent of its biodiversity. Compared to the placid and largely empty deep waters around it, a coral reef boils with life. As well as 8,000 species of fish, coral reefs are home to sponges, crustaceans, starfish, turtles and sea snakes. Some, like the crown-of-thorns sea star, eat the coral directly but most reef creatures are active predators. This, coupled with such a tightly knit environment, leads to a frantic, cut-throat existence.

Reef fish, like the queen angelfish, are adapted to fit into tiny crevices and are often highly flattened, using their pectoral fins to paddle around in short spurts, rather than the energy-efficient cruising of open water fish like tuna. Because of the enclosed nature of a reef, swimming speed is less of a consideration than close range defences. Reef fish are often brightly coloured and this may be to camouflage themselves against the equally bright corals or to confuse predators with false eyespots, such as those of the four-eyed butterflyfish. Many fish have poisonous spines to make themselves less appetising. Gobies have eyes that can swivel independently, like a chameleon, to let them scan for predators.

© Laszlo Ilyes, 2006

A queen angelfish is perfectly adapted to reef living

© Thinkstock

Reef fish have developed many different ways of deterring predators

ON THE MAP

Where do coral reefs grow?

Looking for the largest organisms on Earth? Look here

1. Tubbataha Reef Marine Park
2. Great Barrier Reef
3. East Rennell Island
4. Brazilian Atlantic islands
5. Komodo National Park
6. Belize Barrier Reef
7. Greater St Lucia Wetland Park
8. Aldabra Atoll
9. Maldives

THE STATS
STARFISH

| SPECIES **1,800** | LARGEST **9.4 in (24cm)** | DEEPEST **6,000m** |
| OLDEST **35 yrs** | HEAVISEST **11lbs (5kg)** | FASTEST **2.5 feet p/min** |

DID YOU KNOW? *A sea star can crawl at speeds of up to 2.5 feet per minute if pursuing prey*

Plankton under the microscope

A critical part of the marine food chain, plankton come in all shapes and sizes

'Plankton' is a catchall name for a diverse group of marine or freshwater organisms that are so small and/or weak that they can't swim against a current. Indeed, this inability alone is what classifies an organism as planktonic, with bacteria, algae, molluscs, crustaceans and more all falling under this label.

Despite their minuscule size, plankton species number in the hundreds of thousands and are a critical component of food chains. Fish and marine mammals – including those as massive as whales – feed extensively on plankton (some

exclusively) and without them many ecosystems in the ocean would simply collapse.

Plankton are subdivided according to size, with those larger than 20 millimetres (0.8 inches) – such as jellyfish – referred to as megaplankton, while at the other end of the scale, organisms less than 0.2 micrometres – such as marine viruses – are known as femtoplankton. In between these two extremes there are several other categories, containing a wide array of organisms ranging from cephalopoda (like octopus hatchlings) through to flagellates. ✿

Planktonic organisms

Copepod
Feeding on even smaller microscopic plants and animals than themselves, copepods are parasitic organisms and a key constituent of plankton. They are found in all of Earth's oceans, and there are about 13,000 described species.

Rotifer
Measuring just 0.1-0.5 millimetres (0.004-0.02 inches) in length, rotifers have to be one of the most weird-looking members of the plankton family. Interestingly, despite their tiny size, they are related to nematodes, or roundworms.

Diatom
There are over 100,000 species of diatom, which are photosynthetic, single-celled algae. They play an important role in the base of marine food chains and are a common type of phytoplankton (micro plants).

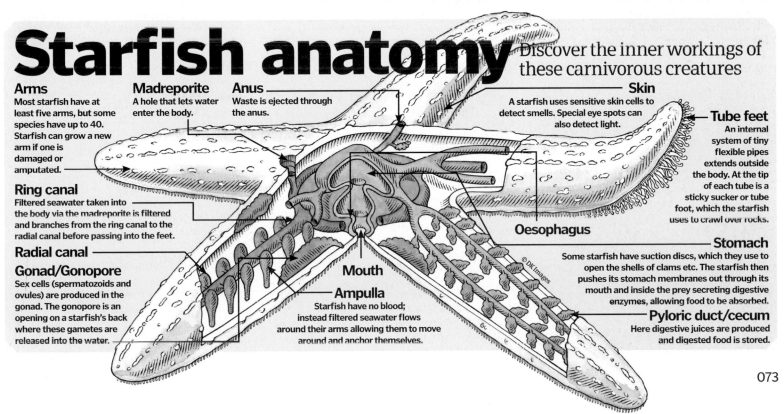

Starfish anatomy
Discover the inner workings of these carnivorous creatures

Arms
Most starfish have at least five arms, but some species have up to 40. Starfish can grow a new arm if one is damaged or amputated.

Madreporite
A hole that lets water enter the body.

Anus
Waste is ejected through the anus.

Skin
A starfish uses sensitive skin cells to detect smells. Special eye spots can also detect light.

Tube feet
An internal system of tiny flexible pipes extends outside the body. At the tip of each tube is a sticky sucker or tube foot, which the starfish uses to crawl over rocks.

Ring canal
Filtered seawater taken into the body via the madreporite is filtered and branches from the ring canal to the radial canal before passing into the feet.

Radial canal

Gonad/Gonopore
Sex cells (spermatozoids and ovules) are produced in the gonad. The gonopore is an opening on a starfish's back where these gametes are released into the water.

Mouth

Ampulla
Starfish have no blood; instead filtered seawater flows around their arms allowing them to move around and anchor themselves.

Oesophagus

Stomach
Some starfish have suction discs, which they use to open the shells of clams etc. The starfish then pushes its stomach membranes out through its mouth and inside the prey secreting digestive enzymes, allowing food to be absorbed.

Pyloric duct/cecum
Here digestive juices are produced and digested food is stored.

© DK Images

SPIDERS & INSECTS

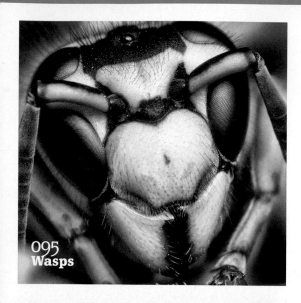

095
Wasps

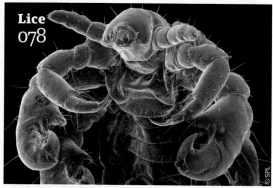

Lice
078

085
Exoskeletons

083
Grasshoppers

074

Scorpions
086

Spiders & insects

088
Spiders

093
Compound eyes

080
Termites

094
Honeybees

090
Black widows

A velvet mite, what a site!

Micro monsters

Largely invisible to all but the most powerful microscopes, a menagerie of micro monsters live all about us – in our homes, on our food and even on human beings themselves

5 TOP FACTS
MICRO MONSTERS

Vampiric
1 A fully grown head louse bites the human scalp between three to five times each day in order to drink the blood, sucking it directly into their digestive tract.

Host
2 A louse's eggs, from which the next generation emerges, are actually attached to its host's hair directly, allowing for an instant transition post-hatch.

Bee-gone
3 One specific variant of mite, Varroa destructor, lives on bees alone. It is an external parasitic mite and spreads viruses that can kill entire colonies.

Sneezy
4 Mites are the cause of numerous allergies, including hay fever, eczema and asthma. They exacerbate these most in warm, humid conditions.

Mighty
5 The tropical variant of mite, Archegozetes longisetosus, is one of the strongest animals on Earth, capable of lifting 1,182 times its own weight.

DID YOU KNOW? Scientists have identified over 48,000 species of mites, only five per cent of their estimated total

"This is the reality of the unseen world operating all around us, a massive multitude of micro beasties feeding off carbon in all its forms"

Mites, lice, silverfish and termites – but a small selection of the microscopic creatures living in your home and, if you refer to bath time as an annual event, on you as well. This is the reality of the unseen world operating all around us, a massive multitude of micro beasties feeding off carbon in all its forms, be that a human hair, a piece of cheese, inside your skirting board or on each other; it is a cut-throat world of silent, unseen organisms that have inhabited our planet for over the last 400 million years. Well, considering they have been alive so long, maybe it is we who inhabit their planet, as not only have they existed far longer than modern humans, but they are more numerous too, with their species numbering hundreds of thousands and their diversity unparalleled.

However, now with the usage of powerful scanning electron microscopes (SEM), scientists are prising open the doors to this unseen world and watching as beasts akin to the creations of the most fevered dreams take form in their millions, marching over a world that has long-since been their home, one in which they have adapted and evolved furiously and efficiently to exploit. Indeed, their appearance – grotesque by human standards – actually betrays their success as species: minimal, streamlined, sense-orientated and above all efficient, it is secondary to function, and gives us a valuable insight into the development and evolution of carbon-based life forms. After all, what use is it looking pretty if you cannot defend yourself from predators, scavenge food, and live in the most demanding of environments?

So strap yourself in as we give you a tour of some of the more common micro monsters living in your own home, as while they aren't for the squeamish, they are fascinating and intriguing life forms nonetheless which tell us much about organisms and evolution. ✿

No it's not an image from *Starship Troopers…*

Cheese mite
FOUND: Food
Cheese mites infest cheese and other foods, and are usually seen as pests, causing spoilage and asthma in people breathing contaminated air. Some cheeses however, such as Mimolette, are deliberately infected with certain mites to create the correct flavour.

Meal mite
FOUND: Kitchen
The Meal species of mite is a common pest of granaries, mills and kitchens, feeding particularly on grains and cereals. It reproduces rapidly under good conditions, while under unfavourable conditions it forms a resting stage in which it can survive for over two years.

Dust mite
FOUND: Everywhere
Millions of dust mites inhabit homes, feeding on shedded skin cells. They mainly live in furniture, and are usually harmless. However, their excrement and dead bodies may cause allergic reactions in susceptible people.

Mites

One of the oldest forms of micro monster inhabiting your house, the mite is among the most diverse and successful invertebrates on Earth

48,200 species have already been identified and scientists postulate that this figure is only five per cent of the total number of mites on Earth. They are strong (for their size), durable and – most importantly – highly adaptable to change, evolving quickly to exploit the different environments presented to them over millions of years. In fact they have proved so good at adapting to Earth's changing environment that mites – or more accurately, their sub class Acari – have lived on Earth since the early Devonian period (416-359 million years ago), inhabiting the warmest and coldest climates and a vast array of living creatures. This evolutionary adaptability has granted mites almost unparalleled diversity and now, with the advent of the electron microscope, their numbers and types are visible for the first time.

Take the common house dust mite (Dermatophagoides pteronyssinus) from the pyroglyphidae family. This variant of mite dwells in human residences – including, as probability suggests, your home – and feeds entirely on organic detritus such as flakes of shedded human skin, flourishing in the stable environment and on a perpetual food supply. The dust mite is tiny and unseen, with a size of roughly 420 micrometers in length and 320 micrometers in height, highly reproductive – a female mite will lay 60 to 100 eggs in the last five weeks of her life – and impervious to all temperatures between 0°C and 60°C.

In essence, the dust mite is perfectly suited for life on Earth now, with the numbers of humans and houses in suitable climates (count yourself immune then in you live in Antarctica) in abundance. The ancestor that the common dust mite once shared evolved to take advantage of the rise of mammals (especially those which emerged from the nomadic tribal groups to set up permanent residences) and did so extraordinarily quickly. For while modern humans have only been around for 125,000 years, the Acari sub-class of mites has been around for over 400 million. This efficiency and adaptability is common in many micro monsters, as we will see over the page.

Main image and 3 x mites pictures © Science Photo Library

© SDaniel Schwen 07

SEM

The micro monster images contained within these pages come courtesy of scanning electron microscopes (SEM), which without we would not be able to observe. Electron microscopes produce electronically magnified images of specimens by utilising a particle beam of electrons. These electrons interact with the target's atoms and produce signals that contain information about the specimen's topography, composition and chemical properties. The electron microscope – due to electrons having wavelengths roughly 100,000 times shorter than protons (visible light) – allows for a magnification of up to 1,000,000x, which is vastly greater than the most powerful optical telescopes, which are limited to just 2,000x magnification.

Lice

Parasitic wingless insects, lice can be found on the majority of birds and mammals… including you

Pubic louse

FOUND: Pubic hair
Pubic lice are infamous for their inhabitation of human genital regions, living like head lice on individual strands of hair and descending to pierce the skin and drink blood.

Head louse

FOUND: Hair
The common head louse inhabits the hair of humans and sucks blood from the scalp. The head louse is closely related to the body louse and both subspecies are capable of interbreeding.

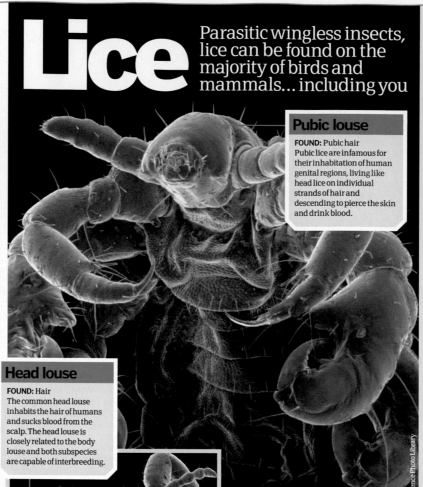

© Science Photo Library

Louse eggs

A louse with its egg – it has been glued to a hair strand. The egg has a perforated lid, which is removed by the emerging nymph. A female louse lays between 80-100 eggs in a lifetime.

© Science Photo Library

Lice are another species of micro monster that are close to home – literally – as not only are they found in your home but they live on humans themselves. In fact, lice cannot exist without a host (an obligate parasite), so it is rare to find them on non-organic matter. Most lice are scavengers by nature, feeding off the skin, blood and detritus found in and on the host's body, and often dwell in hair. There are over 3,000 species of louse (although only three are found on humans) and they live exclusively on avian and mammalian orders.

Head lice live on individual strands of human hair, clinging to them with crab-like limbs and measure two to three millimetres in length. To feed, the lice descend down to the scalp where they consume dead skin and drink blood – a process that involves the louse biting the scalp, injecting its saliva to clot the blood, and then extracting it into its body. When reproducing, female lice produce eggs that they attach to the strand of hair that they are clinging to with their sticky saliva. This means that when the egg hatches – young lice are called nymphs – they can move directly onto the same strand as their parent.

Scientists have discovered from analysing DNA evidence from modern humans' ancestors that lice spread to humans approximately 2,000 years ago from gorillas, who still share a susceptibility to lice.

You talkin' to me? You talkin' to me!

Silverfish

FOUND: Bathroom / kitchen
Silverfish are minute and fast-moving insects covered in silvery scales. Adults range in length from 1.2-2.5 centimetres in length, with a tapering body, two long antennae and three bristles at the rear.

© Science Photo Library

Silverfish

Nocturnal, razor-fast, silent: introducing the fastest micro monster your house has ever seen

Another ancient species that has inhabited Earth for millions of years, the common household silverfish (Lepisma saccharina) is a tiny but visible insect in the Thysanura order. Often found in areas of high humidity – such as bathrooms – silverfish are elongated, flattened insects that measure between 1.2-2.5cm in length. They are not parasitic creatures,

unlike mites and lice, consuming matter that is high in starches and sugars such as: cotton, paper, carpet, synthetic fabric and leather. Their speed comes courtesy of six legs and streamlined physical construction, allowing them to scuttle quickly and dynamically with minimal resistance.

As with mites and lice, the silverfish is aesthetically unpleasant, but as

with its fellow microscopic brethren it doesn't need to be and it is another good example of evolutionary priority. Despite the majority of its variants fitted with compound eyes, the silverfish technically doesn't require them – indeed, some varieties have none at all – as their finely tuned and large antennas and triple-arrayed cerci (largely rear-mounted

appendages used as sensory organs) give it excellent positional awareness, and thanks to its monumental speed considering its size, it is an almost predatorless species, with only certain centipedes and spiders capable of hunting it. Finally, the silverfish can live for up to a year without eating, greatly enhancing its ability to survive and reproduce.

BAD

1. Louse
Found on mammals and birds, the louse clings to its host via individual strands of hair, descending three to four times a day to drink its blood.

BADDER

2. Tapeworm
A worm that lives inside the digestive tract, the tapeworm absorbs nutrients through its skin from food consumed by its host as it is digested.

BADDEST

3. Mosquito
One of the most feared and prevalent parasites alive today, the mosquitoes suck the blood of their host and transmit various diseases including malaria.

DID YOU KNOW? *A species of ant, Globitermes sulphurous, protects its colony by exploding, trapping invaders in its sticky remains*

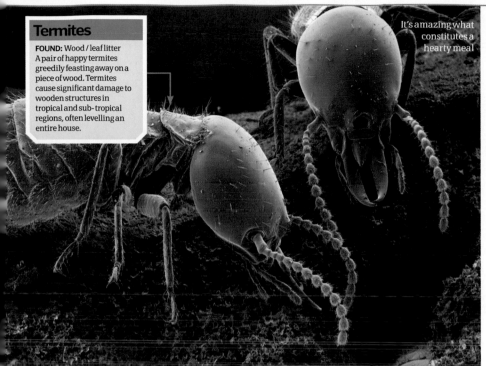

Termites

FOUND: Wood / leaf litter
A pair of happy termites greedily feasting away on a piece of wood. Termites cause significant damage to wooden structures in tropical and sub-tropical regions, often levelling an entire house.

It's amazing what constitutes a hearty meal

Termites

The bane of wood in all its forms, termites may be micro in size but they are capable of macro levels of destruction

While the other micro monsters featured here are potentially damaging to your health and belongings, the termite – a member of the Isoptera order – is neither a parasitic organism nor one that has a taste for your bookazine collection. Instead, they are major detritivores – organisms that feed by absorbing nutrients from detritus – that consume mainly dead plant material such as wood, leaf litter and soil. In nature this is a common behaviour and one that is invaluable to the ecosystem, contributing greatly to the effects of decomposition and the recycling of nutrients. However, when it is the wooden beams of a human home, this becomes more of a problem.

Termites – albeit in a slightly devolved ancestral form – have existed on Earth from the early cretaceous period (145 million years ago) and are reasoned by scientists to be close relatives of cockroaches and mantids. They are eusocial and, arguably, more highly evolved organisms however, living in decentralised, self-organised colonies of hundreds to millions of individuals – split into job roles such as reproductives, workers and soldiers – each guided by a swarm intelligence that allows them to exploit a range of food sources and environments that a singular termite would not be able to do so. Further, their nests or mounds are toughened structures and provide protection against predators.

Home invasion...
Where in our homes do these invaders reside?

Bathroom/toilet
- Silverfish
- Silverfish nymphs
- Dust mites

Plants/pets
- Thread-footed mites
- Spider mites
- Gall mites

Carpets/curtains
- Velvet mites
- Dust mites

Bedroom
- Bed bugs
- Dust mites

Termites
FOUND: Wood
Termites are social insects of the order Isoptera and have strong chewing mouthparts and beaded antennae. Akin to ants, termites have different body forms to perform different functions (castes).

Living room
- Dust mites
- Termites

Kitchen
- Cheese mites
- Meal mites
- Silverfish
- Dust mites

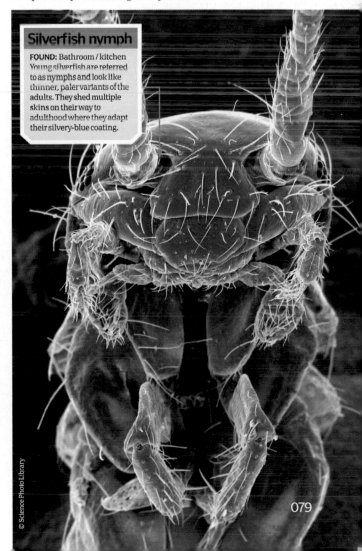

Silverfish nymph
FOUND: Bathroom / kitchen
Young silverfish are referred to as nymphs and look like thinner, paler variants of the adults. They shed multiple skins on their way to adulthood where they adapt their silvery-blue coating.

© Science Photo Library

Termite mounds

How does the wood-loving termite construct its home?

Termites are cellulose-eating insects that share many similarities with ants and bees, although, perhaps surprisingly, their closest relative is believed to be the cockroach. There are about 2,750 species of termite around the world, living in habitats as varied as tropical forests and the African savannah, through to the Pacific coast.

The eating habits of termites make them very important insects in an ecosystem. By consuming wooden structures and plant life they help convert dead trees into organic matter to trigger new life. However, this can cause problems, as they can eat through structural supports in buildings, eventually leading to their collapse.

Termites have evolved to eat wood largely because few other animals can; they carry a special bacteria that enables them to digest the tough cellulose fibres. This innate survival mechanism means termite colonies can be around for a very long time – indeed, some last up to 100 years. A termite mound (or termitarium) will reach its maximum size after four to five years, when it can be home to as many as 200,000 inhabitants.

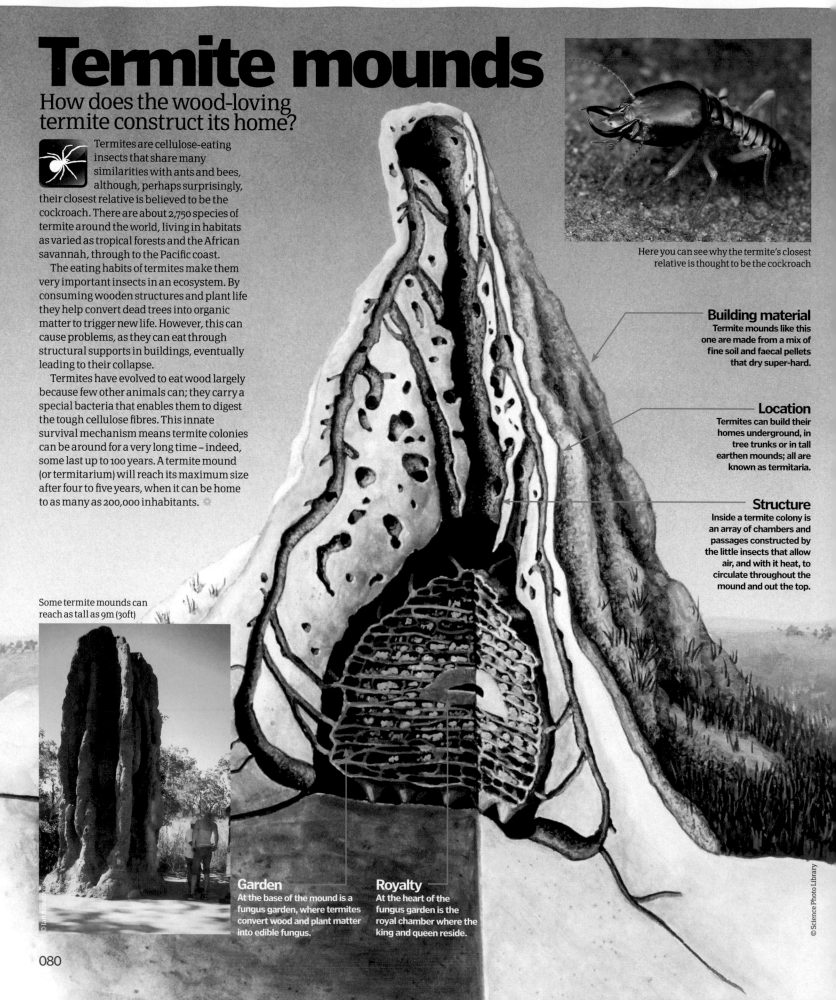

Here you can see why the termite's closest relative is thought to be the cockroach

Building material
Termite mounds like this one are made from a mix of fine soil and faecal pellets that dry super-hard.

Location
Termites can build their homes underground, in tree trunks or in tall earthen mounds; all are known as termitaria.

Structure
Inside a termite colony is an array of chambers and passages constructed by the little insects that allow air, and with it heat, to circulate throughout the mound and out the top.

Some termite mounds can reach as tall as 9m (30ft)

Garden
At the base of the mound is a fungus garden, where termites convert wood and plant matter into edible fungus.

Royalty
At the heart of the fungus garden is the royal chamber where the king and queen reside.

©Science Photo Library

Strength in numbers

1 There are approximately 12,000 known species of ant, composing around about 1.4 per cent of the world's total insect species.

Survival of the fittest

2 The family Formicidae are hardy little critters, who have existed on Earth for more than 140 million years, and aren't going anywhere soon!

Life expectancy

3 An ant Queen can live up to three years. Worker ants expect to live for a maximum of two, still impressive for an insect species.

Ant army

4 Eciton burchellii, a species of army ant, attack in formation with their swarm broadening to 15 yards, including up to 200,000 drones.

What's in a word?

5 In Japanese the word ant is intricately written by linking two separate characters, one meaning insect and the other meaning loyalty.

DID YOU KNOW? Ants communicate primarily with pheromones, chemicals secreted and smelled or tasted by nest mates

The inner workings of an ants' nest

The fascinating social structures of the mighty yet minuscule ant species

Ants, or the family Formicidae, are an interesting species of insect, which show a distinct and complex social infrastructure. Known as an ant colony, this social cycle is dependent on hierarchy, with the Queen starting the proceedings.

Once an ants' nest is successfully built, the Queen, or reproductive female, will take up residence after nuptial flight and shed her wings. One or a few male ants then inseminate her. This can take place in the nest, while stationary in the air or on low vegetation or the ground when food foraging. She then resides in an excavated chamber. Here she will lay her eggs, emerging as larvae, feeding them from regurgitate liquefied musculature, related to the wings.

These initial numbers of worker ants are referred to as nanitics, spawning from eggs no bigger than 1mm in size. This life cycle – from larva, to pupa, to ant – often lasts from six to ten weeks. These are much smaller than subsequent workers, due to the ability of the Queen to only provide a limited amount of food, comparative to that which foraging workers later provide.

Initially the Queen is responsible for nest maintenance and defence, once larvae have reached maturity the Queen is only responsible for reproduction and populating the ant colony. It's now the ant workers turn to feed and sustain her majesty. This allows the colony to expand in population as well as territory and residence.

This of course takes a period of several years, after which the colony produces its first generation of sexuals, who will fly on the same day all at the same time, enhancing their chance to meet in the nuptial flight and to close the cycle. The reason behind this is also that the death of the Queen has devastating effects on a colony as ants seldom replace her, and have a survival expectancy of only several months after her demise. ✿

Ants' nests house complete colonies, so they have to be pretty big. The majority of this species decide to build intricate layouts underground, with some recorded at reaching six metres down.

Home sweet home

Ant colonies are built and maintained by legions of worker ants. They carry tiny bits of dirt in their mandibles, depositing this near the exit of the colony. This forms what is know as an ant hill.

Each nest is an intricate labyrinth of tunnels and chambers that serve different functions and house different members of the ant colony. Each is interconnecting and has an opening that is connected with the surface.

The Queen ant understandably has the freedom of her own chamber. It's here, in this excavated area, that she will repopulate the colony, laying all her eggs.

Other chambers are used as nurseries tending to larvae. There are also food larders, stocking sustenance for the colony, and resting quarters for those hard-working ants.

Ant social types

Every ant knows its place, and the job of each one is just as vital as the next. But just what are the roles of the different ant classes?

NAME OF ANT:
Ant Queen
ROLE:
The Queen establishes but does not rule. Her role is to reproduce, and ensure the longevity of the colony.

NAME OF ANT:
Worker
ROLE:
Perhaps the smallest, these ants care for the Queen and her young, build and repair the nest and forage for food.

NAME OF ANT:
Soldier
ROLE:
Significantly larger worker ants that are named as such due to their larger heads, and stronger mandibles.

NAME OF ANT:
Drones
ROLE:
Male ants, or drones, live only a few weeks or months, and are solely responsible for inseminating young queens.

© Thinkstock

Slugs and snails

The gardener's least favourite visitors, slugs and snails are quite incredible little slime balls

22. Shell
Made of calcium carbonate, a snail's strong shell will remain so if the animal's diet contains enough calcium.

1. Stomach
This section of the digestive tract receives food to be digested.

2. Kidney
During digestion, harmful side-products can accumulate and poison the snail. The kidney can expel this poison.

3. Mantle
Covering the body is a layer called the mantle, which can secrete a shell in snails but not in slugs.

5. Foot
This consists mainly of muscle tissue that contracts and expands enabling the snail to move.

6. Mucous gland
The mucous gland in the foot secretes thick, sticky slime to help the snail traverse tricky ground without injury.

20. Lung
Not all snails have lungs but those that do have a single cavity containing a network of blood vessels that functions like a lung.

21. Liver

4. Heart

7. Dart sac
Some land snails shoot a mucus-covered 'dart' into mates, delivering a substance that improves sperm survival.

19. Anus
The intestine opens outside near the anus. As the snail crawls away it leaves behind a dark trail of faeces.

12. Crop
The crop is a sack where food pulp is stored before heading to the stomach. Digestive fluids are produced by the main gland or hepatopancreas.

11. Salivary gland
Found in the buccal cavity, the salivary gland secretes saliva to aid digestion.

8. Vagina
Female reproductive organ located on the ventral surface of the foot.

9. Penis
Male reproductive organ is located internally when not in use and is found on the ventral face of the foot.

10. Genital pore
Found at the side of the head, this opening allows copulation and exchange of sperm.

18. Respiratory pore
Also called a pneumostome, this breathing pore is an opening through which air is breathed into the lung.

16. Tentacle
Snails have one or two sets of retractable tentacles projecting from the top of the head depending on the species.

17. Eye
If there are two tentacles, the shorter front set will be sensitive to touch and the longer set behind will bear eyes.

15. Cerebral ganglia

14. Salivary duct

13. Mouth
The mouth features a jaw and a rough ribbon-like tongue called the radula for grazing on plants.

Although they look very different, slugs, snails, octopuses, oysters and cuttlefish are all molluscs – Latin for 'thin shelled' – and either have a calcium-carbonate external shell, a small shell under the surface, or no shell at all. Slugs are shell-less while adult snails have coiled shells big enough to withdraw into.

Slugs and snails belong to the large group of molluscs called gastropods and make their home in a variety of locations from back gardens to oceans and everywhere in-between. They are the only molluscs that can live on dry land, and breathe using either lungs, gills or both.

Gastropods are hermaphroditic, which means they have both male and female reproductive organs, and can mate with themselves if no partner is available. During an elaborate mating ritual slugs entwine and stimulate each other until sperm is exchanged via their disproportionately large genitals. Another peculiar trait is apophallation, whereby one slug chews off the other's penis after mating. The apophallated slug may now only reproduce using its female genitalia.

Why do ticks suck blood?

Discover how these little bloodsuckers make a tasty meal of their warm-blooded hosts

Ticks are small parasites that feed on the protein-rich blood of other animals through a process called 'hematophagy'. As they are arachnids they have eight legs, the first pair of which features a special sensory pit called the 'haller' organ, which can sniff out prey. After finding a suitable host, the tick anchors itself to the victim using its claws as well as its spiny legs and the special sucker pads on its feet. To puncture the skin and get to the blood, the tick uses its two fang-like chelicerae, and then extends a long serrated proboscis called a 'hypostome'. The hypostome makes it difficult to remove an attached tick as, like a fishhook, it's covered with backwards-pointing barbs. The tick then sucks up blood until its body, also known as the 'idiosoma', is so bloated it can't take any more – this can take several days.

Engorged
This image shows a tick filled with blood.

Ticks can swell to many times their size after feeding

© Science Photo Library

How to remove a tick

Always consult a doctor if you are at all concerned about a tick bite. However, it's best to remove a tick as soon as possible, as they carry such infectious diseases as lyme disease. You should avoid touching the tick, so it's a good idea to use tweezers or wear protective gloves. Then, firmly but gently, take hold of the arachnid as close to the skin as possible and pull it straight out – don't wiggle or twist, as the delicate mouthparts can break off in the skin.

Once the tick has been removed, clean the area with antiseptic (soap and water will do) to help reduce the chance of bacteria and infection.

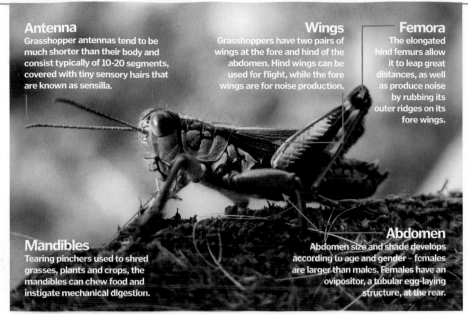

Antenna
Grasshopper antennas tend to be much shorter than their body and consist typically of 10-20 segments, covered with tiny sensory hairs that are known as sensilla.

Wings
Grasshoppers have two pairs of wings at the fore and hind of the abdomen. Hind wings can be used for flight, while the fore wings are for noise production.

Femora
The elongated hind femurs allow it to leap great distances, as well as produce noise by rubbing its outer ridges on its fore wings.

Mandibles
Tearing pinchers used to shred grasses, plants and crops, the mandibles can chew food and instigate mechanical digestion.

Abdomen
Abdomen size and shade develops according to age and gender – females are larger than males. Females have an ovipositor, a tubular egg-laying structure, at the rear.

Grasshoppers

Renowned for their jumping prowess, grasshoppers are a diverse species of insect

Similar to the locust and cricket, the grasshopper is a species of insect in the orthoptera order, however it is non-migratory and tends to exist in isolation (ie, it does not swarm), meeting up generally only to mate.

Grasshopper anatomy consists of a long abdomen (females are equipped with an ovipositor for laying eggs), short forelegs, powerful hind legs (responsible for its jumping prowess), two pairs of wings and a short antenna. Its nervous system is controlled by a series of ganglia, a collection of nerve cells located in each part of the body – the largest occurring in the head. Information is fed to the ganglia via its antenna, sensilla (tiny exterior hairs) and cerci (paired appendages at its rear). Sound's detected by a pair of tympanal organs,

a set of membranes stretched across a frame, and backed by an air sac and sensory neurons.

Grasshoppers are herbivores and tend to eat grasses, plants and leaves, dissected by their mandibles. Food is digested in a series of three guts – the stomodaeum, mesentreron and proctodaeum – running from the fore of the abdomen to the rear respectively. Food is broken down by a selection of secreted enzymes including amylase, protease, lipase and invertase. Reproduction occurs through a lengthy ovulation process (up to nine months), with eggs laid by females typically one to two inches underground.

There are currently roughly 11,000 species of grasshopper recorded worldwide, and they tend to be found residing in tropical forests and grassland planes. ✿

A female grasshopper laying her eggs in sand. Female abdomen tips are fitted with two pairs of triangular valves to ease the digging process

Animal moulting

It's the circle of life in all its skin-shedding glory

Creatures throughout the animal kingdom undergo the process of moulting – the replacement of their horns, hair, skin or feathers. Insects moult to allow their growing bodies to expand beyond the constraints of their rigid exoskeleton, forming a new shell in the process and often eating the old one. Most mammals shed their hair in autumn to grow a thicker layer of protection for the winter, and vice versa for the summer.

Birds moult their feathers regularly as they become worn with use, growing fresh new ones in their place. Water birds, however, often lose all their feathers at once and thus the ability to fly, meaning that they must remain hidden from predators until their feathers have re-grown. Camouflaged animals keep their pattern when they're moulting except for decorator crabs, who transfer the camouflage from their old to new exoskeleton. ✿

Out with the old, in with the new...

The timescale of moulting for a southern hawker dragonfly is a little over three hours

© Böhringer Friedrich

Animals with exoskeletons

Why do some critters have their skeletons on the outside?

The rhinoceros beetle is considered by many as the world's strongest creature, able to carry up to 850 times its own weight!

It might come as a surprise but 98 per cent of the animals on Earth don't have a backbone, and 95 per cent don't have any bones at all. So how do all these creatures support and protect themselves? Well, many invertebrates – and all arthropods – have a protective external casing called an exoskeleton. This literally means 'outside skeleton' and its role is to cover the animal's soft tissues and also provide a rigid structure to which the creature's muscles can attach.

Insect exoskeletons are made of chitin, which is embedded into a kind of tough protein matrix. Chitin is a nitrogen-based biopolymer – similar, at least in function, to keratin, which is the stuff our hair and nails are made of. Arthropods such as crustaceans, meanwhile, have additional calcium carbonate in their exoskeletons for extra armour plating.

As well as supporting and protecting the creature, an exoskeleton also creates a watertight barrier that prevents the animal from drying out. The exterior of an exoskeleton can also contain sensory hairs or bristles, while some animals can secrete various pheromones and chemicals onto the surface of their shell as a means of repelling predators.

Though an exoskeleton consists of flexible leg joints to enable the creature to move about, once it's formed this armour does not expand with the rest of the body. Therefore, the animal will eventually outgrow it. At this point a process called ecdysis, or moulting, takes place whereby the creature will shed its overly tight outer skin in order to make way for a new one.

There are three main types of skeletal system in the animal kingdom: exoskeletons (on the outside), endoskeletons (on the inside, like humans) and hydrostatic skeletons, which are a bit different as they have no real framework but rather maintain their shape by the pressure of fluid in their bodies. Examples of creatures with hydrostatic skeletons include slugs, worms and jellyfish. ✿

Which creatures have exoskeletons?

Spider
The discarded cuticle left behind after a spider has outgrown its exoskeleton and wriggled out is complete with all the legs and you can even see the fine hairs on its body.

Scorpion
Baby scorpions start out all soft and squishy, riding around on their mothers' backs, but their exoskeletons soon harden. One unusual trait about the scorpion's exoskeleton is that it glows fluorescent under ultraviolet light.

© SPL; Thinkstock; Getty

In Chinese medicine, cicada shells, or slough, are used to treat certain ailments

Outgrowing your shell

Until an arthropod reaches maturity, its body will continue to grow. The exoskeleton, however, does not. Whenever the shell begins to feel tight – maybe once or twice a year – it's time to grow a new one and dispose of the old. This process of moulting is known as ecdysis.

The new soft exoskeleton is produced beneath the old one, and when the time's right the old cuticle will separate from the body, enabling the animal to slip out.

Once the outer shell is cast off, the creature needs to temporarily inflate its new soft body as much as possible to create room for growth before the cuticle becomes hard again. This rapid expansion is achieved by the transferral of fluids from the animal's soft body parts to other areas. Insects that breathe through tracheal tubes can also pump up their bodies by taking in extra air.

The hardening and darkening of the cuticle is a process called sclerotisation. Superficial hardening can take a few hours, whereas permanent structural integrity and colouration can take a number of days or even weeks. Before the new exoskeleton has toughened up, the pale-bodied creature remains quite soft and is therefore very vulnerable to predators. As a result the animal will often hide away until its new shell has fully hardened.

Arthropod exoskeletons

All arthropods have an exoskeleton, aka cuticle, consisting of two main protective layers: the thin, waterproof outer epicuticle and the thicker chitinous procuticle just below it...

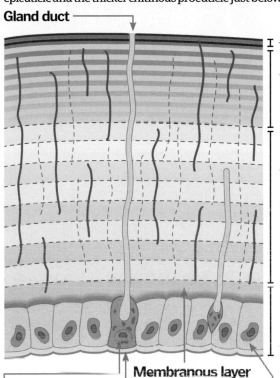

Gland duct

Membranous layer

Basement membrane

Epidermal cells

Dermal gland
Found in the epidermis, the dermal glands are responsible for producing predator-repelling chemicals, which are released on the surface of the exoskeleton through minute ducts.

Epicuticle
A thin, waxy layer, the epicuticle is both water and solvent-resistant. It contains no chitin and makes up the hard exterior of the exoskeleton.

Hardened exocuticle
The thick procuticle layers are made of chitin, which is like nature's plastic. Compacted layers of this structural biopolymer produce the exoskeleton's characteristic hardness.

Flexible endocuticle
Located below the exocuticle is a criss-crossing network of further chitinous layers, which together form the tough yet flexible endocuticle layers.

Procuticle
The procuticle is made up of two main layers: the exocuticle and the endocuticle. The procuticle contains chitin microfibres bound by a protein matrix, each layer aligned differently for strength.

Epidermis
Below the cuticle layers is the epidermis, which is a single layer of secretary cells from which the epicuticle is produced.

Millipede
Its long, tubular exoskeleton is reinforced by hard minerals. Toxic chemicals can also be secreted onto the surface of the outer shell to deter predators or when millipedes feel threatened.

Crab
A crab's broad protective plate across its back is called the carapace. The decorator crab's exoskeleton comes in handy for disguise too, as it features tiny hooks onto which coral attaches. The coconut crab (above), meanwhile, is so big it can spend a whole month shedding its shell and waiting for the new one to harden.

Spiny African flower mantis
A mantis will moult between five and ten times during its lifetime, and usually it will stop growing and shedding once it's an adult with fully functioning wings.

Lobster
Crustacean exoskeletons are reinforced with calcium and made up of plates. Hormones that originate from the lobster's eye tell it when it's time to shed its shell. When a chef boils a lobster its outer skin will turn from blue-black to bright red. This is because certain pigments in the exoskeleton turn red when exposed to heat.

© Thinkstock

Scorpions

The mascot of choice for international supervillains, these sinister stingers are also fearsome hunters

Scorpions are arachnids, like spiders. However, whereas spiders are mainly ambush predators, scorpions go out looking for their lunch instead. Scorpions have between two and ten eyes, depending on the species, but their eyesight is poor and most scorpions are nocturnal anyway.

Instead they rely on vibration-sensitive legs, and hairs on their body that can detect the lightest touch or air current. A desert scorpion can feel the vibrations caused by the footsteps of a walking insect from a metre away. By comparing the time it takes the surface vibration to reach each leg, the scorpion can triangulate the position of its target. When it is close enough, the scorpion makes a brief dash to snatch its prey in powerful pincers. These claws, or chelae, are not true legs but are instead modified feelers. With the victim firmly grasped in its clutches, the scorpion arches its tail over its back to inject a powerful venom that incapacitates its meal within seconds.

Scorpions can't eat solid food directly, so they feed in a two-stage process. First they tear off small pieces with claw-like mouthparts, called chelicerae. These morsels are placed in a small cavity under the mouth and digestive juices are squirted up from the gut like ketchup. After the enzymes have liquidised the food, it can be slurped down into the stomach. Scorpions can eat several times their body weight at a single sitting and store this away for leaner times. They have very slow metabolisms and many species live for over ten years. If necessary they can manage with just one or two meals a year. ✦

Claw
The outer half of the claw is fixed and called the tarsus. The inner, movable, section is called the manus. Collectively, the pincer is called a chela.

Cephalic ganglion
It's not complex enough to call it a brain but this bundle of nerves controls all the actions of the scorpion.

Claw muscle
The bulge in the claw contains a large bundle of muscle fibres to allow a powerful crushing and slicing grip.

ON THE MAP

Finding scorpions
Scorpions have a very wide distribution and are found on every continent apart from Antarctica. The dark zone on the map represents the greatest scorpion diversity but they can be found as far north as Kent in the UK and as far south as New Zealand.

DEADLY

1. Box jellyfish
The venom in the stinging tentacles will cause excruciating pain for weeks and can stop your heart. The venom also eats away your skin.
© GG

DEADLIER

2. Deathstalker scorpion
The most venomous scorpion. It rarely kills adults but children and the elderly are at great risk and the sting is difficult to treat.
© Tola Kokoza, 2009

DEADLIEST

3. Funnel web spider
This large spider produces more venom than any other spider. Most mammals are immune to its bite but it will kill humans in 15 minutes.

DID YOU KNOW? Occasionally, scorpions will be born with two tails. This is caused by a random genetic mutation

Party animals

How do scorpions glow in ultraviolet?

All scorpions are fluorescent. This means that they glow when shone with ultraviolet light. This rather funky property is an accidental side effect of the way their armour plating is constructed. When scorpions first shed their skin, the new skin underneath is soft and vulnerable. To harden it up, the protein chains are cross-linked using other compounds. This process is called sclerotisation and is similar to the way that cowhide is turned into leather. In scorpions, the cross-linking compound is beta-carboline, which is strongly fluorescent. As a result scorpions glow more and more brightly under UV light with each successive moult.

A deadly and bright creature
© Fritz Seiler-Grimm

Hairs
These tiny hairs allow the scorpion to detect touch and air currents.

Telson
A hollow needle that injects venom into its prey.
© Thinkstock

Only 25 species have venom capable of killing a human
© Siga

Telson
The sting or telson is a hollow needle that injects the venom. The two poison glands can adjust the dose according to the size of prey.

Metasoma
The tail is made from the last six segments of the body. The anus opens at the end, just before the sting.

Intestine
Scorpions do most of their digestion externally and have quite a simple digestive tract.

Prosoma
This is also sometimes called the cephalothorax, as with spiders, and it is a fused head and body segment that holds the sensory organs and the legs.

Mesosoma
This corresponds roughly with the abdomen of an insect or spider. The digestive and reproductive organs are contained here.

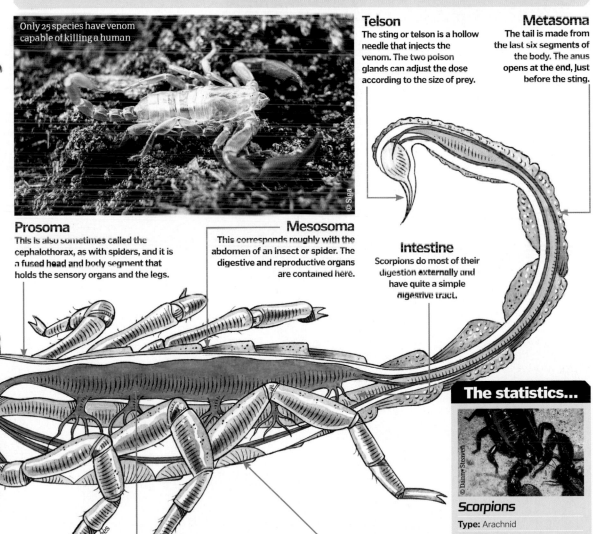
© DK images

Sting in the tail

Scorpions are fast, strong and armoured, but they aren't invulnerable and relying on sheer brute strength when you are tackling prey almost as large as you is always risky. To tilt the scales in their favour, all scorpions are equipped with fast-acting venom which is delivered through a hollow barb located on the end of their tail.

Scorpion venom is a cocktail of hundreds of different neurotoxins and enzyme inhibitors. This broad spectrum of chemicals allows the scorpion to target several different biological systems at once; some compounds paralyse muscles, others cause cell damage. Scorpions have also evolved different toxins to target different animals. For example, insect and mammal nervous systems work in quite different ways, and by combining all these chemicals into a single venom, scorpions have created a silver bullet that can take down almost anything. Despite this, our sheer size is our biggest defence and only 25 species of scorpion are deadly to humans.

Dorsal blood vessel
This also functions as a primitive heart, sloshing blood between the lungs and the bodily extremities.

Book lung
Four simple folded structures on segments three to seven of the mesosoma supply oxygen to the blood.

The statistics...

© Danny Steaven

Scorpions

Type:	Arachnid
Diet:	Carnivore
Average life span in the wild:	4-25 years
Weight:	4-60g
Size:	12mm-20cm

Anatomy of a spider

Inside the animal behind the most common phobia in Britain

Part of the arachnid class of animals – which actually includes scorpions, ticks and mites – spiders are eight-legged arthropods with two body sections. With its ability to inject venom into its prey, immobilising them for ease of eating, the spider has become both feared and revered.

Fancy a bite?

The poison gland connected to a venomous spider's fangs contains dangerous chemicals that are released into a victim by digging the fangs into the victim's body. Unless the spider feels threatened, these fangs will remain tucked away. Some spider poisons have horrible side effects, including tissue degeneration, cell death, and sickness, and yet even if a deadly venomous spider does bite you, your chance of dying as a result of it is less than ten per cent. Male funnel-web venom contains robustoxin, which affects the nervous systems of humans and monkeys, but not of other mammals.

Cephalothorax
The cephalothorax is the fusion of head and thorax that distinguishes spiders from insects, which have three separate head, thorax and abdomen sections. This large section of the spider's body carries four pairs of legs and two pairs of mouthparts.

Brain

Forward-facing eyes
Despite having numerous eyes, the spider is not known for its good eyesight. Forward-facing eyes enable the spider to better judge distances. Most spiders have four pairs of eyes – a main pair and three small pairs – but some species have fewer.

Pedipalps
This pair of small feelers are ideal for controlling and tearing up food.

Chelicerae
These fangs are small but deadly projections that inject poison into the spider's prey.

Mouthparts
The mouthparts enable the spider to inject victims with digestive enzymes and then use their fangs to liquefy the body, which can then be sucked up as food.

Leg joints
The spider's jointed legs have seven individual sections, helping them to move quickly. The hairs on a spider's legs can detect vibrations in the air, helping them to anticipate predators.

Poison gland

Coxa

Trochanter

Femur

Patella

Tibia

Metatarsus

Tarsus

Tarsal claw

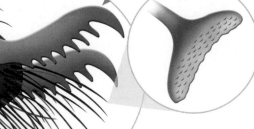

Feet
A spider's foot is covered in hairs, each of which is covered in microscopic feet. These mini feet allow the spider to grip on to any surface.

Good vibrations
1 Spiders do have eyes but they aren't very effective. Instead, spiders use vibrations. The tiny bristles all over a spider's body surface are sensitive to touch, vibration and airflow.

Spiders' digest
2 Spiders digest food outside their body. They cover the insects in digestive enzymes which break down the body, and allows the spider to suck up the liquid prey.

Arthropods
3 Spiders are arthropods, so the skeletal system of their body is the outermost layer. The hard exoskeleton helps the spider maintain moisture and not dry out.

Special silk
4 Spider silk has other uses than spinning webs. Black widow silk was at one time used in military gun sights because of its strength and uniform thickness.

Flying spiders
5 Young spiders, or spiderlings, can travel great distances by doing something called 'ballooning' – the process of floating on the breeze using a strand of silk.

DID YOU KNOW? If a train was to hit a sheet of spider's silk the thickness of a pencil it would stop the vehicle in its tracks

Pedicel
This thin section of the body connects the cephalothorax and the abdomen.

Abdomen
The abdomen, which is covered in hairs that stand on end to deter enemies, is where you will find the heart, lungs, liver and silk-producing spinnerets.

How do spiders breathe?

There are two kinds of respiratory system inherent to the spider – trachea and book lungs. The trachea system consists of tubes running the length of the body. The natural movements of the spider forces air into the body, where it diffuses into the blood. Carbon dioxide is then diffused back into the air and forced out of the body again by the spider's movements. The book lungs, meanwhile, consist of very thin leaf-like structures filled with blood that also exchange oxygen and carbon dioxide through diffusion.

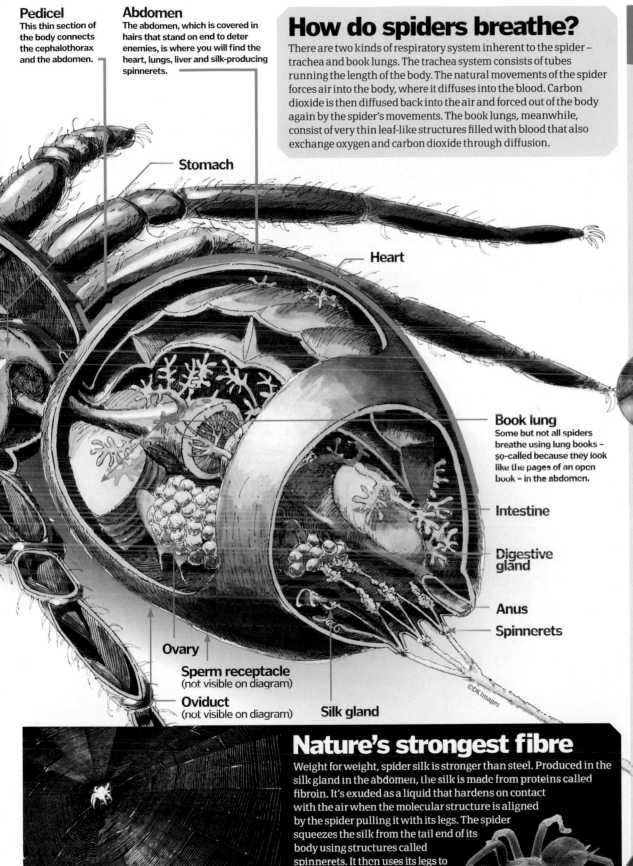

Stomach

Heart

Book lung
Some but not all spiders breathe using lung books – so-called because they look like the pages of an open book – in the abdomen.

Intestine

Digestive gland

Anus

Spinnerets

Ovary

Sperm receptacle
(not visible on diagram)

Oviduct
(not visible on diagram)

Silk gland

©DK Images

MOST WANTED

Some of the most notorious spiders on the planet

1 Brown recluse
The brown recluse can be distinguished by the dark violin-shaped marking on its back. It uses stealth – not a web – to catch its prey by sneaking up and sinking its venomous fangs into the victim. Most bites to humans are accidental and painless, until three to eight hours later when the site becomes red and painful. In bad cases the wound becomes necrotic causing the cells and tissue to die, which can leave severe scarring.

2 Black widow
Identified by their vivid red-on-black markings, black widows are found in the more temperate regions of the globe. Though the venom can bring about nasty symptoms in adults, a bite from the black widow doesn't actually sound the death knell for its victims. Children and the elderly, however, are more at risk.

3 Mexican redknee tarantula
The Mexican redknee is most wanted not because it's a deadly creature but because it makes for a popular pet. Found in the mountains of Mexico and often employed for its impressive appearance as a Hollywood prop in the likes of the *Indiana Jones* and *James Bond* films, this spider is actually very docile in nature and moves very slowly.

4 Wolf spider
Mottled brown in colour – and therefore often confused with the brown recluse (above) – the wolf spider is so-named because it was once thought to have hunted in packs. Though wolf spiders are hairy, they are not closely related to the tarantula. Wolf spiders are not poisonous unless you're allergic, and they can be found throughout Europe and in Britain.

5 Funnel-web spider
A native to the coastal and mountain regions of eastern Australia, the funnel-web is a small but deadly part of the family. Its glossy, almost hairless body gives it a menacing appearance and some species can serve a highly toxic, fast-acting venom. The female funnel-web will spend most of her life inside her burrow, which is lined with white silk.

Nature's strongest fibre

Weight for weight, spider silk is stronger than steel. Produced in the silk gland in the abdomen, the silk is made from proteins called fibroin. It's exuded as a liquid that hardens on contact with the air when the molecular structure is aligned by the spider pulling it with its legs. The spider squeezes the silk from the tail end of its body using structures called spinnerets. It then uses its legs to stretch the material into long threads for weaving into webs to catch prey.

Latrodectus females can be identified by the distinctive red hourglass marking found on the underside of their abdomen

sxc.hu

Black widows

How do these deadly spiders kill their prey?

The black widow spider (genus Latrodectus) begins by using its silk glands (spinnerets) at the rear of its abdomen to create a sticky web. It waits at the edge of the trap until its prey either flies or walks into it. When an insect is trapped in the web, the black widow can sense the vibrations caused by the struggling prey. From these vibrations it can tell how big and strong the prey is, and if it is too big, it will leave well alone.

If the prey is small enough, however, the black widow will use its spinnerets to cover it in stronger webbing. It then firmly holds the prey with its chelicerae, which is a pair of hollow appendages above its mouth that send poison into the victim.

The spider's latrotoxin, neurotoxic poison, causes the prey to suffer spasms, paralysis and death within ten minutes. After this, enzymes inside the victim liquefy its body allowing the spider to feed on it. ✿

DID YOU KNOW?

The poison of the black widow spider is 15 times stronger than a rattlesnake's venom. It rarely bites humans and although painful, less than 1% of them cause human death.

While their bites are dangerous to humans, black widows don't usually bite unless acting defensively

How does a spider construct its web?

Learn how arachnids create their spiral orb webs in which to ensnare prey

Building a spider web is a very complex process. Referring to the stages below, first the spider (at point A) dangles a length of sticky silk, which can be carried in the air until it sticks to an anchor point, such as a branch (see point B). Once the silk is attached to point B, the spider pulls it taut and fixes the original end to anchor point A, creating the 'bridge thread' (red).

Now the spider fixes a second strand (blue) to point A and spins this while crossing the bridge. This thread is looser than the first and droops below the bridge thread. At point B the spider attaches this strand but doesn't pull it taut.

Next the spider travels back halfway along the now anchored loose thread (to point C, the web centre); the weight of the spider bows the thread into a V-shape, and from the bottom of the 'V', the spider attaches a third thread, which is spun as the arachnid descends to another branch (anchor point D). This turns the V-shape into a Y-shape, and creates another integral pathway. The spider continues to create more of these structural strands until a basic framework is in place.

With the main frame lines in position, the spider adds radial threads from the centre to surrounding vegetation, much like the spokes of a wheel. These form the non-stick paths upon which the creature can safely navigate its trap.

Next the spider creates a silk spiral across the radial lines from the inside out. Using this as a template, it repeats this stage, except this time the threads are coated in bug-catching adhesive.

Now all the spider needs to do is position itself at the centre of its trap and wait. These creatures are very sensitive to vibrations and, quick as a flash, the spider can expertly traverse its web to confront a haplessly entangled victim. ●

The spinnerets in action, here being used to cocoon a victim

© Alamy

Stage 1: Creating a framework

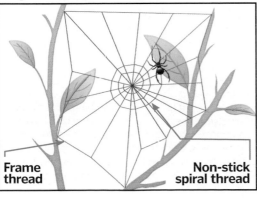

Stage 2: The orb takes shape

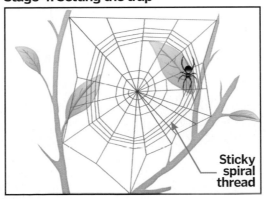

Radial thread

Stage 3: The spiral template

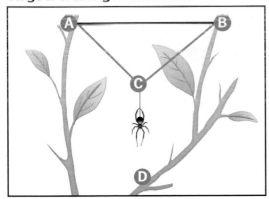

Frame thread

Non-stick spiral thread

Stage 4: Setting the trap

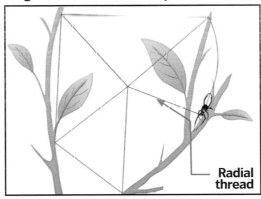

Sticky spiral thread

The science of silk

Spider silk is made of proteins called fibroins. It's very strong – in fact, weight for weight it's tougher than steel – yet also extremely elastic. These two characteristics, together, make for one unique substance in nature that the world's greatest material scientists have been trying to re-create artificially.

Silk is secreted as a liquid from the spider by the spinnerets, which are special glands located in the tip of the arachnid's abdomen. Upon contact with air the liquid instantly hardens to become a fine but strong silk. As the material is produced, the spider pulls it into long, thin threads using its legs.

The reason the spider itself does not become caught in its own web is that, first, it knows which sticky strands to avoid and, second, the adhesive hardens if the unwitting victim makes a sudden movement, but not with the gentle, considered movements of the spider.

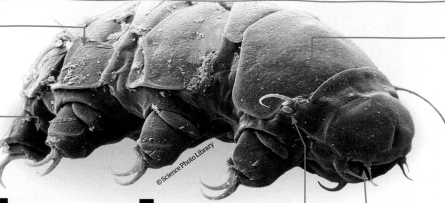

Cell count
Tardigrades are eutelic, which means that individuals of the same species all have the same number of cells.

Legs
All tardigrades have eight legs. Their name means 'slow walker'.

©Science Photo Library

Moulting
Some species only defecate when they shed their skin, leaving the faeces behind inside the old skin.

Senses
Some species have very simple, non-image-forming eyes, as well as sensory bristles.

Mouthparts
Tardigrades have a circular mouth that pierces and sucks. Most feed on plants.

Tardigrades

They may be small but are these minibeasts really the toughest creatures on the planet?

Tardigrades are tiny aquatic invertebrates, sometimes called water bears because of the loping way that they move. The largest species are 1.5 millimetres long, the smallest are under 0.1mm. Despite their squishy and vulnerable appearance, they are virtually indestructible. Experiments in laboratories have shown that they can survive pressures of 6,000 atmospheres, temperatures as low as -272°C or as high as 151°C and radiation doses that would most certainly kill us a thousand times over.

They achieve this by dehydrating their own bodies using a special sugar called trehalose, which acts as scaffolding to protect the cell contents. Their water content drops to one per cent of normal in this state and their metabolism slows by 99.99 per cent. Ice can't form in a body this dry and all the chemical reactions that might harm them simply happen too slowly to be dangerous. ✿

ON THE MAP

Tardigrades are everywhere!
1 The top of the Himalayas
2 The bottom of the Mariana Trench in the Pacific Ocean
3 Tropical rainforests
4 The Atacama desert
5 Antarctica, frozen deep in the ice
6 On the moss in your garden

Bombardier beetle self-defence

What explosive technique does this insect use to protect itself?

Bombardier beetles have a unique means of self-defence, seeing off predators by blasting them with a disorientating caustic jet of steam and liquid. A violent explosion erupts from the rear end of the insect when two chemicals are combined and then catalysed.

The concentrated substances are secreted from glands into a reservoir where they are mixed inside the creature's abdomen. When the beetle feels threatened a muscular valve then forces the concoction into a second chamber. Here a catalyst causes an exothermic reaction that raises the temperature of the liquid to boiling point.

It is then ejected under great pressure out the tip of the insect's abdomen. This turret ejector can aim the stinky stream in all directions as it uses muscles to swivel the nozzle. The blast of fluid is released in super-fast pulses up to 500 times per second to prevent the beetle itself from being scalded.

The noxious jet of boiling fluid, which is also extremely smelly, confuses and, in some cases, can even immobilise the would-be assassin. ✿

Ejection nozzle
The catalysts cause a violent exothermic reaction that releases a lot of heat energy. This vaporises most of the liquid in the chamber causing it to explode out of an opening at the end of the abdomen.

Reaction chamber
Danger triggers a fast response from the beetle that opens a valve in the reservoir and releases the acidic concoction into another chamber where enzyme catalysts are added.

Taking aim
Muscles around the exit passage direct the jet of boiling steam in almost any direction with incredible precision, temporarily stunning the bug's foe.

Chemical stores
Two concentrated primary reagents (hydrogen peroxide and hydroquinone) are secreted from glands in the beetle's abdomen into a chemical reservoir.

© Getty

5 TOP FACTS
EYES

Eye-spy
1 There are ten eye layouts falling into two categories. Simple eyes have one concave photoreceptive surface, while compound eyes have a number of lenses on a convex surface.

Seven
2 Simple eyes such as those of humans are very common on our planet and have evolved at least seven times from just a small grouping of photosensitive cells.

Mosaic
3 Adult dragonflies can have 30,000 ommatidia, giving them incredibly detailed, mosaic-like images to process. The quantity also grants them excellent movement sensing.

Different forms
4 Compound eyes come in two forms. Apposition eyes work by combining individual points of info together to form an image, while superposition eyes create one whole image.

Cambrian
5 Apposition eyes are almost certainly the original type of compound eye. The oldest eyes found are from the trilobites of the Cambrian Period (542-488.3 million years ago).

DID YOU KNOW? The ommatidia that make up compound eyes are between 5-50 micrometers in size

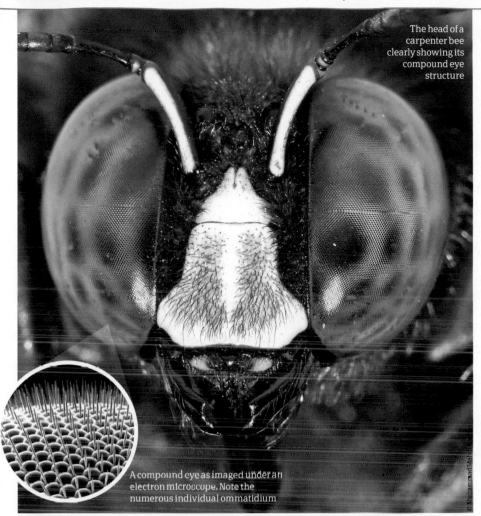

The head of a carpenter bee clearly showing its compound eye structure

A compound eye as imaged under an electron microscope. Note the numerous individual ommatidium

© Muzammmad Mahdi

Inside a bee's eye

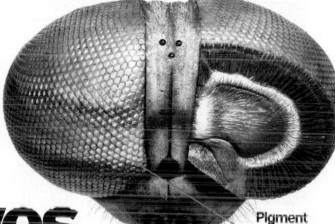

Cornea
The outer part of each ommatidium is overlaid with a transparent cornea that refracts incoming light.

Crystalline cone
Beneath the cornea of the ommatidium is a crystalline pseudocone that helps focus the light further into its body.

Photosensing cells
The inner 90 per cent of the ommatidium contains six to eight long, thin photosensing R cells.

Rhabdom
The portion of the R cells at the central axis of the ommatidium form a light guide, a tube referred to as the rhabdom.

Optic nerve
At the base of the rhabdom it meets an optic nerve which transmits the picture element to the brain.

Pigment cells
In apposition compound eyes, pigment cells line the walls of each ommatidium to block light from other ommatidia.

© DK Images

Compound eyes

Allowing for an incredibly wide viewing angle and the detection of fast movement, compound eyes are highly technical biological structures

Compound eyes are made up of numerous small optical systems arranged around the outside of a convex surface. There are two types of compound eye; apposition and superposition. The former is the more common and works by having each photorecepting system (the eye's ommatidia) independent from every other, each viewing light from just a small part of the overall picture, only to be then pieced together by the brain into a comprehensible whole.

This differs from superposition compound eyes where the individual optical systems do not work separately from each other, but instead pool their light together to produce one single erect image at the back of the eye.

Indeed, apart from an external aesthetic similarity, with an array of facets positioned around a convex structure, the two compound eye types differ greatly in how they work. The main difference is most evident in how the two eyes' ommatidia process light to form an image. In apposition eyes, each ommatidium consists of a thin, tapered tube capped with a cornea, beneath which is a transparent crystalline cone through which rays converge to an image at the tip of its receptive structure, referred to as the rhabdom. Each ommatidium is hexagonal in shape and lined with pigment cells, which act as a light barrier between each tube. Because of this, each ommatidium only receives an incredibly narrow proportion of incoming light from directly in front of it, each contributing a small part of the overall picture.

In superposition compound eyes, however, beneath the optical elements there is a wide transparent clear zone, unimpeded by pigment cells. This means that unlike apposition compound eyes where the ommatidium form small isolated images to be pieced together at the brain, the optical elements in superposition eyes superimpose all light rays received across the ommatidia to form one erect image on a deep-lying retina, only then having the whole image sent to the brain for processing.

There are benefits of each type of compound eye, compared to each other and standard lens-bearing eyes as sported by humans. The main benefits include a very large viewing angle – due to the convex array – fast movement tracking due to the amount of photorecepting units that do not have to individually move to track, and the ability to detect the polarisation of light. However, negatively, because the individual elements are so small, due to the principle of diffraction of light, resolution in compound eyes is considerably worse than in normal variants with large lenses (this is why astronomical telescopes have such large lenses or mirrors). The main benefit of superposition eyes over apposition eyes is their ability to deliver a picture in lower light conditions due to the convergence of gathered light rays. ❖

A honeybee collecting pollen from a daisy

© Science Photo Library

Anatomy of a honeybee

Wings
Wings grant the honeybee good flight agility and the ability to cool and set the wax walls of the hive.

Stomach
The primary stomach is used to digest consumed food.

Pollen basket
A polished concavity surrounded by a fringe of hairs, used to carry collected pollen.

Antenna
Twin smell-sensing antennas give honeybees great positional awareness.

Mouth
Honeybees have two mouthparts, one for biting and one for sucking.

Crop
A smaller internal second stomach sac, where nectar is stored.

Pollen comb
Situated on the honeybee's hind legs, the pollen comb is used to brush and compact collected pollen into the pollen basket.

Ovipositor
The stinger of the bee. Only the female workers and queen have them.

Honeybees

Rapidly in decline worldwide, honeybees play a crucial role in sustaining ecosystems. But how do they work?

A prominent member of the apis genus, the western honeybee (apis mellifera) is one of the most valuable insects in the world, producing harvestable beeswax and honey, as well as extensively pollinating a multitude of crops and plants.

As larvae, honeybees emerge from eggs laid by the colony's queen (a large female who is sexually active and controls the hive) into the waxen cellular walls of the hive. They are fed on royal jelly, a goo-like substance excreted from bee glands. Through the consumption of royal jelly the larvae grow into pupae (adolescent grubs) and then, dependent on their lineage and growing environment, turn into one of three adult castes: workers, drones or queens.

Worker honeybees are the smallest of the three classes and consist of females who did not reach sexual maturity during growth. Equipped with a sting, the workers aid the construction of the hive, and are also responsible for foraging for nectar and pollen, raising young and protecting them if attacked. Drones are larger than workers and are male. Not equipped with a sting, their primary purpose is to mate with the queen, who does so with many of them to ensure the best possible genetic diversity (great for colony strength and health). The queen is the largest class of all and runs the colony. Queens are identified early and fed more royal jelly in order to develop egg-bearing ovaries.

Honeybees produce honey by collecting nectar from plants and crops, a clear viscous liquid made from roughly 80 per cent water and 20 per cent sugar. Once collected by the bees – stored in a special secondary stomach called a crop and taken back to the hive – it is processed by the workers internally using enzymes to break it down into raw honey. This raw honey is then stored by the bees in the combed walls of the hive and capped with a layer of wax. The wax is forced to dry by the drones flapping their wings to create cool air. If the hive is put in threat by fire or predation, the colony will gorge themselves on the reserves before flying off.

Remarkable systems of communication revolve mainly around a series of dances to alert one another to the size, location and distance of food supplies. Most common is the 'waggle dance'. Here, a honeybee that has located a food source returns to the hive before conducting a waggling motion in the source's direction repeatedly, forming a figure of eight. The duration of the movement indicates the distance of the source from the hive.

Since 2006 honeybee colonies have declined rapidly, with some parts of the US and Canada seeing drops of up to 70 per cent. Colony collapse disorder is associated with impaired protein production and is seen to be caused by a combination of severe weather conditions, habitat loss, pesticide usage and various viruses. ✿

The honeybee's wings offer great control

© Firoooz/Flagstaffotos

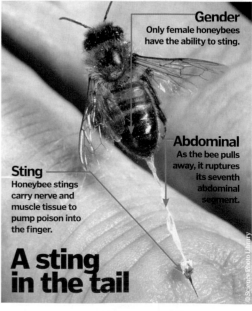

Gender
Only female honeybees have the ability to sting.

Sting
Honeybee stings carry nerve and muscle tissue to pump poison into the finger.

Abdominal
As the bee pulls away, it ruptures its seventh abdominal segment.

A sting in the tail

© Science Photo Library

While wasps have earned something of an unpopular reputation, they are actually invaluable for keeping pests in check

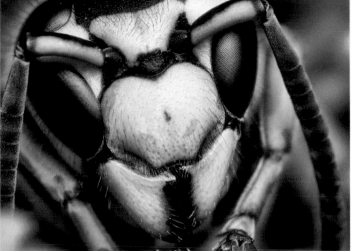

What's inside a wasp nest?

Find out how this predatory insect constructs its papery home

When a queen wasp comes out of hibernation she will begin looking for a site to build a nest. She starts by creating a petiole, which forms the main stalk from which the rest of the nest will hang (like the petiole stalk that attaches a leaf to its stem). To produce the material from which the nest is made, wasps collect weathered wood and plant matter with their powerful mandibles and chew it up. The papery matter is combined with saliva to generate a paste ideal for nest construction even in awkward crevices and cavities, such as a roof's eaves.

The next job for the queen is to begin construction on a small framework of downward-facing hexagonal cells that form the main body, which is used for brood rearing. After building the first cell at the end of the petiole she adds another six around that, and so on until the nest has grown to about the size of a walnut.

Inside each cell the queen lays an egg to create a starter brood of worker females. Eventually these hatch into larvae and the queen will stop nest building to spend about a month looking after these young wasps. Once they are mature enough to fend for themselves, the young wasps then take on the role of workers and resume construction. The world's biggest recorded wasp nest reached a length of 3.7 metres (over 12 feet). With the workers now active, the queen can concentrate on egg-laying and rearing larvae. ✿

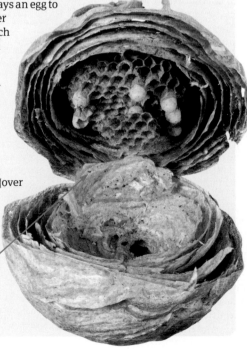

Core
The heart of the wasp nest is where not only the structure itself begins, but the colony too, as the queen lays the first of many broods of eggs.

© SPL

Wasp stings

The wasp holds a potent and reusable form of attack

A wasp stings by transferring venom from an internal venom sac through its egg-laying tube into its victim. The wasp's sting differs from the bee's sting due to the smooth surface of its egg-laying tube, allowing retention of it after an attack for reuse. The bee's jagged equivalent sting however, does not allow for such action, forcing it to literally wrench itself in two and leaving its rear end and stinger stuck in its victim.

The wasp's sting holds another unique ability. While the venom of a wasp contains many active ingredients, it also carries a pheromone that alarms all other wasps in the area, calling for backup in its attack on its target. This talent is an evolutionary bonus card the bee does not share. Therefore, while bees are more likely to be seen flying in swarms there is greater probability that a sting by a solitary wasp will end up leading to a mass attack. ✿

Inside a wasp's abdomen

Venom sac
Housing the venom, before being passed through the egg-laying tube and into the victim.

Egg-laying tube
The smooth surface allows the wasp to retain the tube after stinging.

© DK Images

Mosquitoes explained

We take a look inside these miniature bloodsuckers

Mosquitoes are nectar-drinking insects, which – in the case of the females – also drink blood (haematophagy). This is undertaken as the female needs to obtain nutrients there within – such as iron and protein – to help develop her eggs. Vis-à-vis, the common mosquito has developed a highly complex form and system in order to extract these substances from their target host, including a saliva that negatively affects vascular constriction, blood clotting, platelet aggregation and angiogenesis, allowing it to drink freely. We take a look at the mechanisms it has evolved in order to do so. ✿

Thorax
This part of the mosquito is specialised for locomotion, with its three pairs of legs and single set of wings attached.

Abdomen
Comprised of seven segments, blood and nectar are directly sourced here. It is also the digestive area.

Wing
The wings consist of a series of longitudinal and cross veins through a lightweight outgrowth of the exoskeleton.

Head
The head has been honed to acquire sensory data information for feeding, with sensitive antenna, compound eyes and a stinger-like proboscis.

Compound eye
The compound eye is constructed from thousands of individual photoreceptor units and has been developed to detect fast movement.

Legs
The three pairs of legs are long and covered with minuscule hairs which help it stick to surfaces and provide sensory feedback.

Proboscis
The proboscis is used to inject the exploitative negative saliva needed to circumvent the target's vertebrate physiological responses, and also to extract blood from a target.

Antennae
The antenna is highly sensitive and plays a major role in detecting odours of potential targets.

© DK Images

How do fireflies produce light?

Understanding this natural phenomenon

Lampyridae, or fireflies, are not flies at all. This beetle species is celebrated at many cultural festivals for their ability to produce biological lights. They are able to achieve this through a natural heat-resistant substrate enzyme known as luciferase. The cells in the insect's tail produce this enzyme, which chemically reacts with oxygen; the fuel that allows them to produce this impressive natural phenomenon.

But why do they create light? Fireflies are noted for blinking their lights and the female of the species does this, alternating the rate and wavelength of each flash, to attract fertile males. This is a fundamental interaction, due to the fact that varying species of Lampyridae will occupy the same space. This flashing can distinguish appropriate mates. Firefly larvae are also capable of creating this bioluminescent spectacle, hence the affectionate nickname glowworm. ✿

Image: Art Farmer 2006

Why light attracts moths

Understanding their obsession with light

You're likely to have seen it, a moth fluttering near an outside light at night, spinning around aimlessly. The insect's intriguing behaviour is down to phototaxis, an animal's automatic reaction to or away from light. A moth is a positively phototactic bug, which means it's fascinated and charmed by bright lights, for example a car's headlight, a porch light, or a candle flame. The latter unfortunately doesn't have a happy ending. It is also believed that a moth uses a light at night as a form of navigation. It is mainly the moon that guides a moth, but lamps and other such bright, glowing objects can confuse the creature as it passes by. This sends it in a bit of a dazed and circular pattern around the light, until the Sun comes up when it uses the day to regain its strength.

DID YOU KNOW?

World's largest moth...
Found mainly in southeast Asia, the Atlas moth (or attacus atlas) can have a total wing surface area of 65 square inches and their wingspan can reach up to 12 inches (30cm).

H2O
1 Female dragonflies lay their eggs on plants next to, in, or on top of water. This is due to the fact that all dragonflies start their life span as water-dwelling nymphs.

Adder
2 In the Welsh language the dragonfly is called 'gwas-y-neidr' ('adder's servant') derived from the fact that dragonflies are often found in the same habitat.

Oding
3 In the US the capturing and studying of dragonflies is referred to as 'oding', a process similar to the more traditional hobbies of birding and butterflying.

Giant
4 The recorded maximum flight speed of a dragonfly was that of a southern giant darner, at just under 60mph. Typically, however, dragonflies tend to fly between 10-34mph.

Anisoptera
5 The infraorder of dragonflies is Anisoptera. Stemming from the Ancient Greeks, this means 'not equal wings' because their hind wings are broader than their fore wings.

DID YOU KNOW? *Dragonflies can fly at speeds of up to 60mph and have almost 360-degree vision*

A yellow-winged darter dragonfly, commonly found in northern China

Eyes
Large, bulging compound eyes can view up to 360 degrees.

Abdomen
This streamlined part of the body helps to increase power and speed.

Wings
Intricately veined membrane wings need to be warmed up before flight.

Legs
Six bristle-covered legs help the dragonfly to catch its prey.

Dragonflies

One of the world's largest and most exotic insects, dragonflies are valuable, carnivorous predators

Similar to but typically much larger than damselflies, dragonflies are large, agile insects that undertake a valuable role in the Earth's ecosystems, eating mosquitoes and other smaller insects. Their powerful flight abilities stem from their streamlined abdomen and dual sets of intricately veined membrane wings, which allow them to fly at speeds up to 60mph. Dragonfly wingspans range from one inch up to six inches. Their agility also stems from large bulging compound eyes, which on some of the larger species grant them almost 360-degree vision.

Unfortunately, this high performance comes at a cost – dragonfly muscles need to be warm in order to function properly. Therefore, for dragonfly wings to function optimally, the insect has to engage in a series of stationary wing-whirring exercises and elongated periods of basking in the Sun to generate requisite heat before taking off. However, when in flight, the large, warm and toned muscles deliver the dragonfly complete six-way propulsion, moving from a stationary/hovering position directly upwards, downwards, forwards, backwards and left to right.

Young dragonflies are called larvae and are aquatic rather than aerial predators. At this stage of their lifespan, they don't possess any wings but sport a formidable anatomical structure not present in adults called the 'mask'. The mask is a disproportionately large structure, to which a set of larger fangs is attached. When not in use, the mask is concealed under the larvae's thorax, extended to capture prey such as tadpoles and aquatic worms. Larvae transform into full-grown dragonflies through a series of moultings, the final one leaving a distinctive exuvia (cast skin) behind. ✿

Metamorphosis

We explore how Lepidoptera metamorphosis takes shape

Belonging to the Lepidoptera family, butterflies are insects that achieve four life stages before turning into all manner of beautiful specimens, including the Hesperiidae, Papilionidae and Nymphalidae. This amazing journey sees Lepidoptera begin life as a plain egg that hatches into a larva, or caterpillar, after a period of six days.

The caterpillar eats constantly for up to four weeks – until pupation – and is adept at consuming plant matter. Using three pairs of true legs and pairs of 'prolegs' – sucker-like structures with hooks on the end – it grips to leaves and plant stems, munching with powerful mandibles. Caterpillars have 4,000 muscles to enable this and a long gut tract to quickly digest food. This feasting fuels tremendous growth and a caterpillar will shed its husk several times, becoming stronger and larger each time. At this stage larvae begin to secrete signature hormones that prompt them to produce a protective silk cocoon – a pupa or chrysalide – and initiate the metamorphic stage. The cocoon, built using modified salivary glands known as spinnerets, may take the form of a small hollow in the earth lined with silk, or a roll of leaves, camouflaged to deter predators. What goes on inside is fascinating: larva anatomy and organs are rapidly dissolving and re-forming into new tissue, limbs and the adult butterfly's wings. This process varies from species to species, some taking no more than two weeks, others over winter, but eventually emerging as a butterfly. Blood is pumped into the insect wings, making them expandable and ready to fly.

Beautiful butterfly
Emerging butterflies range in size, from 1/8 of an inch up to 12 inches, and can fly at speeds up to 12 miles per hour. There are 24,000 catalogued species of butterfly.

Baby butterfly
Butterfly and moth eggs are very small and cylindrical in shape. Females lay their eggs on or near the plants that will later become larva food supply.

Hungry caterpillar
The caterpillar, or larva, consumes copious amounts of plant matter with powerful mandibles, before secreting signal hormones, setting the metamorphic stage in motion.

Chrysalides
Inside the chrysalides, larvae go through dramatic biological changes. Just before the adult butterfly hatches, the pupa skin becomes transparent and the wing pattern is visible inside.

Attack of the giant insects

Massive moths, colossal crickets and blooming big beetles – the supersized bugs are here...

Insects are the most successful animal class on the planet. They show the greatest diversity in shape and size and can be found in every land habitat. Around 90 per cent of all animal species are insects; the beetles alone represent one fifth of all known species. Despite this incredible variation, all insects are built from the same basic body plan. Insects are arthropods – the group of animals that includes arachnids like spiders and also contains crustaceans.

The basic arthropod design has an exoskeleton divided into segments, with one pair of legs on each segment. Some arthropods – such as millipedes – stick quite closely to this primitive plan. Others specialise by fusing segments or modifying legs for other uses. The word 'insect' means 'cut into three', and the distinguishing feature of this class is that the body segments have been fused and organised into three different parts: head, thorax and abdomen. The head has legs modified to form mandibles, pincers and antennae, the abdomen may have a stinger or ovipositor (egg-laying organ), but is otherwise clear of limbs. Only the central thorax has legs. All insects have three pairs of legs and most have two pairs of wings, though in many orders, one or both pairs of wings may be modified or absent.

Insects provide us with honey and silk and they have a huge impact on agriculture. The herbivorous insects are often major pests of crops, but the carnivorous insects, such as wasps and ladybirds, eat the herbivores and keep the populations under control. Insects, especially bees, are also crucial for pollinating flowering plants. One in every three bites of food that you eat relies on insect pollinators for its production.

Most insects are quite small and go largely unnoticed. A square mile of empty field contains more insects than there are humans in the world. Insect size is limited by several factors. An exoskeleton quickly becomes too heavy to support its own weight as size increases, and since they are cold-blooded, their metabolic rate depends on the temperature of the environment.

© Science Photo Library

That's one beetle you wouldn't want to find in your tent...

5 TOP FACTS
BIG BUG FACTS

Most expensive
1 The Queen Alexandra's Birdwing is the largest butterfly in the world. It is also one of the most expensive. Specimens have sold for $12,400 (£7,600).

Most refreshing
2 The jungle nymph stick insect is one of the heaviest insects in existence. In Malaysia they are fed guava leaves and the droppings are used to make tea.

Longest
3 Chan's megastick (phobaeticus chani) is the longest insect in the world; one specimen is 56.7cm (22 inches) long. It was only discovered in 2008.

Most dangerous
4 The Asian giant hornet is the largest wasp in the world. Its sting kills more people in Japan each year than all other wild animals combined, including bears and snakes.

Largest actual bug
5 True bugs belong to the order hemiptera and have piercing and sucking mouthparts. The largest is the giant water bug, which can be 10cm (four inches) long.

DID YOU KNOW? *Cockroaches aren't radiation-proof; just 6-15 times the lethal dose for humans will kill them*

However, in tropical climates, a few species have reached sizes of 15cm long or more. At this size, insects are restricted by how much oxygen they can get to their organs. This is because insects don't have lungs; they rely instead on a network of tubes connected to openings called 'spiracles' that run down the side of the abdomen. Insects can pulse their abdomen and flap their wings to ventilate the spiracles, but as the insect gets bigger the proportion of the body that is taken up by spiracles gets rapidly out of hand.

Oxygen comprises 21 per cent of our planet's atmosphere and the largest insects today are only the size of the smallest mammals. However, during the carboniferous period around 350 million years ago, oxygen levels rose to as high as 35 per cent. This, combined with the fact that mammal predators hadn't evolved yet, drove some species to become enormous. Dragonfly-like insects the size of seagulls and a 2.6m millipede called arthropleura lived at this time. The current record holders are a little more modest, but you still wouldn't want to find any of these inside your bed! Let's see how these not-so-little critters measure up... ⚙

Inside an insect

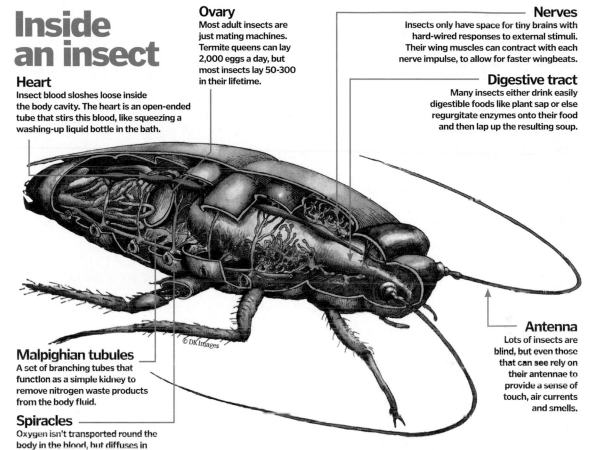

Heart
Insect blood sloshes loose inside the body cavity. The heart is an open-ended tube that stirs this blood, like squeezing a washing-up liquid bottle in the bath.

Ovary
Most adult insects are just mating machines. Termite queens can lay 2,000 eggs a day, but most insects lay 50-300 in their lifetime.

Nerves
Insects only have space for tiny brains with hard-wired responses to external stimuli. Their wing muscles can contract with each nerve impulse, to allow for faster wingbeats.

Digestive tract
Many insects either drink easily digestible foods like plant sap or else regurgitate enzymes onto their food and then lap up the resulting soup.

Malpighian tubules
A set of branching tubes that function as a simple kidney to remove nitrogen waste products from the body fluid.

Spiracles
Oxygen isn't transported round the body in the blood, but diffuses in through the spiracles and along a network of tubes called tracheae.

Antenna
Lots of insects are blind, but even those that can see rely on their antennae to provide a sense of touch, air currents and smells.

© DK Images

THE WORLD'S LONGEST BEETLE

Titan beetle
Titanus giganteus

When you're as large as the titan beetle, your armoured carapace is thick enough to protect you from any insect predator. But now you represent a large enough meal to attract much larger carnivores, you'd better be ready to defend yourself.

As well as its spiky thorax, the titan beetle has mandibles that are said to be capable of snapping pencils and slicing flesh. Despite its large size, the titan beetle can still fly. It can't take off from the ground, so it uses its claws to climb trees for a gliding start. Adults don't eat at all – their mandibles are purely for self-defence and they spend their lives searching for mates. The larval form has never been found, but probably lives in rotting wood and may be as much as 30cm long and 5cm wide.

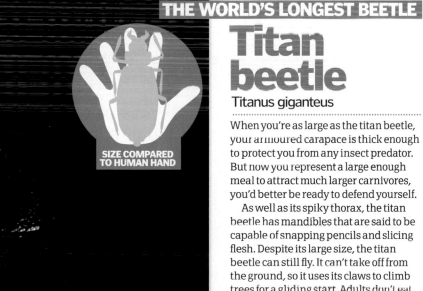

SIZE COMPARED TO HUMAN HAND

The statistics...

Titan beetle

Size:	167 x 66mm (6.5 x 2.6in)
Weight:	80g
Diet:	None
Average life span in the wild:	Unknown, probably several years
As big as:	Your hand

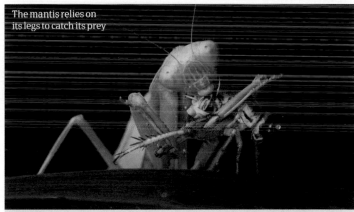

The mantis relies on its legs to catch its prey

In the forests of the carboniferous period, the Earth was inhabited by huge insects and other invertebrates

© Science Photo Library

Regal moth caterpillar

Citheronia regalis

It's absolutely huge, brightly coloured and covered in spikes, but the regal moth caterpillar is quite harmless. There are no poisonous spines or hairs, and the 'horns' are actually just soft appendages to scare off predators. Regal moth caterpillars hatch from eggs just 2mm across, laid in groups of no more than four on the top surface leaves from any of several different tree species. They are a solitary species, which is just as well, because a single caterpillar can strip several branches completely bare.

The caterpillars moult five times during their life, to make room for their growing bodies. The smaller stages, or instars, feed at night and resemble bird droppings to discourage birds. Only the last instar has the bright colours and the scary-looking horns, and at this point the caterpillar is hungry enough to eat round the clock. The adult regal moth lives just a few weeks.

It's not called the 'giant weta' for nothing...

The statistics...

Regal moth caterpillar

Size: 150 x 20mm (6 x 0.7in)

Weight: ~100g

Diet: Hickory, walnut and cotton leaves

Average life span in the wild: ~1 month

As big as: A carrot

SIZE COMPARED TO HUMAN HAND

The regal moth caterpillar is also known as the hickory horned devil... with good reason

© McEvoy, 2010 / Science Photo Library

Chinese mantis

Tenodera sinensis

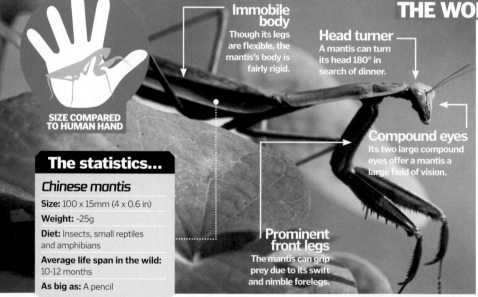

Immobile body
Though its legs are flexible, the mantis's body is fairly rigid.

Head turner
A mantis can turn its head 180° in search of dinner.

Compound eyes
Its two large compound eyes offer a mantis a large field of vision.

SIZE COMPARED TO HUMAN HAND

Prominent front legs
The mantis can grip prey due to its swift and nimble forelegs.

The statistics...

Chinese mantis

Size: 100 x 15mm (4 x 0.6 in)

Weight: ~25g

Diet: Insects, small reptiles and amphibians

Average life span in the wild: 10-12 months

As big as: A pencil

Mantises are voracious predators. The Chinese mantis is large enough to take on virtually any insect, and even small frogs and lizards. There are several documented cases of Chinese mantises catching, killing and eating hummingbirds. The mantis has no venom and relies instead on lightning-fast strikes with its folded forelegs. These have a forward-facing spike on the end, which is used to impale the prey, and rearward-facing spines lining the inside surface of the longest two leg segments. The legs create a serrated scissor grip that will hold struggling animals in place, so that the mantis can feed. Once those powerful front legs have slammed shut, it is very difficult indeed for even large prey to escape. The species was introduced to North America around 1895 to control insect pests, and is now fairly common in the north-eastern United States.

Goliath beetle

Goliathus

There are six known species of goliath beetle, all of them truly massive. The larvae live in decaying leaves and wood on the forest floor, but they need more protein than other beetle larvae and will also eat insects and carrion (decaying animal flesh). When they reach full size, the larvae build a cell out of hardened soil to protect themselves while they pupate. Once the adult beetle emerges from the pupa, it stays inside the cell, hibernating until its carapace has hardened and the dry season ends. The first rains wash away the cell walls and the beetle emerges. Just like the titan beetle, the adult goliath beetle spends its time looking for a mate. It has working mouthparts and so can sustain itself with sugar-rich foods and live for as long as a year.

Armour
The goliath beetle has a reinforced pair of outer wings called 'elytra', which protect another set of wings beneath.

Horny
Further improving upon the goliath beetle's standing as the heaviest beetle, it also has a sturdy Y-shaped horn for added protection.

The statistics...

Goliath beetle

Size: 110 x 55mm (4 x 2in)

Weight: 100g

Diet: Tree sap and fruit

Average life span in the wild: ~1 year

As big as: A computer mouse

© H.Zell

SIZE COMPARED TO HUMAN HAND

COOL

1. Orchid mantis
Over the course of several moults, the orchid mantis's body shape and colour change to match, as it waits for prey to visit.

COOLER

2. Hercules beetle
The Hercules beetle grows to over 15cm (six inches) in length and can support 850 times its own weight on its shell.

COOLEST

3. Puss caterpillar
The fluffiest insects in the world are the larvae of the megalopygidae moth. Those hairs are highly venomous though, so no touching!

DID YOU KNOW? The Malaysian giant stick insect hatches from an egg just 4mm across, but uncurls to 700mm long!

THE WORLD'S LARGEST CRICKET

SIZE COMPARED TO HUMAN HAND

The weta has been stalking the Earth since prehistoric times

The statistics...

Giant weta

Size: 100 x 20mm (4 x 0.7in)

Weight: 50g

Diet: Plants and insects

Average life span in the wild: 2 years

As big as: A sparrow

Giant weta
Deinacrida

New Zealand had no mammals until they were introduced by western settlers. Instead, many insects evolved to fill the same ecological niches that are occupied by small rodents elsewhere. In a sense, the native species weta fulfils the same role as a mouse. Without mammal predators, weta have already evolved to be quite large compared with other temperate insects, but the giant weta is found on the small islands off the coast of the main New Zealand islands. Small islands tend not to support large predators (such as the owls that hunt other weta on the mainland), and so the weta there have evolved into larger species. Giant weta can bite but they aren't venomous, and their primary defence is from the spines on their hind legs. When threatened, they scrape their legs against the side of their abdomen to make a warning hissing sound and slash with the hind legs.

The statistics...

Atlas moth

Size: 300mm (12in) wingspan

Weight: 25g

Diet: Citrus & evergreen leaves

Average life span in the wild: ~4 months

As big as: A handkerchief

THE WORLD'S LARGEST MOTH

Atlas moth
Attacus atlas

Measured by wing surface area, the atlas moth is the largest in the world. Their huge size makes them very unsteady fliers and when the females emerge from the cocoon, they simply hang there, broadcasting pheromones into the air and waiting for a mate. The males are only slightly smaller, but extremely active. Every night they will fly several kilometres in search of females, using their incredibly sensitive, feathery antenna to home in on the pheromone trail.

Atlas moths have a very short lifecycle for such large insects – they spend just six weeks as larvae, then six-eight weeks as a pupa. The caterpillars are rapacious eaters, going from an egg 2.5mm across to a caterpillar the size of a pork sausage. But when they emerge as an adult moth they have no mouthparts and live for just a week, using stored fat reserves to sustain themselves.

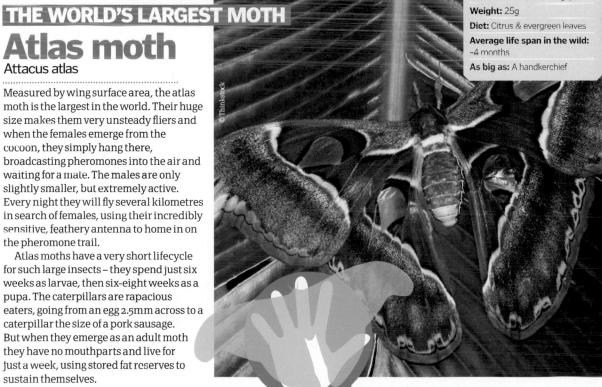

© Thinkstock

SIZE COMPARED TO HUMAN HAND

RECORD BREAKERS

Biggest butterfly
Queen Alexandra's birdwing
Size: Up to 305mm

Biggest dragonfly
Giant petaltail dragonfly
Size: 152mm

Biggest praying mantis
Chinese mantis
Size: 100 x 15mm

Biggest grasshopper
Giant grasshopper
Size: Up to 90mm

Biggest earwig
Saint Helena earwig
Size: Up to 84mm

Biggest moth
Atlas moth
Size: 300mm

Biggest bee/wasp
Asian giant hornet
Size: 50mm

Biggest ant
Siafu ant
Size: Up to 50mm

Biggest fly
Gauromydas heros
Size: 100 x 60mm

Biggest beetle
Goliath beetle
Size: 110 x 55mm

Biggest water insect
Giant water bug
Size: Up to 100mm

Biggest millipede
Giant pill millipede
Size: up to 80mm

Biggest stick insect
Lord Howe island phasmid
Size: Up to 120mm

REPTILES & AMPHIBIANS

106
Saltwater crocodiles

112
Snakes

115
Pythons

104
King cobras

120
Turtles

108
Crocodiles

116
Amphibian life cycle

117
Frog leaps

© Thinkstock

© Thinkstock

World's deadliest reptiles

We take a look at the most dangerous reptiles on Earth

From snakes to crocodiles, the deadliest reptiles on our planet have a variety of ways to kill, stun or disable a foe. Some, like the king cobra, possess a fatal amount of venom that they inject into their prey, while others like the saltwater crocodile use their strength to overpower enemies.

Across all corners of the globe lurks a reptile with the potential to cause harm. While some are unjustly feared despite their timid nature, others are not nearly feared enough. Attacks on humans in most cases are rare due to the knowledge of how dangerous these creatures can be. However, they are not unheard of, and when one of these animals is cornered or threatened its aggressive nature can quickly become apparent.

Here we take a look at five of the most lethal carnivorous reptiles, pitting them head-to-head to find out which is the most deadly. ❂

King cobra

The largest venomous snake in the world, it strikes fear into the heart of its prey

Fortunately for us, the king cobra is generally shy and will slink away from humans. However, when defending itself or its eggs it is one of the most deadly reptiles known to man. When facing an attacker the cobra is able to raise 1.8 metres off the ground and move forward to attack.

They live in undergrowth present in rainforests and humid jungles. One of their terrifying characteristics is the ability to slide up trees, surveying the area and finding prey from above. They primarily eat other snakes and smaller reptiles, preferably non-venomous snakes. To find prey, it can "smell" nearby chemicals with its forked tongue.

To kill, the king cobra strikes and pierces its prey with its fangs, injecting a lethal amount of venom. A single bite from a king cobra will typically contain 6-7ml of neurotoxin, which is enough to kill up to 20 people. It then devours the creature whole. They are the only snakes that make nests for their eggs, and a female king cobra will lay anywhere from 20-40 eggs at any one time. King cobras are generally found in South East Asia, with the largest living king cobras in Malaysia.

Fangs
Two short, fixed fangs inject venom into prey like a needle, killing them in minutes.

Jaws
King cobras can open their jaws very wide to swallow large prey.

Neck
The ribs on its neck can flatten when it is threatened, extending its hood.

Stomach
They digest their food slowly as it is pushed down their body. They can go without food for months after eating a large animal.

Not the friendliest pet in the world...

© Renaud d'Avout d'Auerstaedt

TIME TO DEATH
15 mins

Cold blooded

1 Reptiles are able to regulate their inner body temperature depending on the environment they are in, helping keep them alive in a number of different places and situations.

Skin

2 Reptiles have a dry and scaly skin that contains high levels of keratin, which prevents water loss and helps regulate the internal body temperature.

Heart

3 All reptiles have a three-chambered heart to pump blood around the entire body except crocodiles, which have four chambers just like humans.

Eggs

4 Most reptiles lay eggs with a hard shell, and baby reptiles develop within the eggs from which they hatch, requiring both food and air immediately.

Air

5 Although some reptiles reside in or near water, they need a constant supply of air unlike amphibians, who live underwater when they are born.

DID YOU KNOW? There is enough venom in one bite from a king cobra to kill an elephant

King of the cobras

What makes this snake so deadly?

Eyes and ears

King cobras can see 100m away, and although they have no ears they can "hear" sound vibrations.

Skin

They shed their smooth-scaled skin about five times a year.

The statistics...

King cobra

Genus: Ophiophagus

Length: 3.6-5.5m

Weight: 6-9kg

Top speed: 10mph

Life span: 20 years

Kill factor

King cobra

Aggression: Generally shy, but make it mad and you'll quickly discover its bad temper.

Intelligence: Uses its hood, hiss and speed to its advantage when confronted.

Speed: Agile and quick, they can pounce forwards up to an incredible two metres.

Strength: On rare occasions they will use their muscular body to constrict prey.

Other: The fatality rate from its venom is up to 75 per cent, and can be as quick as 15 minutes.

Deadly rating:
☠️ ☠️ ☠️ ☠️ ☠️

Gila monster

The only venomous lizard which lives in the United States is shy but can be very deadly

Found across several states in America including Nevada and California, the Gila monster is known for being timid but potentially very deadly. Its main source of attack is its venom. The teeth of a Gila monster have grooves which channel the venom into the wounds of its prey. They are average-sized lizards with powerful jaws and short legs adapted for digging.

Identifiable by their characteristic black bodies interspersed with orange, pink and yellow, Gilas are lethargic creatures that spend about 95 per cent of their lives underground in burrows. They eat mainly bird or reptile eggs and on occasion small birds, lizards and mammals. They are commonly thought to be very deadly and dangerous reptiles. However, their venom is primarily used for self-defence. They tend to bite their prey by surprise and come back when the venom has taken effect. Unless threatened, Gila monsters will only attack when seeking a meal.

TIME TO DEATH 1 hour

Caution! Handle with care!

Good looks
A stout body and headlike scales, the Gila monster tends to reside in harsh desert environments.

Kill factor

Gila monster

Aggression: Generally run or hide rather than fight.

Intelligence: Coloured scales allow limited camouflage when avoiding predators.

Speed: Sluggish and slow. Avoiding one shouldn't be too hard for a human.

Strength: Quite weak. They use venom to assist in hunting prey.

Other: Although deadly to smaller animals, its venom is rarely fatal in humans.

Deadly rating:
☠️ ☠️

Is it a monster?
The human risk is low, but this beast can be deadly

A hungry Gila can deliver a nasty nip

Fatty deposits
Gila monsters store fat in their tails – like a camel does in its hump – to be used during hibernation.

The statistics...

Gila monster

Genus: Heloderma

Length: 30-60cm

Weight: 1.3-2.2kg

Top speed: 15mph

Life span: 30 years

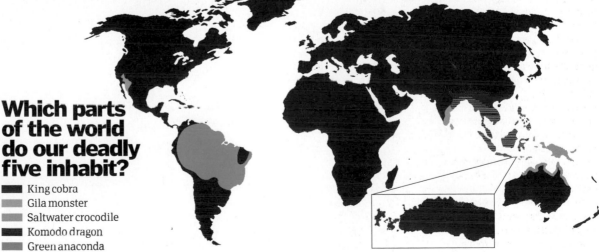

Which parts of the world do our deadly five inhabit?

■ King cobra
■ Gila monster
■ Saltwater crocodile
■ Komodo dragon
■ Green anaconda

© Midori

Kill factor
Saltwater crocodile

Aggression: Very dangerous, particularly in mating season.

Intelligence: Use very clever hunting tactics.

Speed: Fast swimmers and slow walkers but have a quick leap.

Strength: A powerful bite and a muscular tail. Very strong.

Other: Young crocs are forced out of their home territory by domineering adults.

Deadly rating:
☠ ☠ ☠ ☠ ☠

TIME TO DEATH
60 secs

The statistics...
Saltwater crocodile

Genus: Crocodylus

Length: 2.1-7.0m

Weight: 408-1,000kg

Top speed: 25mph

Life span: 70 years

Who knew they could do camouflage too?

Tail
The strong tail of a Komodo dragon is often longer than its body.

Kill factor
Komodo dragon

Aggression: Multiple attacks on Indonesian villages back in 2009 showed the dragon's aggressive potential.

Intelligence: Komodo dragons are smart animals, particularly when hunting.

Speed: Appear clumsy but can move as fast as a dog, and are excellent swimmers.

Strength: Weak bite but strong claws, and their tail can knock down large mammals like pigs.

Other: Slow acting but deadly venom. Dragons are typically quite solitary.

Deadly rating:
☠ ☠ ☠ ☠

The statistics...
Komodo dragon

Genus: Varanus

Length: 2-3m

Weight: 68-91kg

Top speed: 15mph

Life span: 30 years

Saltwater crocodile

The largest living crocodilian on Earth eats anything, even humans

When tackling large prey or attackers, the saltwater crocodile will typically overpower, drown and then dismember them. The crocodile can hold its prey underwater as it can separate its mouth from its throat, allowing it to open its massive jaw when fully submerged. To finish off its prey it will either drag it to land or hold it above water and swallow it vertically.

They are very intelligent creatures, lurking beneath the surface of the water until potential prey arrives for a drink. Using their powerful tail, they then suddenly leap out of the water and drag their prey back underwater. In the last 25 years they have been responsible for the death of about a dozen people.

They mostly eat small fish and land vertebrates but they are not picky eaters. Any mammal in its vicinity is good food as far as a saltwater crocodile is concerned. They have even been known to attack boats, mistaking them for enemies. Their jaws have a biting force of up to 2,300kg per square inch, the

most powerful bite on the planet. On land they use their strong legs to move, while underwater they use their giant tail for propulsion.

They are generally found in brackish (slightly salty) waters such as rivers, swamps and estuaries. They are also occasionally seen in the open sea as they can swim up to 620 miles (1,000km), but they are most commonly found in northern Australia, southeast Asia and eastern India.

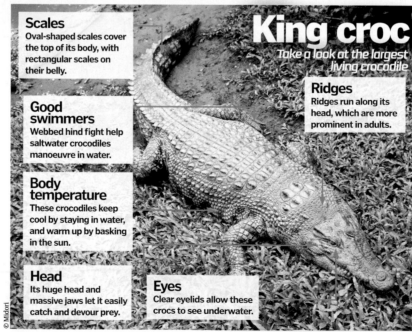

King croc
Take a look at the largest living crocodile

Scales
Oval-shaped scales cover the top of its body, with rectangular scales on their belly.

Good swimmers
Webbed hind fight help saltwater crocodiles manoeuvre in water.

Body temperature
These crocodiles keep cool by staying in water, and warm up by basking in the sun.

Head
Its huge head and massive jaws let it easily catch and devour prey.

Ridges
Ridges run along its head, which are more prominent in adults.

Eyes
Clear eyelids allow these crocs to see underwater.

A beast that can kill in just seconds

DAYS

1. Bite
Some reptiles seep venom into their prey when they bite, coming back to finish off their enemy up to a week later when the venom has taken effect.
© Mats Stafseng Einarsen

HOURS

2. Venom
Toxins target the nerves and muscles in prey which provide movement, often rendering animals completely immobile in under an hour.
© Thinkstock

MINUTES

3. Constriction
Reptiles such as the anaconda asphyxiate their prey by coiling their body around that of the prey, stopping them breathing and killing them in minutes.

DID YOU KNOW? The Komodo dragon was discovered in WW1, when a pilot saw the reptiles after swimming to Komodo Island

Deadly dragon

What makes one of the last living relatives of the dinosaurs so deadly?

Skull
The skull of a dragon is designed to withstand large amounts of stress, so they can stop their prey pulling away.

Poison
Large glands channel venom between the animal's teeth, which then seeps into their prey.

Teeth
60 razor-sharp teeth help them literally tear their prey into shreds, known as pull-feeding.

Claws
Dragons use their long and powerful claws to climb trees, and also to attack prey.

TIME TO DEATH
3 days

The world's deadliest hand puppet...

Tongue
The long yellow forked tongue of a dragon detects the chemicals of nearby prey.

Komodo dragon

The world's heaviest living lizard is also one of the most dangerous reptiles

These huge lizards like to live an isolated existence except during mating season, when males will patrol and defend a territory up to 1.2 miles long per day. They are found only on a small group of Indonesian islands in the Flores and Bali seas.

Komodo dragons are cannibalistic, but will also eat large prey such as pigs and deer of a similar size to themselves. Like saltwater crocodiles they are not fussy eaters, and will eat almost anything they can overpower including other dragons. They are very quick eaters; a 45kg dragon was observed to eat a pig almost its own weight in 20 minutes, equivalent to a human eating 320 quarter-pound hamburgers in the same time.

It was only discovered in 2009 that Komodo dragons possess a deadly amount of venom, which they use to kill their prey. When hunting, a dragon will keep a vice-like grip on its prey with its mouth. Venom then seeps into large wounds on the prey made by the teeth. The prey goes into shock and bleeds to death. Although they have a similar-sized skull to that of a saltwater crocodile, the bite of a dragon is only one-sixth as strong.

Kill factor
Green anaconda

Aggression: Short-tempered reptiles, and even more so when in captivity. Not good pets.

Intelligence: These ambush predators wait for the perfect opportunity to attack prey.

Speed: Slow on land but quick and deadly in the water.

Strength: Capable of killing large animals such as jaguars with their strong body.

Other: One of the few reptiles that gives birth to live young.

Deadly rating:
☠ ☠ ☠ ☠

Green anaconda

The biggest snake in the world is at its most dangerous when underwater

Although its cousin, the reticulated python, might be longer than the green anaconda, it pales in girth comparison, as the anaconda is not only long but also incredibly thick. They are one of the few reptiles where the females outsize the males. They tend to live in swampy marshes and streams in the tropical rainforests of the Amazon and Orinoco basins. On land they are slow and clunky but in water they are reptiles to be reckoned with. Like the saltwater crocodile, they wait submerged in water for prey to approach, using their eyes and nostrils on the top of their head to see around and breathe.

Like the king cobra the green anaconda swallows its prey whole, digesting it as it moves down its body. Its teeth are angled backwards, so that once it has bitten its prey, any attempts to escape will only impale the animal further. They feed on animals as large as jaguars and also pigs and deer. Their main method of attack is constriction; they are known as nonvenomous constrictors. They wrap their bodies around prey and squeeze until asphyxiation occurs. Again, they can go months without eating after a large meal.

The statistics...
Green anaconda

Genus: Eunectes
Length: 6-9m
Weight: 132-227kg
Top speed: 13mph
Life span: 10 years

TIME TO DEATH
2 mins

Attack
When killing prey, the green anaconda coils around and constricts its prey until it can no longer breathe.

Giant snake

Why this massive reptile can be so dangerous

Mouth
The green anaconda can open its mouth through a jaw-widening 180 degrees.

Body
These nocturnal creatures have a characteristic olive-green body covered in black spots.

Head
Narrow head is small when compared to its thick, muscular body.

Eyes and nose
Green anacondas can still see and breathe when almost fully submerged.

How crocodiles hunt prey

They outlived the dinosaurs but these hunters are anything but elderly

Crocodiles are often described as living fossils, but despite the fact that their body shape hasn't changed much in the last 200 million years, they are actually some of the most sophisticated reptiles on Earth.

Like all living reptiles, they are cold blooded but that doesn't make them sluggish. Crocodiles have a four-chambered heart and muscles that mimic our diaphragm to ensure they can quickly pump oxygen around their bodies for explosive bursts of speed. Crocodiles are ambush predators; their preferred tactic is to lurk in the river with just their eyes and nostrils visible above the surface and burst out of the water to surprise animals that have come to the bank to drink. If their initial lunge fails, they can chase prey over land at speeds of 17kph. The galloping gait of the crocodile was dismissed as a folk legend for many years, simply because hardly anyone who witnessed it lived to tell the tale.

Once a crocodile has grabbed its prey, it will drag it into the water and pull it under. Crocodiles need air to breathe but they can hold their breath for 30 minutes and drowning your prey is easier and more reliable than risking it escaping if you unclamp your jaws. Crocodile teeth are only designed for gripping and puncturing; they have no incisors or carnassials to slice meat off a carcass. Instead they will grip a chunk of flesh with the front teeth and spin violently on their long axis to twist off a bite-sized piece. Crocodiles don't have lips so they can't seal their mouth shut when eating. This means they can't swallow food underwater without drowning themselves so each torn off mouthful has to be brought to the surface and tossed into the back of the mouth.

When food is scarce, their cold-blooded metabolism allows crocodiles to go for as long as two years without eating at all. This, combined with their ability to scavenge rotting meat, was probably what allowed them to survive the event that killed the dinosaurs. ✿

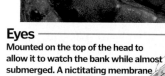
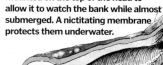

A stealthy croc sp[...] prey from the [...]

Eyes
Mounted on the top of the head to allow it to watch the bank while almost submerged. A nictitating membrane protects them underwater.

Teeth
Crocodiles have 64 to 70 teeth, which are replaced continuously throughout the animal's life.

Tongue
A crocodile can't stick its tongue out of its mouth because it is anchored to the floor of the mouth all the way along.

Salt glands
Special glands on the top of the tongue allow crocodiles to excrete salt that builds up in their blood in saltwater environments.

Jaw muscle
The massive muscle and its placement a long way forward of the hinge provides a bite pressure almost twice that of a great white shark.

Although the teeth are deadly [...] its death grip that kills

ON THE MAP

Where to find crocodiles
1 Central America
2 The Amazon Rainforest
3 Sub-Saharan Africa
4 Tropical regions of Asia and the Far East
5 Northern Australia

DID YOU KNOW? The largest crocodile in the world is called Utan and measures over six metres long

Anatomy of a river killer
Inside the body of the oldest killer on the planet

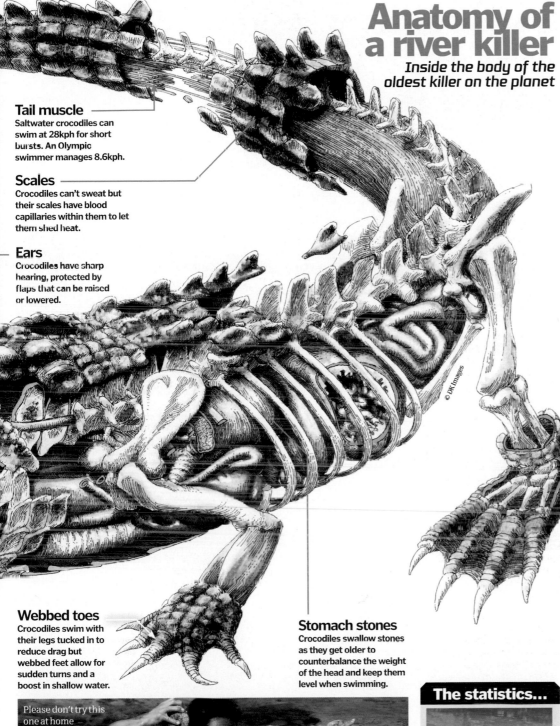

© DK Images

Tail muscle
Saltwater crocodiles can swim at 28kph for short bursts. An Olympic swimmer manages 8.6kph.

Scales
Crocodiles can't sweat but their scales have blood capillaries within them to let them shed heat.

Ears
Crocodiles have sharp hearing, protected by flaps that can be raised or lowered.

Webbed toes
Crocodiles swim with their legs tucked in to reduce drag but webbed feet allow for sudden turns and a boost in shallow water.

Stomach stones
Crocodiles swallow stones as they get older to counterbalance the weight of the head and keep them level when swimming.

Please don't try this one at home

© Cameloctober

Crocodile or alligator?
A field spotter's guide to carnivorous reptiles

Crocodile
Location: Crocodiles live in Africa, Asia, Australia and the Americas, in both fresh and saltwater.

Snout shape: The V-shaped snout is a general-purpose design for catching fish, reptiles and mammals.

Jaws/teeth: The upper and lower jaws are the same width, so the fourth tooth in the lower jaw sticks up.

Colour: Mottled green or sandy yellow, with slightly darker scales along the back and tail.

Skin: Each scale has a pore near the edge, visible even on crocodile handbags and wallets.

Alligator
Location: Alligators are only found in the southern United States and China and vastly prefer freshwater.

Snout shape: A heavier, U-shaped snout provides extra strength for cracking turtle shells.

Jaws/teeth: A wider upper jaw completely covers all the teeth in the lower jaw when the mouth is closed.

Colour: Much darker, sometimes almost completely black, depending on the water quality.

Skin: Alligators only have pores on the scales that are covering the upper and lower jaws.

Other
A crocodile with a very long, thin snout, is actually a gharial. Caimans look like a slightly smaller alligator, but you can tell them apart because the large scales on their head form a four-four-two pattern, instead of two-two-two.

The statistics...

Crocodiles
Type: Reptile
Diet: Carnivore
Average life span in the wild: 70 years
Weight: 1,200kg
Size: 4.85m

The strongest jaws on the planet

Why do crocodiles have the strongest bite of any creature known, yet are not able to open their jaw if we place an elastic band around it?

A crocodile has the strongest bite of any known creature, producing a phenomenal force of around 5,000 pounds per square inch. By comparison, the great white shark only has a bite of 400 pounds per square inch. The sets of muscles that control and give power to the crocodile's bite have evolved and developed to be extraordinarily strong, and give crocodiles a natural weapon the likes of which mostly went extinct along with the gargantuan jaws of the dinosaurs.

Alongside their relatively quick speed over short distances on land – an Australian freshwater crocodile was recorded as running at just over 17kph (11mph) for around 20-30 metres – and the immensely sharp teeth that crocodiles prominently display, this incredible bite forms an immense weapon for the crocodiles to successfully hunt and kill with inside a competitive aquatic environment.

However, although the jaw muscles used to snap the jaw shut are well developed, the muscles that are used to open the jaw in the first place are considerably weaker. So much so that if the jaw is taped shut or a large rubber band is put around it, the muscles are not strong enough to push up against the force created by these. ✿

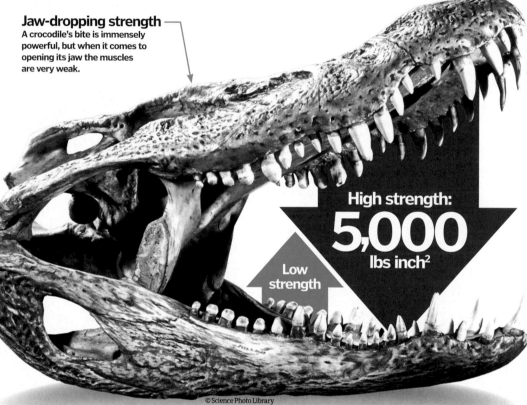

Jaw-dropping strength
A crocodile's bite is immensely powerful, but when it comes to opening its jaw the muscles are very weak.

High strength:
5,000 lbs inch²

Low strength

© Science Photo Library

He hasn't lost a game of snap yet!

© Sias van Schalkwyk

Death rolls

How crocs employ this tactic

Commonly misunderstood, the crocodile death roll is a unique method to feed off previously killed prey, not a method to kill them. The most famous user of the death roll is the Nile species of crocodile, common to the Nile River in Egypt. Here, crocodiles use their camouflage and speed to grab large prey and drag them into the water. Once there, the crocodile proceeds to drag the target underwater, holding it there until it drowns. Once the prey is dead, the crocodile then performs the death roll in order to tear large chunks of flesh off its body quickly and efficiently. To do this, it buries its large teeth into the creature's flesh, before rolling its body 360 degrees. The muscular force of the crocodile's body in partnership with the sharpness of its teeth proceed to tear the prey open, something that would prove difficult within the water while stationary. ✿

"The death roll is a unique method to feed off killed prey, not a method to kill them"

Marsh crocs basking in the sun

© Kmanoj

© Science Photo Library

The statistics...

Snakes

Type: Reptile

Diet: Carnivorous

Average life span in the wild:
Up to 25 years

Weight: 1.4-97kg (3-214lb)

Size: 0.1-9m (0.3-30ft)

Snakes' jaws are adapted to swallow their prey whole

Snakes

Feared and respected in equal measure throughout human civilisation, discover the incredible life of snakes

Snakes are not legless lizards. They evolved from lizards about 112 million years ago but have since changed their body shape and habits quite radically. Modern legless lizards, like the slow worm and grass lizard, have short bodies and long tails, but snakes are nearly all body with a relatively short tail on the end. This means that the skeleton of a snake has ribs running for most of its length. Snakes also lack eyelids and external ear holes. Their eyes are protected by an unblinking, transparent scale called a brille and their poor hearing is made up for by their other senses. Snakes can smell the air by collecting molecules on their forked tongue, then passing them back to the Jacobson's organ at the front of the mouth. They can also sense vibrations through the ground and some species have 'thermal

imaging' that enables them to detect the infrared radiation from live prey, even in complete darkness. The coral snake (aipysurus laevis) has light receptors in its tail, so that it can check it hasn't left the tip poking out, when it hides in a dark crevice.

Snakes have scales to conserve moisture and allow them to grip the ground. These aren't loose, like feathers or skin, but are anchored to the deep layers of the epidermis. When a snake moults, it sheds the entire skin in one go. Moulting isn't to allow room for growth (as with insects), but a way of replacing worn scales and getting rid of parasites.

You can find snakes in tropical seas and on every continent except Antarctica, but there are a few islands that they have never conquered, including Iceland, New Zealand and, perhaps most famously, Ireland. ✤

How snakes hunt

Snakes attack with a fast lunge and a single bite. Their jaws and teeth aren't strong enough to take bites out of their quarry so they must swallow everything whole. Small, non-venomous snakes will strike for the head of a mouse or frog and either try to crush its skull or asphyxiate it by engulfing its mouth and nose.

Venomous species will strike and withdraw to avoid injury while the venom takes effect. Boas and pythons use their muscled bodies to constrict. This doesn't kill by crushing; the coils slide past each other so that the scales act as a ratchet. As the victim struggles, they can only tighten further. Sometimes the prey will die of asphyxiation, other times the pressure in the chest cavity becomes so immense that their heart simply stops.

Snakes don't actually dislocate their jaws to swallow large prey, but the lower jaw is very flexible and has some extra joints at the back of the skull to allow it to 'hinge' open extra wide. The left and right halves of the lower jaw aren't joined and so can 'walk' down an animal, drawing it into the serpent's mouth as they go.

DID YOU KNOW? Even a severed snake head can still bite and will automatically inject the maximum dose of venom!

Getting around

With no legs, snakes have developed some clever ways to get from A to B

Snakes have many ways of propelling themselves forward, depending on their environment. These use completely different muscle sequences and are much more distinct than, say, the differences between walking and running. All snakes can use lateral undulation but each species has other techniques unique to its habitat. Sea snakes, for example, can use lateral undulation to move backwards, while the chrysopelea snakes of Southeast Asia can even flatten their body into a gliding wing and launch themselves up to 100 metres (328 feet) from one tree branch to another

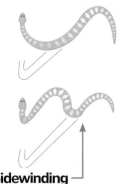

Sidewinding
Sidewinding is an adaptation to loose or slippery surfaces, so the contact points between the snake and the ground don't slide backwards. This maximises grip and uses less than one-third of the energy of a lizard which is running the same distance.

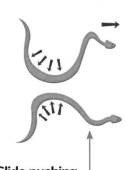

Slide pushing
In tunnels, there's no room to move side to side, so the snake alternately braces against the tunnel walls and stretches its body forwards. It's slower than lateral undulation and uses seven times more energy, but it's still faster than rectilinear movement.

Concertina
The snake pulls its body into a tight series of coils and then braces the tail section as it straightens out again. This needs good grip or something to push against, and it isn't efficient for long distances, but it's a quick way to lunge forward when striking.

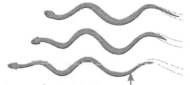

Lateral undulation
The most common form of locomotion involves the snake gripping obstructions or small irregularities on the ground with the side of its body, and rippling a wave down their length that slides past the obstruction. Aquatic snakes swim like this by pushing against the water itself.

Rectilinear
The slowest way to move uses the tiny muscles that attach the skin to the ribs. By alternately pulling the skin up off the ground and putting it down again slightly forward, the snake creates a travelling wave that creeps it forward almost silently. This form of movement is employed by pythons and boas when stalking prey.

A deadly cocktail

2,900 species of snake have been identified but only a quarter of them are venomous. Out of those, 250 species are deadly enough to kill a human with one bite and around 100,000 people are killed by snakebites worldwide each year.

Snake venom is produced in modified salivary glands and stored in reservoirs behind the eyes. Snakes can choose the dose they deliver with each bite and will sometimes 'dry bite' without injecting at all. Each species has a different venom that is a mixture of hundreds or thousands of different proteins and enzymes. Between them, they can affect every organ system in the body if left unchecked.

MAIN SYMPTOMS

Rubbery, minty or metallic taste in the mouth

Fear and panic

Vomiting

Diarrhoea

Dizziness and fainting

Severe pain

Blurred vision

Convulsions

Rapid, weak pulse

Spontaneous bleeding

Numbness

Breathing difficulty

Tissue necrosis

Heart failure

The anatomy of a snake

Heart
Snakes have no diaphragm, so the heart is free to move out of the way when swallowing large prey.

Left lung
Shrunk to almost nothing to save space, the left lung isn't used for breathing.

Right lung
Only the front portion is used for breathing. The rear section acts as a swim bladder in sea snakes.

Liver
Like most of the snake's organs, this is long and thin to fit in the narrow body.

Tracheal lungs
This extension of the windpipe allows limited breathing when the stomach is so full that it compresses the true right lung.

Intestine
Because there is no room to coil it up, snakes actually have a very short intestine, which gives them a slow digestion.

Testes
Where snakes retain paired organs, they are staggered one in front of the other.

Kidneys
Snakes don't produce urine. Instead they excrete uric acid, which is a dry white paste and lets the snake conserve water.

Pancreas, gall bladder and spleen
Secrete digestive enzymes and produce immune cells.

Belly scales
Unlike legless lizards, snakes have wide belly scales with just a single column of scales on the underside.

The snake uses its tongue to smell by bringing air molecules into contact with the Jacobson's organ

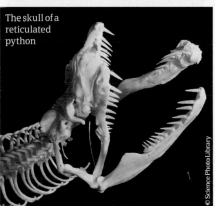

The skull of a reticulated python

© Science Photo Library

Why do snakes shed their skin?

How and why do these slippery reptiles moult so frequently?

Snakes shed their skin for two main reasons. The first is to facilitate continued growth. This occurs as snakeskin does not grow in partnership with the snake itself, unlike in humans, where millions of skin cells are shed each year continuously on a microscopic, unseen level. On the contrary, snakes cannot shed skin in this microscopic way, necessitating them to literally outgrow the outer layer of skin whole on a frequent basis. The frequency that snakes shed their skin is largely dependent on the stage of life cycle they are in, with sheddings incredibly frequent during infancy and teenage years (bi-monthly in some species), but slowing to a couple of times per year as adults.

The second reason why snakes shed their skin is to preserve their health. Poor living conditions (lack of humidity, lack of vegetation, excess heat, and so on) as well as an inadequate food source can lead to skin damage and parasites. If left unchecked for a long period of time in the wild, this would be highly detrimental to the snake's well being. By shedding its skin, the snake can mitigate these potentially damaging conditions and start anew.

Interestingly, however, the shedding process brings with it complications. For the week or two preceding the shedding, the snake's vision is impaired due to the loosening of the skin's outer layer, and the week or two after the event, the new outer layer is soft and vulnerable to attack from predators. For this reason, snakes tend to be overly protective around sheddings, and largely inactive if possible. The snake initialises each shedding by rubbing itself against a sharp object such as rock, to pierce the outer layer of skin. ✿

A close-up view of a snake's shedded skin

Venom
Venom is modified saliva containing neurotoxins and hematoxins.

Fangs
Pit vipers have hinged fangs that collapse against the roof of the mouth.

Pivot
Tiny lower teeth act as a pivot during the lightning-fast strike.

How do snakes bite?

Call them cold-blooded, but they have death down to a science

Snakes are highly adapted killers. Non-venomous snakes kill by constriction (suffocation) or swallowing prey alive. Venomous snakes – which make up only ten per cent of the world's snake species – inject their victims with powerful toxins that either paralyse the respiratory system or attack red blood cells, instantly rotting flesh and bone.

Only venomous snakes have fangs, a set of long, hollow teeth in either the front or back of the mouth that act as hypodermic needles. As fangs enter the flesh, the snake flexes its jaw muscle, squeezing toxic saliva out of the venom gland, through the fang's venom canal and deep into the victim's tissue. Snakes can control the release of venom, so many defensive strikes against humans are non-lethal 'dry bites'. If bitten, never try to cut open the wound or suck out the venom. Keep the victim calm and get to a hospital quickly for a dose of antivenin.

How do snakes smell?

Nose not work? No problem!

While snakes have both nostrils and nasal cavities, they do not use them to smell with. In fact, snakes smell through the combination of a specialised organ located in their oral cavity and a flicking motion of their elongated tongue. The organ in question is referred to as the vomeronasal organ (or Jacobson's organ) and is located in the roof of their oral cavity. Due to its internal positioning, the snake utilises its forked tongue to flick air particles from the surrounding environment into contact with it. From here the vomeronasal organ translates the smell into electrical signals to be sent to the snake's brain, enabling it to determine whether prey or predators are in its locale. In addition, due to the tongue's role as a smelling device, it is not used by snakes to aid the swallowing process. ✿

3. Jacobson's organ
This organ translates the particulate matter into sensory signals.

2. Oral cavity
The air particles are drawn into the mouth along with the tongue.

1. Tongue
An elongated tongue redirects air particles from the environment.

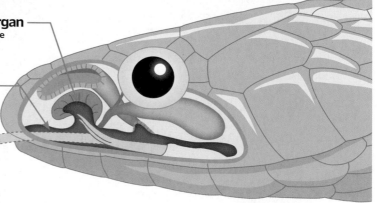

Record breaker
1 The longest python recorded was a reticulated python called Fluffy. Although native to SE Asia and the East Indies, Fluffy lived at a zoo in Ohio, USA, and measured a whopping 7.3m (24ft).

The pits
2 Before killing their prey through constriction, pythons seek out their warm-blooded dinner with special heat-sensing pits located in their mouths, between their eyes.

Mini me
3 Pythons can lay up to 100 eggs at a time – usually in the vacated burrows of other animals. The baby pythons are born alive and look just like miniature versions of their adult counterparts.

Pythons can swim
4 There are some 30 different species of python, all of which are good swimmers. Most species are ground-based, but some climb trees while others burrow underground.

Vestigial hind limbs
5 Like boas, pythons possess visible pelvic spurs, which are the evolutionary remnants of back legs. These tiny bones towards the tail end suggest they descended from lizards.

DID YOU KNOW? The African rock python is a protected species which plays a vital role in controlling rodent populations

Rock pythons have a diverse diet which includes everything from small antelopes to crocodiles

© SPL

Rock pythons

Discover how Africa's largest snake kills and consumes its prey

© GJ Alexander

Despite being non-venomous, the python remains one of the world's most dangerous serpents. The African rock python, in particular, is a very deadly assassin, also notorious for being ill-tempered.

Pythons incapacitate their prey by literally squeezing the life out of them, coiling their long – sometimes seven-metre (23-foot) – bodies round the victim and tightening their grip until the animal, unable to breathe, eventually suffocates. That done, the python then sets about consuming their meal... in one go.

Equipped with a set of highly flexible jaws, stretchy skin and ribs hinged with extra-supple tissue, the African rock python can down its quarry whole. First the python slides its mouth over the head of the prey and then gradually moves its body along the length of the animal with the help of an expandable throat and abdomen. The animal is then digested over a matter of hours, or even days if it's particularly large. Following such a meal, the python need not eat again for several weeks. ✿

Tropical rainforest
(equatorial Africa)

Tropical savanna

Deserts and semi-arid regions

Semi-tropical southern Africa

African rock python range

© NASA

The statistics...

© Tigerpython

Rock pythons

Type: Reptile

Genus: Python sebae

Diet: Carnivore

Life span in wild: Up to 25 yrs

Weight: Up to 100kg (220lb)

Size: Up to 7m (23ft)

Amphibian skin

Skin is the body's main protective barrier against the outside world, and although an amphibian's skin is only very thin it has many qualities vital to keeping them alive

Amphibians can breathe in and out through their skin – both on land and under water – and they can take in water not through their mouths but instead through absorbent skin found on their underside, called a seat patch. Most adult amphibians do have lungs, but additional oxygen is taken in through the skin to supplement that provided by these organs. Some species of salamander have no lungs or gills and breathe exclusively through their skin.

The reason that amphibians feel slippery is that their skin is full of glands that produce mucus, which spreads across the surface of the skin. This mucus moistens the skin,

making it softer and therefore more oxygen absorbent. Although amphibians have few defences against predators, they do have additional poison glands on their skin that secrete irritating toxins for repelling would-be diners. Most are only mildly poisonous, but some species, such as the South American poison dart frog, are deadly to the touch.

Amphibian skin must stay moist in order to prevent the body from becoming too hot or cold, and also to avoid the risk of desiccation (drying up), which would spell the end for Mr Toad. This constant need for moisture means that, as well as producing protective mucus, amphibians should live close to a water source. ✿

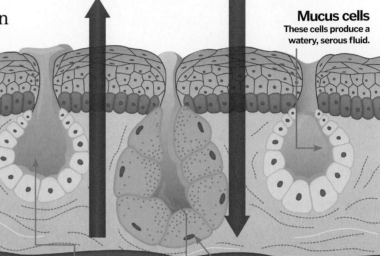

Breathe out
Carbon dioxide leaves the body through the skin.

Breathe in
Oxygen passes into blood vessels via the skin.

Mucus cells
These cells produce a watery, serous fluid.

Mucus gland
Mucus cells group together to form a sac-like gland.

Poison gland
Groups of poison glands are located in areas most likely to be attacked by predators.

Poison cells
The toxicity of the poison secreted is reliant on the amphibian's diet.

The life cycle of an amphibian

The incredible journey from spawn to tadpole to frog

4. Tadpole
At six days old, the egg hatches and becomes a tadpole. External gills develop to filter water and take in tiny bits of food. A sucker protrudes beneath the head end, which can suck onto plant matter.

3. Tail bud
The tail bud forms at around the four-day mark. Muscles have begun to develop and the embryo feeds on the yolk inside itself.

2. Mutation
Following a mere matter of hours after the egg has been laid, the metamorphosis has begun.

1. Egg
Several layers of absorbent watery jelly swell to protect a single tiny embryo that has been fertilised by the male frog. Water is vital to the development of these aquatic babies.

5. Internal gills
Nine days into metamorphosis, a flap of skin grows over the external gills and replacement internal gills develop. A spiracle (pore) remains on the left-hand side where water can escape. The tadpole's eye is not yet fully formed.

6. Hind legs
Next the internal gills develop and a pair of hind legs form.

7. Front legs
The final stage of a frog's development (around 75 days) includes the arrival of front legs and lungs to replace the internal gills. Amphibians can also breathe through their mucous-covered skin.

8. Froglet
For the next one to two years, the young frog's tail will become increasingly short until it's barely a tail at all.

9. Frog
A frog becomes an adult at the tender age of three years. It will breathe using its fully formed lungs and will take to the land to seek out a mate and begin the whole process again.

Elastic energy in the leg muscles transforms into mechanical energy during the leap

How do frogs leap?

Discover what enables this amphibian to jump up to 50 times its own body length

The secret to why frogs can jump so far is all in their legs. The ideal way for a frog to evade predators is to leap away in a split second. The amphibians have evolved extremely strong hind legs with specially fused leg bones and proportionally big feet, which are perfect for launching into the air over huge distances, as they enable the frog to push off against the ground for longer.

Using high-speed cameras to examine the anatomy of a frog as it jumps, researchers have discovered the mechanics of how a frog can travel so far. Pre-jump the muscles in a frog's powerful hind legs are lengthened and stretched as they sit in the typical crouching position. Upon takeoff the muscles connecting the pelvis to the knee contract as the frog flies into the air, pulling the upper hind leg backwards and propelling the frog forwards. The muscles then stretch again once the frog has reached the ultimate height of its jump. These super-stretchy muscles store a huge amount of elastic energy, which in turn is transferred into mechanical energy.

The appropriately named rocket frog can jump a massive two metres (6.6 feet) – that's over 50 times its own body length. This is the equivalent of Olympic triple-jumper Jonathan Edwards jumping around 90 metres (295 feet) in just a single stride – let alone three.

One mighty leap can be the difference between life and death for a frog

READY FOR TAKEOFF...

1. Stretched and ready
In a crouching position, the super-flexible frog leg muscles are stretched like springs and ready for release.

2. Forelegs
The frog flexes its forelegs first to initiate the jump.

3. Hind legs
Simultaneously the hind legs extend to a vertical position and lock straight at the height of the kick. The thighs then swing round to the side and draw the legs back up into a bent position.

© DK Images

Frog anatomy

Often used to teach anatomy, frogs have a body plan much like our own – but with a few important differences…

The statistics…

Frog

Type: Amphibian

Order: Anura

Diet: Usually carnivorous, though often herbivorous at the tadpole stage of development

Average life span in the wild: Estimated at 4-15 years

Size: From 7.7mm (0.3in) up to 33cm (12.9in)

Distribution: Global, except Antarctica

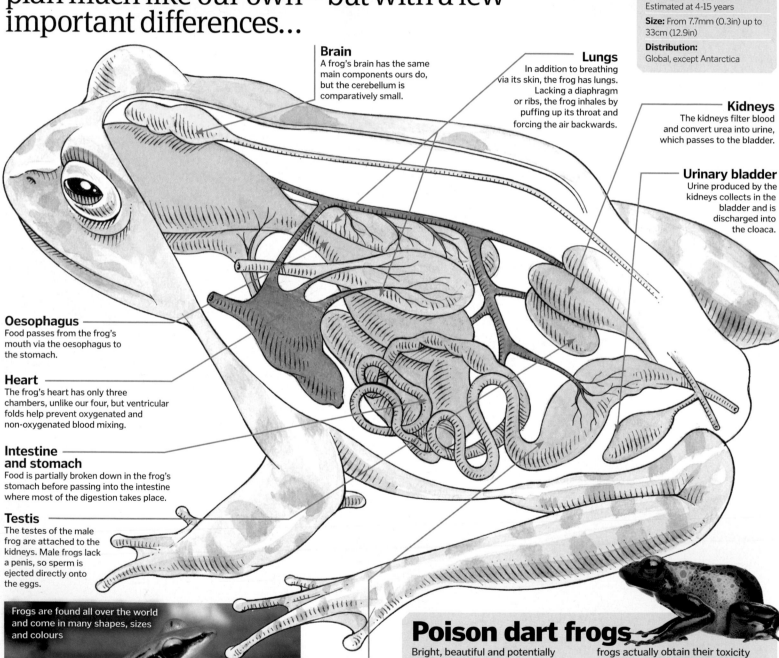

Brain
A frog's brain has the same main components ours do, but the cerebellum is comparatively small.

Lungs
In addition to breathing via its skin, the frog has lungs. Lacking a diaphragm or ribs, the frog inhales by puffing up its throat and forcing the air backwards.

Kidneys
The kidneys filter blood and convert urea into urine, which passes to the bladder.

Urinary bladder
Urine produced by the kidneys collects in the bladder and is discharged into the cloaca.

Oesophagus
Food passes from the frog's mouth via the oesophagus to the stomach.

Heart
The frog's heart has only three chambers, unlike our four, but ventricular folds help prevent oxygenated and non-oxygenated blood mixing.

Intestine and stomach
Food is partially broken down in the frog's stomach before passing into the intestine where most of the digestion takes place.

Testis
The testes of the male frog are attached to the kidneys. Male frogs lack a penis, so sperm is ejected directly onto the eggs.

Frogs are found all over the world and come in many shapes, sizes and colours

Cloaca
Both liquid and solid waste, as well as sperm and eggs, all wind up in the cloaca, where they are ejected from the body via the cloacal vent.

Poison dart frogs

Bright, beautiful and potentially lethal, members of the Dendrobatidae family, aka poison dart frogs, let would-be predators know they should dine elsewhere. Their colourful skin exudes alkaloid compounds that make some of these tiny frogs among the most deadly vertebrates alive. However, they can't do it alone: poison dart frogs actually obtain their toxicity from their arthropod prey, eg mites. This means frogs born and raised in captivity are non-toxic, because they can't synthesise these compounds independently. The most toxic frogs produce batrachotoxins and less potent pumiliotoxins, both of which are cardiotoxins, causing muscle spasm, arrhythmia and death.

STRANGE BUT TRUE
NAME THAT SALAMANDER

Plethodon glutinosus is the 'what' salamander?
A Southern fried B US dyed C Northern slimy

Answer:
Known for being extremely sticky, the northern slimy salamander – found throughout the USA – is said to be the stickiest of its kind. Its skin produces a strong mucus that can essentially glue shut the mouth of any predator that attempts to eat it!

DID YOU KNOW? The Hydromantes salamander's tongue can reach its prey in just 20 milliseconds

Ballistic tongue biology

How do some amphibians and reptiles catch bugs with projectile tongues?

Imagine if your tongue was 80 per cent the length of your body and you could poke it out and reel it back in within 20 thousandths of a second. Well, if you're a lungless Hydromantes salamander that's one ability you already possess.

Creatures like frogs, chameleons and salamanders have a staple diet consisting mainly of insects. In order to make a quick getaway, most of these bugs have evolved sensors that detect even the slightest movements made by their would-be assassins, so the hunter must be able to get close without being detected. To help them grab a bite, some amphibians and reptiles have very long and sticky tongues – perfect for catching flighty prey without having to get so close. While most of these animals strike out using elastic recoil, Hydromantes do things a little differently... ✿

The tip of the chameleon's ballistic tongue can accelerate up to 50 g – five times faster than a fighter jet!

The fastest tongue in the world

See how the web-toed salamander uses ballistics to fire its entire tongue skeleton out of its body

Hydromantes salamander
The Hydromantes salamander is the proud owner of the fastest tongue on Earth. This appendage is not only the longest amphibious tongue, but it's also one of the most accurate tongue-protrusion mechanisms seen in nature. To ensure it doesn't go hungry it uses a built-in ballistic projectile to grab its next meal. Imagine the tongue as a tethered arrow being fired from a bow.

Projectile
The tongue exploding from the mouth is a true projectile in the sense that the entire tongue skeleton is launched outside the body. The tongue is tipped with a sticky mucus pad that adheres to the prey.

Tongue skeleton
The tongue consists of a bony skeleton surrounded by protractor muscles that store elastic energy. Whilst the tongue skeletons of other amphibians are found in the base of the mouth, in this lungless species of salamander the resting tongue skeleton extends over the shoulders.

Retractor muscles
The tongue snaps back into the mouth with the help of long retractor muscles connected to the pelvis. The retractor muscles don't have the same power as the protractor muscles, but the tongue still recoils back into the mouth very quickly.

Protractor muscles
Ringed around the tongue skeleton are stretchy protractor muscles. When the muscles around the hyobranchial apparatus contract, the whole mechanism shoots out of the mouth like a crossbow arrow.

© Thinkstock; Patrick Coin

The statistics...

Turtle

Type: Reptile

Genus: Chelonia

Diet: Varies by species, but generally omnivorous

Average life span in the wild: Typically from 50-100+ years

Weight: From 100g (3.5oz) to 900kg (1,984lb)

Size: From 5-10cm (2-4in) to over 2m (6.6ft)

Keeping clean

When you're covered by a shell and your flippers won't hold a scrub brush, you need a little help to stay clean. Over time, turtles can become covered with algae, ectoparasites and barnacles. Cleaner fish – notably wrasses, but also species, such as the pictured tangs – swim in to remove the debris, earning an easy meal in the process. Although this relationship is apparently mutualistic – ie beneficial to both creatures – there are concerns that cleaner fish may spread disease among turtles.

The life of turtles

Slow and steady wins the race as these armoured reptiles have proven across millions of years

Baby hawksbill turtles make the most perilous journey of their lives as they crawl from their nest to the sea

 One of the most notable things about turtles is their endurance. Arising over 100 million years ago, turtles have enjoyed a fairly stable existence, standing by as the dinosaurs rose and fell, and changing very little across the many millennia.

Specialised adaptations allow turtles to live in a diverse array of habitats. Many freshwater turtles must hibernate to survive the winter, slowing their metabolism down so far that they can go months without eating or drinking. On the other hand, the leatherback sea turtle speeds its metabolism up, enabling it to survive in water far too cold for any other reptile.

Some turtle species are territorial and may have dominance hierarchies, but they form no social bonds. Typically turtles come together only because they share habitat or for mating. Freshwater species tend to breed annually, whereas marine turtles may only reproduce every few years. Female turtles are capable of storing viable sperm in their oviducts for months, or even years! When ready to lay her eggs, she leaves the water and seeks a suitable substrate for digging on land. Freshwater turtles make nests in the soil along the waterways and ponds where they live. Marine turtles, on the other hand, travel widely over the course of a year, following ocean currents, but will swim hundreds, or even thousands, of miles in order to return to their natal beaches.

Once her eggs are buried, a female turtle's parental responsibilities are over. Incubation time varies by species and climate, but is around two to three months. When the baby turtles are ready to hatch they use a sharp egg tooth to cut through their shells and then, as a group, they dig their way out and make for the relative safety of the water. Marine turtles typically emerge at night and instinctively crawl en masse towards the brightest horizon which on a natural beach is towards the ocean.

Young turtles are vulnerable to dehydration, as well as a variety of predators; relatively few survive to adulthood. Even adult freshwater turtles may fall prey to animals such as raccoons or herons, but adult marine turtles have few natural enemies. Although the occasional shark or killer whale may attack, by far the biggest threat to marine turtles is humans. Thousands of turtles are injured by boats or killed in fishing nets each

2,200kg

DID YOU KNOW? *In many species, the gender of a turtle is determined by the temperature at which the egg is incubated*

Anatomy of a turtle
Take a closer look at the unique physiology of these shelled reptiles

Head
Like all reptiles, turtles have bony skulls with eye sockets, but unlike snakes, lizards and crocodilians, they do not have teeth. Although turtles' brains are quite small, they can learn complex behaviours.

Lungs
The primary function of the turtle's lungs is to take up oxygen, but they can also be used as flotation devices.

Reproductive system
Female turtles have two ovaries containing as many as 4,000 tiny eggs. Eggs are fertilised in the oviducts and remain there until they have formed shells and are ready to be laid.

Tail
Male turtles have longer tails than females and use them for assistance in holding on during mating.

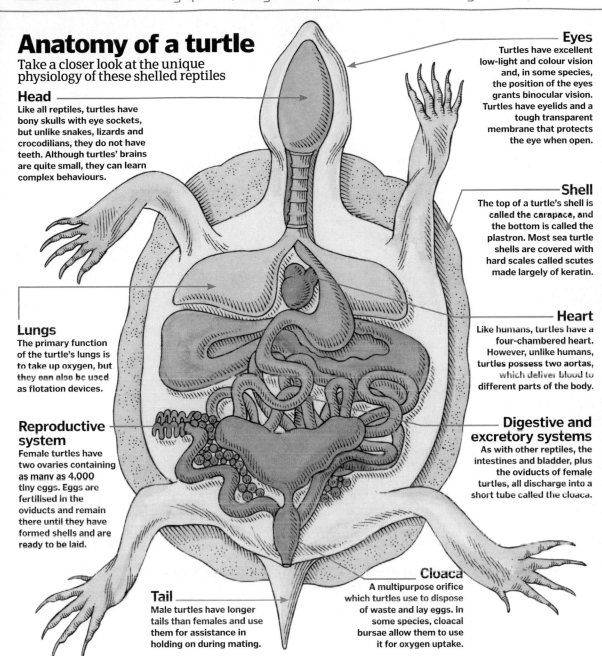

Eyes
Turtles have excellent low-light and colour vision and, in some species, the position of the eyes grants binocular vision. Turtles have eyelids and a tough transparent membrane that protects the eye when open.

Shell
The top of a turtle's shell is called the carapace, and the bottom is called the plastron. Most sea turtle shells are covered with hard scales called scutes made largely of keratin.

Heart
Like humans, turtles have a four-chambered heart. However, unlike humans, turtles possess two aortas, which deliver blood to different parts of the body.

Digestive and excretory systems
As with other reptiles, the intestines and bladder, plus the oviducts of female turtles, all discharge into a short tube called the cloaca.

Cloaca
A multipurpose orifice which turtles use to dispose of waste and lay eggs. In some species, cloacal bursae allow them to use it for oxygen uptake.

year, while others are hunted for their shells or meat, either for food or for traditional medicines.

Today these fascinating animals are among the most threatened in the world, with more than half of turtle/tortoise species facing extinction. All seven species of marine turtles are endangered or critically endangered, and the total populations of certain rare freshwater turtles number in the single digits. ❁

"Turtles will swim hundreds of miles to return to their natal beaches"

An inner compass
Sea turtles are able to travel all over the world and yet many species somehow manage to find their way back to the beach where they hatched, sometimes laying their own eggs mere metres from the place where they emerged. Research indicates that many species use magnetic fields to create a mental map that pinpoints their current location relative to their goal, as well as providing them with a compass bearing. Exactly how they do this is unclear, but scientists have found tiny crystals of the mineral magnetite in turtles' brains, which are known to perceive magnetic fields.

© Corbis; Alamy; DK Images; Thinkstock

Spot the difference

TURTLE
Habitat: Almost entirely aquatic, in the open ocean.
Shell: Teardrop shaped and streamlined, designed for speed in the water.
Mobility: Instead of feet, sea turtles have large flippers so they can 'fly' through the sea.
Size: Varies; some can be 75cm (29.5in), while others exceed 3m (9.8ft).
Diet: More likely to be carnivorous, eg crabs/shrimp.
Geographical distribution: Found in all oceans, but mostly in temperate areas.

TORTOISE
Habitat: Terrestrial but a few species are semi-aquatic when young.
Shell: High domed shell which is thicker and bumpier than aquatic turtles.
Mobility: With rounded, stumpy legs, tortoises are built to walk on land and dig in soil. They can't swim.
Size: Range from 6cm (2.4in) to 1.8m (5.9ft).
Diet: More likely to be herbivorous, eg grass/fruit.
Geographical distribution: Worldwide, from North America to Mediterranean.

TERRAPIN
Habitat: Fresh and brackish water.
Shell: Their shells are quite flat in comparison.
Mobility: Terrapins are more versatile between land/water.
Size: Generally smaller, but some can be tortoise sized.
Diet: Very much omnivorous.
Geographical distribution: Worldwide; the most common in terms of number of species.

MAMMALS

162
Pandas

152
Wolves

131
Bear fishing

126
Killer whales

Mammals

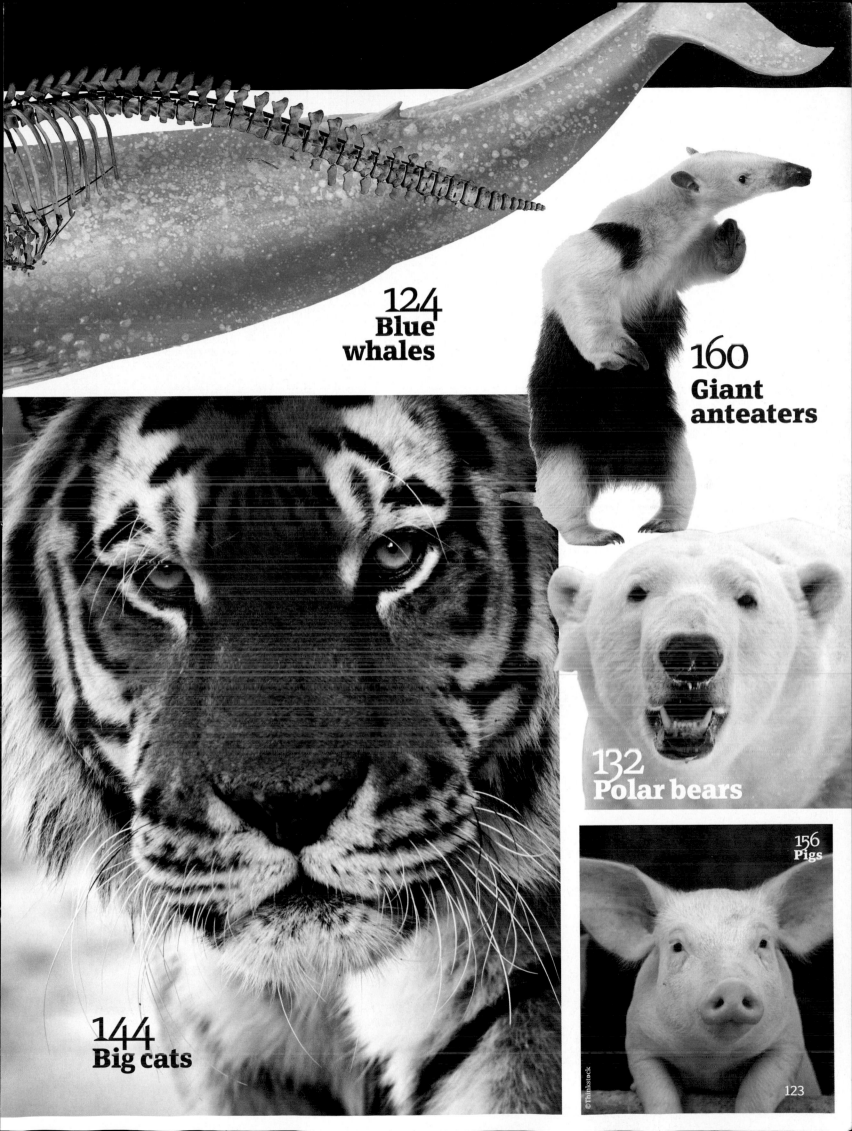

124
Blue whales

160
Giant anteaters

132
Polar bears

156
Pigs

144
Big cats

©Thinkstock

Blue whales

What's as long as three London buses and as heavy as 112 giraffes?

The blue whale isn't just the largest animal alive, it is the largest animal ever to have lived. Even the largest dinosaurs are topped by this leviathan. Everything about the blue whale is huge. It has a heart the size of a small car, a tongue that weighs 2.7 tons and lungs that can hold 5,000 litres of air.

Blue whales spend most of their lives swimming alone or in pairs, unlike other baleen whales such as the humpback. The female gives birth every two or three years to a single calf that weighs as much as an adult hippopotamus. For the first seven months, the calf drinks more than 400 litres of milk a day to enable it to put on 90kg of weight every 24 hours.

Blue whales aren't really very blue. The top half of their body is a bluish grey and the underside is a lighter colour to make them harder to see when viewed from below, against the sky.

Blue whales are also extremely fast swimmers. They cruise at 20kph and can sprint at 50kph. This makes it virtually impossible for barnacles and other parasites to attach themselves. In spring, however, a thin film of diatom algae growing on the skin can sometimes give them a yellow-orange hue and 19th Century whalers referred to them as 'sulphur bottoms'.

Despite their size, blue whales are preyed upon by orcas (killer whales) and 25 per cent of adult blue whales show orca bite scars. ✿

One in four blue whales show scars caused by orcas

© Morningdew 05

Baleen plates
The blue whale doesn't have teeth. Instead the baleen plates hang down to create a colander made of keratin.

Rostrum bulge
This oil and wax-filled chamber focuses sonar pulses, used for echolocation.

Ventral pleats
60 to 90 folded grooves expand the mouth to six times its size after a huge gulp of water and krill.

Pectoral fin
Three metres long and used like the diving planes in a submarine to adjust depth and for steering.

Huge size...

Human
Average length: 1.6m

Blue whale
Average length: 30m

5   10   15   20   25   30

LENGTH IN METRES

A blue whale swimming with her calf

© Andreas Tille

5 TOP FACTS
LARGEST MAMMALS

African elephant
1 SIZE: 5,400kg
The largest land animal currently living. Elephants are large enough to be safe from all predators but must spend 16 hours a day eating.

Polar bear
2 SIZE: 600kg
The largest bear and the largest land carnivore, although it spends much of its time in the sea. Its bite can crush a seal skull.

Mountain gorilla
3 SIZE: 200kg
The largest primate. Although they have powerful canine teeth, they are herbivores with a diet that includes celery, bamboo and stinging nettles.

Whale shark
4 SIZE: 36,000kg
The largest fish, whale sharks are filter feeders like the blue whale, but their food is even smaller than krill – microscopic plankton.

Blue whale
5 SIZE: 180,000kg
The largest animal that has ever lived. Its upper lip bone is the largest bone in the animal kingdom ever discovered.

DID YOU KNOW? *A blue whale's heart beats five times a minute. It pushes ten tons of blood through a million miles of vessels*

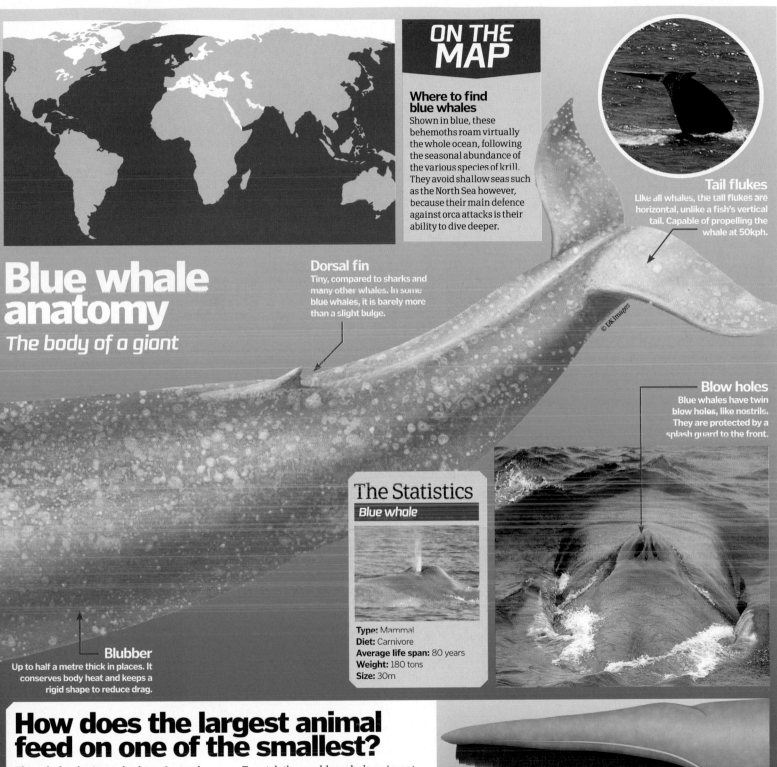

ON THE MAP

Where to find blue whales
Shown in blue, these behemoths roam virtually the whole ocean, following the seasonal abundance of the various species of krill. They avoid shallow seas such as the North Sea however, because their main defence against orca attacks is their ability to dive deeper.

Tail flukes
Like all whales, the tail flukes are horizontal, unlike a fish's vertical tail. Capable of propelling the whale at 50kph.

Blue whale anatomy
The body of a giant

Dorsal fin
Tiny, compared to sharks and many other whales. In some blue whales, it is barely more than a slight bulge.

Blow holes
Blue whales have twin blow holes, like nostrils. They are protected by a splash guard to the front.

Blubber
Up to half a metre thick in places. It conserves body heat and keeps a rigid shape to reduce drag.

The Statistics
Blue whale

Type: Mammal
Diet: Carnivore
Average life span: 80 years
Weight: 180 tons
Size: 30m

© UK Images

How does the largest animal feed on one of the smallest?

Blue whales don't eat plankton. Instead they eat krill, which are one step up from plankton in the food chain. Krill resemble small shrimp, except that they swim in open water in huge swarms. Most krill are only a couple of centimetres long and since a blue whale needs around 1.5 million calories every day, that means it needs to eat a lot of krill – up to 40 million a day, in fact.

To catch them, a blue whale swims at speed towards a swarm and opens its mouth to gulp in 90 tons of water at a time. It then uses its massive tongue to force the water back through the baleen plates. These are 300 feathery bars, each one a metre long, that are attached to the upper jaw. They are made of keratin, like your fingernails. The krill get sieved out by the baleen and then swallowed.

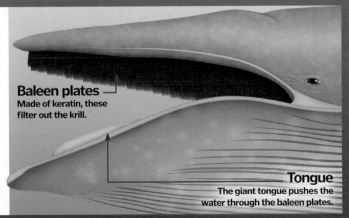

Baleen plates
Made of keratin, these filter out the krill.

Tongue
The giant tongue pushes the water through the baleen plates.

How killer whales hunt

To merely call them the wolves of the sea is a gross underestimation

Killer whales aren't whales (they are more closely related to dolphins) and it's not fair to call them killers either. There are no confirmed cases of fatal attacks on humans by killer whales in the wild. But they are incredibly intelligent hunters – probably second only to humans. Killer whales, or orcas, can swim at 56 kilometres (35 miles) per hour (or 30 knots), they have teeth eight centimetres (three inches) long and their echolocation system allows them to find prey in complete darkness. But what really sets them apart is their ability to plan, improvise and work as a team.

Orcas live in loose family groups called pods, of five to seven individuals. In the wild their life span can be 60 years or more but the infant mortality rate is very high; up to half will die before they are seven months old. This is mainly due to the difficulty of finding enough food. Killer whales are mammals and their warm-blood metabolism uses a lot of energy. An adult needs 230 kilograms (510 pounds) of food a day.

To feed this appetite, some subspecies prey on schools of fish by circling below them and releasing a stream of bubbles to confuse them. Others have learned that they can catch sharks by flipping them on to their backs to induce a sort of panic stun, known as tonic immobility. The killer whales that hunt among the Arctic sea ice catch seals and walruses by knocking them off ice floes into the water (see 'Hunting as a pack').

These are not purely instinctive behaviours; orcas will teach their young, often deliberately catching and releasing a seal several times to allow them to practise hunting. In 2005 scientists observed a killer whale regurgitating fish at the water's surface to lure seagulls down before catching the birds. Four other orcas subsequently learned this tactic. ❁

In April 2012 the first ever all-white orca – named Iceberg due to his 2m (6.6ft) dorsal fin – was spotted off the coast of eastern Russia

Dorsal fin
Provides roll stability when swimming; the male has a larger fin that can reach 2m (6.6ft) tall.

Blowhole
The blowhole closes when relaxed, so a killer whale must consciously think to open it and breathe.

Saddle patch
Grey rather than white for the other patches. The shape varies between individuals and is used by scientists for identification.

The makeup of a maritime mammal

Melon
This lump of fatty tissue acts like a lens to focus the sound waves from the orca's echolocation clicks.

Teeth
The front ones are angled slightly forwards, so they aren't wrenched loose by struggling prey.

Pectoral fin
Unlike the dorsal and tail fins, the pectoral fin has bones, including a five-fingered 'hand'.

Pelvis
This tiny bone is all that remains of the ancestral pelvis, now that orcas have evolved for an aquatic life.

The statistics...

Killer whale

Genus: Orcinus
Type: Mammal
Length: 7-10m (23-32ft)
Diet: Carnivore (eg fish, seals)
Weight: 6 tons
Life span in wild: 50-80 years
Status: Threatened

Tail fluke
Most of the thrust from the tail is generated on the upstroke of the two flukes, not the downstroke.

Median notch
Helps to reduce turbulence in the orca's wake, and thereby keep drag to a minimum.

HUNTING AS A PACK

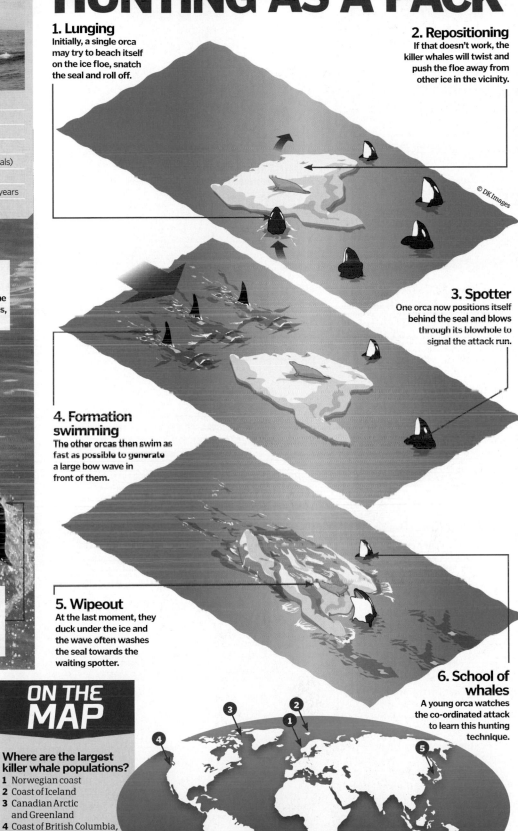

1. Lunging
Initially, a single orca may try to beach itself on the ice floe, snatch the seal and roll off.

2. Repositioning
If that doesn't work, the killer whales will twist and push the floe away from other ice in the vicinity.

© DK Images

3. Spotter
One orca now positions itself behind the seal and blows through its blowhole to signal the attack run.

4. Formation swimming
The other orcas then swim as fast as possible to generate a large bow wave in front of them.

5. Wipeout
At the last moment, they duck under the ice and the wave often washes the seal towards the waiting spotter.

6. School of whales
A young orca watches the co-ordinated attack to learn this hunting technique.

ON THE MAP

Where are the largest killer whale populations?
1 Norwegian coast
2 Coast of Iceland
3 Canadian Arctic and Greenland
4 Coast of British Columbia, Washington and Oregon
5 Sea of Japan
6 Southern Ocean, around Antarctica

© DK Images

Is keeping killer whales in captivity a good idea?

There are 42 orcas currently held in captivity in aquariums and sealife parks around the world. Since 1990, almost all of these have been born in captivity. Orcas put on an impressive show because of their huge size and striking appearance. But they are also extremely intelligent and they can be trained to perform spectacular jumps and a wide range of tricks.

Most zoo animals have longer life spans than in the wild but the reverse is true for orcas. Lack of company from other orcas and the limited size of their tank mean they rarely live beyond 25 years. The male orca's huge dorsal fin nearly always loses rigidity and flops over after a few years in captivity. This is a permanent structural change to the fin cartilage and may be due to insufficient exercise or too much time spent swimming at the surface.

127

How whales communicate

Whales produce a wide range of complex sounds through differing techniques – we explore some of the mystery of whales' songs

 Whales communicate by creating sounds through methods that differ depending on their family type. Toothed whales – which include dolphins – produce high-pitched sounds by the manipulation of air stored in their head through their phonic lips, a structure loosely akin to the human nasal cavity. As air is passed through the phonic lips they contract causing vibrations in the surrounding tissue before being consciously streamed by the whale.

Baleen whales differ in their sound creation, as they do not posses a phonic lip structure, doing so through manipulation of air passing through their larynx instead. The larynx works through the vibrations of internal vocal cords when air is passed over them. However, mystery shrouds this method of communication as baleen whales lack vocal cords, so presently scientists are unsure as to the exact manner in which their low-pitched sounds emanate from their larynx. ❁

How do blowholes work?

Find out why marine mammals have a little hole on top of their heads

 Whales, dolphins and porpoises are all cetaceans and spend their whole lives underwater. Unlike fish however, which have gills, cetaceans are mammals and so have lungs. They therefore need to come to the surface now and then to take in oxygen. The blowhole is a small nostril-like opening located on the dorsal side of the mammal near its head. It enables the animal to take in air without having to stop and lift its mouth out of the water.

A muscular flap covers the blowhole and remains sealed when the creature is relaxed so the lungs don't fill with water. When the animal contracts this flap, the blowhole opens enabling the creature to exhale and take in another breath.

Sperm whales can hold their breath for over an hour. When the whale comes to the surface, air and waste gases are forcefully expelled from the lungs. As this warm, moist air is released, the water vapour condenses and emerges from the blowhole as a misty spout. ❁

All images © SPL

How sperm whales dive

With a diving range of up to a kilometre, how does this animal plunge to such mighty depths?

 Native to all the world's oceans, the sperm whale is one of the largest predators that still hunts individual prey, such as giant squid and octopus, which it dives to immense depths of up to 1,000 metres (3,280 feet) to find. While using echolocation to track down its next meal is a fine talent in itself, descending to these great depths is another matter entirely. So how does it do it? ✿

The statistics...

Sperm whale

Type: Mammal

Genus: Physeter macrocephalus

Diet: Carnivore

Average life span in the wild: Up to 60 years

Length (male): 15-18m (50-60ft)

Length (female): 9-11m (30-36ft)

Weight (male): 32-41 tons

Weight (female): 14 tons

Getting inside a sperm whale's head

It has the biggest brain of any mammal, but what else is going on in this huge noggin?

Nasal passage
Water that travels across the nasal passages helps to cool the spermaceti.

Blowhole
When the whale holds its breath to dive, the blowhole seals. On surfacing, it shoots air out of its lungs forwards and left instead of straight up like other whales.

Spermaceti
This waxy substance has a melting point of around 30°C (85°F), but hardens when it gets colder, matching the density of water.

Spermaceti organ
This produces spermaceti. It's thought that if the whale can control the blood flow to the spermaceti organ, it can make the wax cool, contract, harden and become more dense, which helps the creature sink easier.

Lungs
Like many whales, the sperm whale can hold its breath for an exceptionally long time – up to 90 minutes in some cases. This is because they're great at storing oxygen in their blood and muscles as well as reducing their organs' demand for oxygen.

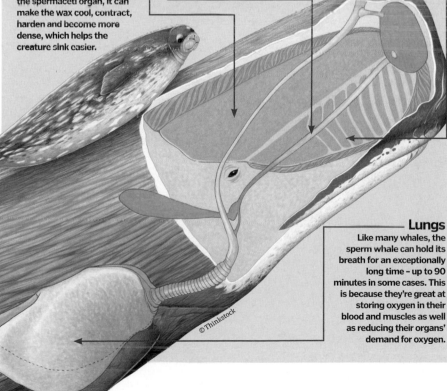
© Thinkstock

© SPL
Once a year beluga whales head to river estuaries to shed their dead skin

How do beluga whales moult?

What makes these white whales so well adapted to Arctic waters?

 Belugas, also known as white whales, are carnivorous mammals that are found in and around the Arctic coastal regions of Europe, Asia and North America. Beluga whale skin is grey at birth (as it serves as better camouflage) and gradually becomes lighter till at around the age of five it becomes creamy white, giving them their unique appearance.

To keep them warm during the freezing Arctic winters, the belugas have extremely thick insulating skin – 100 times thicker than human skin. In the summer months, however, belugas take part in an unusual custom whereby they group together in pods and head for the shallow fresh waters of river estuaries to moult. Once in the shallows, the groups roll around on the mud and rocks to wear away the dead skin. Unlike other whales, belugas don't have fused neck bones and so they are the only whales capable of turning their heads. ✿

The life of a narwhal

A closer look at the 'unicorn of the sea'

They may bear more than a passing resemblance to the mythical unicorn, but narwhals are very much real and are a member of the porpoise family that lives exclusively in the Arctic and northern Atlantic oceans.

With a fairly compact body, a super-thick layer of blubber and the ability to dive as deep as 1,800 metres (5,900 feet) for seabed-dwelling halibut, they are perfectly adapted to surviving in the frozen north.

Their most distinguishing feature – the spiral tusk which can reach up to three metres (9.9 feet) on males – is not a horn but a tooth which grows through the upper lip. The tusk's purpose is not known for certain, but the general consensus is that it's used primarily for courtship and mating rituals. Males are sometimes seen crossing tusks in a practice called 'tusking', but this is believed to be play-fighting – a way of establishing a social hierarchy within the group (similar to a stag's antlers), or even a method of cleaning the teeth, rather than a serious attempt to maim/kill.

Like most cetaceans, narwhals live in pods, though their size can vary from just a few individuals up to several hundred or even several thousand, especially during migration season. ✿

Tusk
This elongated, spiral-shaped tooth can be 3m (9.9ft) long in male narwhals. Although it looks rather formidable its principal purpose is thought to be for bonding, settling a social order in the pod and attracting mates, as opposed to use as a lethal weapon.

Markings
Narwhal skin features a mottled pattern of black-brown over white, which increasingly lightens as they approach maturity. These markings offer some degree of camouflage from predators like killer whales.

Body
The narwhal's body is cylindrical and quite stocky compared to other cetaceans like dolphins and they have no dorsal fin. Along with a 10cm (3.9in)-thick layer of blubber under the skin, this body shape ensures optimal heat preservation in freezing-cold waters.

The statistics...

Narwhal

Type:	Mammal
Genus:	Monodon monoceros
Diet:	Carnivore (eg fish, squid, shrimp)
Average life span in the wild:	50 years
Length:	4-6.1m (13-20ft)
Tusk length:	2-3m (6.6-9.9ft)
Weight:	1,600kg (3,500lb)

Porpoises in demand

Narwhals provide a host of invaluable resources to the native Arctic tribes

People would struggle to live in the Arctic if it weren't for marine creatures to hunt and, in many respects, narwhals are considered the ultimate catch, with not a single part of the creature wasted.

Starting with the tusk, this is often incorporated into everyday tools like harpoon shafts, as well as in many traditional handicrafts; it's sometimes also used for bartering with other tribes.

Meat from the porpoise is often the main food source for hunters' dog teams, though it's also consumed by people – particularly the fatty layer of skin (sometimes called 'mattak'), which is a rare source of vitamin C in the region.

On top of all this, oil can be extracted from the narwhal's blubber, which is an essential fuel for both cooking and powering lamps, while its sinews can be used to sew boots and other clothing.

© Corbis

Dolphin noises

With no vocal cords, how and why do these intelligent mammals communicate?

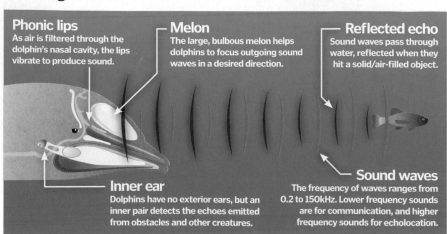

Phonic lips
As air is filtered through the dolphin's nasal cavity, the lips vibrate to produce sound.

Melon
The large, bulbous melon helps dolphins to focus outgoing sound waves in a desired direction.

Reflected echo
Sound waves pass through water, reflected when they hit a solid/air-filled object.

Inner ear
Dolphins have no exterior ears, but an inner pair detects the echoes emitted from obstacles and other creatures.

Sound waves
The frequency of waves ranges from 0.2 to 150kHz. Lower frequency sounds are for communication, and higher frequency sounds for echolocation.

Dolphins produce sound from 'phonic lips', located in their nasal cavity. These muscular tissues, when stimulated by passing air, allow them to form a variety of sounds of varying frequencies, such as clicks, whistles and moans. This is similar to how humans produce sounds by exhaling air from their lungs through the larynx, but differs as dolphins do not shape and project these sounds through their mouth, relying instead on a large fatty structure known as the 'melon' to amplify and focus them.

Dolphins communicate by producing low-frequency noises (0.2 to 50kHz) which travel at 0.9 miles per second (1.4kps), roughly 4.5 times faster than through air. These lower frequencies travel further than higher ones and, along with a signature whistle formed in infancy, enable communication over large distances.

Echolocation allows dolphins to locate and discriminate objects, animals and terrain via a sequence of high-frequency sound waves (the characteristic clicking sounds). Clicks range in frequencies from 40-130kHz and usually last between 50 to 128 microseconds. Echolocation sound waves are amplified and directed by the melon and their echoes (when the waves hit an object and bounce back) are received by an inner ear, then sent to the brain in the form of nerve impulses. As dolphins have two phonic lip complexes, they can communicate and echolocate at the same time. ✿

The ones that get away
At the height of the salmon run, a bear can catch one fish every 20 minutes and will eat 40kg of salmon every day. Despite this, more than 200 fish will get past for every one the bear catches.

DID YOU KNOW? Bears don't like to get their ears wet and use their hind legs to kick fish out of deep pools, rather than dive in

"Please, after you, I insist"

Bear diet

Bears are relentless omnivores. Whatever is in abundance, they will eat. Bears will climb trees to eat acorns and use their claws to carefully strip berries from a bush. The grizzlies in Yellowstone National Park even eat moths, getting through up to 40,000 a day.

But for pure nutritional value, almost nothing beats salmon. Spawning salmon are full of eggs and their skin is rich in fat. Bears get ten times as much energy from fish as they do from berries. Through summer and early-autumn they will eat 20,000 calories a day – as much as ten adult humans – to put on enough weight to last through the winter.

The statistics...

Brown bear

Class: Mammal

Family: Ursidae

Diet: Omnivore

Average life span in the wild: 25 years

Weight: 300-550kg

Size: 1.5-2.7m long

How do bears catch fish?

Need to catch a 30-pound salmon without a rod or net? Just grin and bear it

In July and August each year, tens of thousands of fat salmon migrate back up the rivers of Northern America and Eastern Russia to spawn. For an opportunistic hunter like the brown bear, this is too good to miss.

A bear perched at the top of a low waterfall catching fish in mid air makes for a great photograph, but the right sort of waterfall is relatively rare and competition from other hungry bears at these spots can be very fierce. It also requires perfect reflexes. The bear has just one chance to snatch the slippery, struggling fish with a grip firm enough to make it back to the shore without it wriggling free. If he drops it, the fast-flowing water will whisk away his prize, even if the fish is already dead.

A much better hunting ground is where the river becomes broad and shallow. In ankle-deep water, the bear can outrun the salmon as they frantically flap themselves over the stones, and pinning one to the riverbed with heavy claws is much easier. Bears also watch from the bank as salmon rest in calmer pools close to shore. They will then suddenly leap and try to snatch a fish in their jaws.

The bear's fearsome claws may be deadly weapons on land, but against salmon they aren't much use. Bears don't

have opposable thumbs so they can't grip the fish and brown bear claws are quite blunt. But they have very powerful jaws with huge, backward-curving canine teeth. Bears will attempt to snag the fish with the front of the mouth when they strike, but they will often then hold the fish against the crook of their elbow. This lets them get a better grip on the salmon with the molars at the back of the mouth, so they can securely carry it to the shore.

Dare you to take it off him...

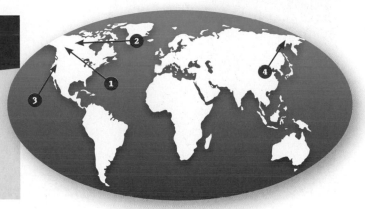

ON THE MAP

Where do fish-eating bears live?
1 Katmai National Park, Alaska
2 British Columbia, Canada
3 Lake Tahoe, Northern California
4 Kamchatka, Siberia

Kings of the Arctic

How polar bears hunt and survive

The polar bear may seem cute and cuddly, but these mammoth mammals of the Arctic are a hardened species, set out to survive in these subzero temperatures, plunging as low as -45° Celsius.

The polar bear, or Ursus maritimus – which means sea bear – have been recorded to weigh as much as 2,209 pounds, and can grow to as big as ten feet tall when standing on their hind legs. That's a massive body mass, which includes a thick layer of blubber nearly 4.5 inches thick. Wrap this up with two additional layers of fur, which covers all of the bear's anatomy except their nose and foot pads, and Ursus maritimus stays as snug as a bug. Pure white to creamy yellow/light brown in colouration, depending upon season and angle of light, makes for a perfect combination for surprising prey.

Other essential parts of the anatomy, such as the paws and snout, help them thrive in these harsh conditions. Polar bears' paws are large compared to its body size. Measuring 12 inches, they include thick, curved, non-retractable claws, essential for catching large prey, as well as for additional traction

A family of polar bears receive a surprise visit from a Russian sub

Polar bears are animals without boundaries, padding across the ice from Russia to Alaska, from Canada to Greenland and onto Norway's Svalbard archipelago

ON THE MAP

Where can you find the king of the arctic?

Found throughout the Arctic circle, polar bears can be found in five countries: Denmark (Greenland), USA (Alaska), Canada, Norway (Svalbard) and Russia. Estimates suggest that only 20,000-25,000 polar bears remain throughout the world.

LARGEST BEAR

1. Brown bear
The largest member of the bear family, brown bears can weigh up to 1,500 pounds. They live across northern Eurasia and the USA.

MEANEST BEAR

2. Polar bear
Rival in all but size to the brown bear, and much more deadly, polar bears are claimed to have actively hunted humans on the ice.

NOT A BEAR

3. Koala bear
Contrary to its misleading name, coastal Australia's cuddly Koala is not a bear at all but in fact a marsupial, which is an infraclass of mammals.

DID YOU KNOW? Polar bears enjoy a relatively extended life span, most dying at a ripe age of 25 years old

to help them when chasing that prey and running on ice.

Small bumps, known as papillae, are also present and these help them keep their grip when manoeuvring. Up to half the length of the bear's toes is covered with a swimming membrane, which enables them to swim at a rate of six miles per hour, and they're known to be competent swimmers as far as 320km from shore.

The bear's sense of smell is extremely acute, and becomes the most important sensory for detecting land prey. Able to smell a seal from over one kilometre away, under three feet of snow, this is extremely important to this species' survival, as snowy weather conditions impair its eyesight, which is no better than ours. These factors firmly put Ursus maritimus at the top of the Arctic food chain.

Unfortunately, despite their great prowess, the polar bear population is dropping quickly, mainly due to the damaging effects of global warming. As the Earth heats up, larger quantities of ice are melting earlier in the year, removing the vital hunting platforms which polar bears use to hunt seals. This habitat loss is preventing polar bears from building up the requisite fat reserves to survive in the harsher and leaner parts of the year, with many succumbing to malnutrition. In addition, the loss of ice is forcing the bears to swim further and further between landmasses, draining energy that is vital for healthy reproduction, body conditioning and general survival.

> "Polar bears can smell a seal from over one kilometre away, under three feet of snow"

Ice fishing is sometimes about the long game...

A sperm whale provides a nutritious and hearty meal

Every family has its fall-outs...

5 TOP FACTS
POLAR BEARS

1 Diving depths
The polar bear makes shallow dives to catch prey, but can stay submerged for up to two minutes, in depths of up to 15 feet.

2 Female of the species
A female polar bear can bare offspring as young as four or five years old. Cub litters are most commonly twins.

3 Boys are bigger
The male is the larger of the two sexes, growing up to ten feet tall and weighing in at over 1,400 pounds. The female is a little more slender, at seven feet tall and only 650 pounds.

4 Translucent fur
Ever wondered why a polar bear looks white? Well, each hair is a transparent and pigment-free hollow tube, reflecting the light around it. Perfect camouflage for hunting prey.

5 Bear on standby
The polar bear can slow down its own metabolism, which enables it to conserve energy at any time of the year.

Learn more

For more information about polar bears head over to polarbearsinternational.org where you can learn more about these incredibly cute but ultimately deadly beasts, and even adopt your very own cub!

Locating prey
To catch prey, polar bears wait in silence outside seal breathing holes in the ice, before dragging them out when they surface to breathe. They then crush the seal's skull to kill it.

Big diet
Polar bears' diet consists mainly of land-caught seals and their pups. During the summer months they also eat a plethora of sea creatures and fish.

Devouring prey
Polar bears tend to be selective in what parts of their prey they consume, focusing on the calorie-rich skin and blubber.

On the hunt
Land or sea, nothing stops the polar bear

Primates

There's more to primates than just monkeys. This diverse group also contains some of the strangest and most specialised animals in the world. We go looking for the King of the Swingers

 Primates are mammals with grasping hands and feet, good vision and large brains for their body size. They evolved from squirrel-like tree-dwelling animals around 65 million years ago, just before the dinosaurs became extinct. Primates are divided into the lemurs (who only live in Madagascar), lorises, tarsiers and simians. Somewhere between 33 and 70 million years ago, a few simians made the journey from Africa to South America, probably floating on impromptu rafts of vegetation. From there, they evolved into the New World Monkeys, and they are the only primates native to that continent. The simians left behind became the Old World Monkeys – who have tails – and the apes – who have lost their tails.

There are approximately 424 species of primate currently known, mostly living in the midst of tropical rainforests. Primates are very successful mammals. Even ignoring the fact that the dominant species on Earth (homo sapiens) is a primate, this group of animals has still spread out widely across the tropical regions of the world; from the humid forests of Central America to the arid African savannah, and from the swamps of the Congo basin to the Ethiopian highlands, which are a massive 5,000m above sea level.

Primates account for as much as 40 per cent of the fruit-eating animals (by weight) in tropical rainforests and their preferences have had a major impact on the evolution of plants there. Bananas and oranges, for example, use monkeys to spread their seeds and so they have evolved skins that are very hard to peel unless you have opposable thumbs.

Primates live longer than other mammals of the same size, partly because they are often able to co-operate to defend themselves against predators. They also reproduce more slowly though, with infants hugely dependent on their parents for much longer than most other animals. Their reasonably large brains require time to fully develop, and to fill with knowledge about their environment.

Although most primates eat fruit as part of their diet, many of them have specialised for other foods as well. Lemurs eat leaves, marmosets strip tree bark to eat the gum underneath and the aye-aye has an elongated middle finger to winkle insects out of trees, like a woodpecker. ✿

Mouse lemur

1 Madame Berthe's mouse lemur weighs just 30 grams (1.1 ounces) and has a body that measures 9.2cm long (3.6 inches). It lives only in a small part of Madagascar.

Mountain gorilla

2 At the other end of the scale, the mountain gorilla weighs 200kg (440lb). Despite its ferocious bulk, it is completely herbivorous and mostly eats leaves.

Male proboscis monkey

3 The male proboscis monkey has a nose the size, shape and colour of a large sweet potato. Amazingly, it seems that this feature actually attracts females.

Gelada

4 The gelada is a grass eater. It has the most opposable thumb of any primate apart from humans, used to pick apart grass stalks to reach the most nutritious parts.

Howler monkey

5 The howler monkey is the loudest primate. Using the enlarged hyoid bone in its neck, it makes a hooting noise that can be heard three miles away.

DID YOU KNOW? *Female lorises bathe their young with toxic saliva licked from patches near their elbows to discourage predators*

The skeleton of a swinger

Primates show a high degree of specialisation and adaptation between different species, but even those primates that have climbed down from the trees still show plenty of evidence that their ancestors used to swing overhead. Primate skeletons are adapted to provide maximum mobility and reach in their arms and forward-facing eyes to give depth of perception.

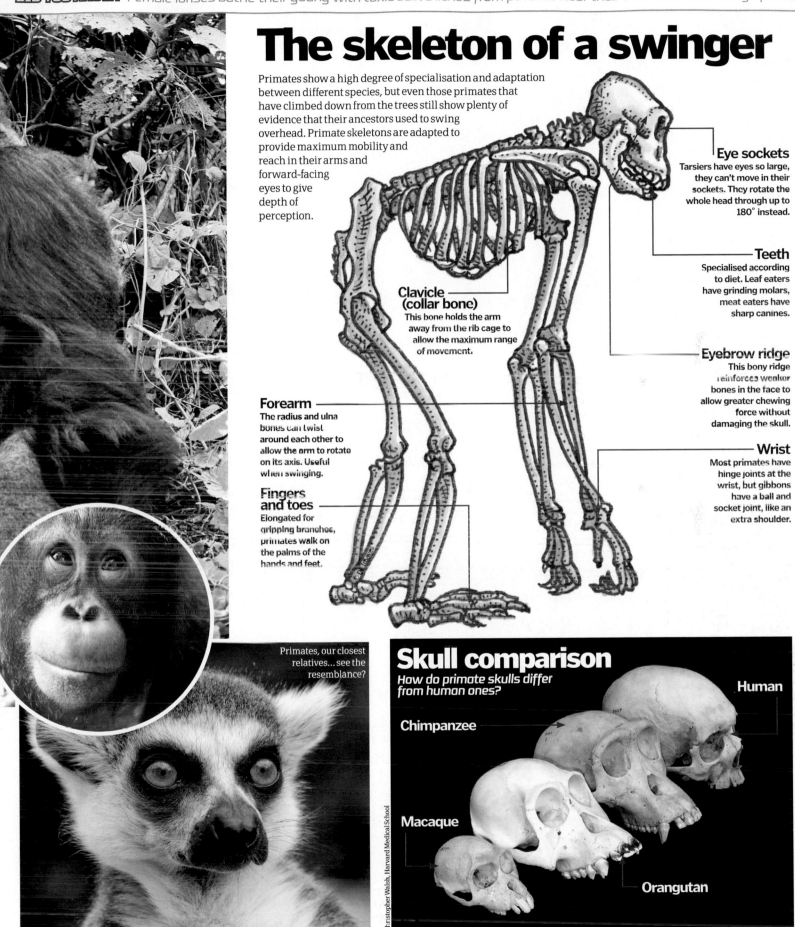

Eye sockets
Tarsiers have eyes so large, they can't move in their sockets. They rotate the whole head through up to 180° instead.

Teeth
Specialised according to diet. Leaf eaters have grinding molars, meat eaters have sharp canines.

Eyebrow ridge
This bony ridge reinforces weaker bones in the face to allow greater chewing force without damaging the skull.

Wrist
Most primates have hinge joints at the wrist, but gibbons have a ball and socket joint, like an extra shoulder.

Clavicle (collar bone)
This bone holds the arm away from the rib cage to allow the maximum range of movement.

Forearm
The radius and ulna bones can twist around each other to allow the arm to rotate on its axis. Useful when swinging.

Fingers and toes
Elongated for gripping branches, primates walk on the palms of the hands and feet.

Primates, our closest relatives... see the resemblance?

© Christopher Walsh, Harvard Medical School

Skull comparison
How do primate skulls differ from human ones?

Human

Chimpanzee

Macaque

Orangutan

Brushing twice a day keeps those teeth pearly white

Wise monkeys

Monkey see monkey do

Primates have binocular vision and fingers and thumbs that can grip small objects with precision. This is useful enough already, but it is their large brains that allow them to explore and manipulate the world around them in more complex ways. Chimpanzees use sharpened sticks to poke for termites and as weapons; gorillas carry a walking stick to gauge the depth of the water as they cross a river; Japanese macaques wash their food in seawater to remove dirt and season it with salt. These behaviours aren't innate; they are passed from generation to generation.

Most primates are highly social, with complicated power struggles and sexual relationships worthy of any soap opera. The New World species form monogamous relationships and look after the young together. In Africa and Asia, only gibbons do this. Old World monkeys and great apes have dominance hierarchies to establish one male in a group with mating access to most of the females.

Taste the rainbow

The complex, three-dimensional world of the forest makes accurate depth perception essential. This requires forward-facing eyes and a flattened nose that won't get in the way. For this reason primates rely much more on their vision than they do on their sense of smell. Most mammals can see in just two basic colours but primates have evolved a three-colour vision that is sensitive to red, green and blue wavelengths. This allows them to easily distinguish between ripe and unripe fruits.

In New World monkeys, the males all have two-colour vision, which is slightly better for identifying succulent leaves, while most females see three colours, so they can find fruit. Most species gather food co-operatively, to get the best of both worlds.

Depth perception is vital to aid swinging

1. Orangutan
The fluffy orangutans have been seen using leaves as makeshift megaphones, to amplify the 'kiss squeak' sounds that they make.

2. Gorilla
Gorillas show complex emotional attachments to each other in the wild and Koko, a female gorilla at San Francisco Zoo, has pet cats.

3. Chimpanzee
Captive chimpanzees have been taught to use American sign language to ask for food and can remember the numbers one to nine as well as their values.

DID YOU KNOW? In 2005 the naming rights for the newly discovered Callicebus aureipalatii were auctioned off for £450,000

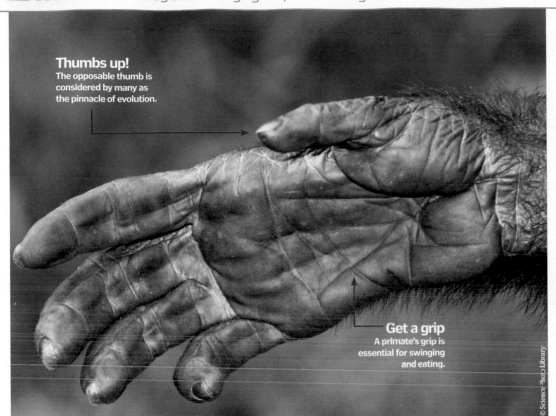

Thumbs up!
The opposable thumb is considered by many as the pinnacle of evolution.

Get a grip
A primate's grip is essential for swinging and eating.

© Science Photo Library

All fingers and thumbs

Primates evolved in the trees and even those species that have since climbed down to solid ground still carry the legacy of hands and feet that were designed to grip branches. Primates have five fingers and toes on each foot with nails, rather than claws, an opposable thumb and often an opposable big toe as well. Primate fingers are much longer than in other mammals and tend to curve inwards when relaxed, so their natural position is a loose grip.

As well as being good at gripping, primates have long arms with very freely rotating shoulders and wrists. This makes it easy to swing from branch to branch. This form of movement is called brachiation. Gibbons can brachiate at 55km/h, travelling 6m with each swing.

"Can you bring a cup and saucer next time"

Where do they live?

Primates evolved from tree-dwelling animals. In South America, where forests tend to be very dense with lots of trailing lianas, most species still spend all their lives high in the trees, away from predators. In the Old World, colobus monkeys and gibbons live in the trees but the great apes spend a lot of their time on the forest floor. Baboons and mandrills don't climb much at all.

Primates mostly live in tropical regions, avoid water and are active during the day. But with such versatile animals, there are always exceptions. Galagos, or bushbabies, are nocturnal; Allen's swamp monkey has webbed feet and can swim; and the Japanese macaque lives in an area that is snow-covered for eight months of the year.

ON THE MAP
Where to find primates

1 New World Monkeys – South/Central America
2 Old World Monkeys, Apes – Sub Saharan Africa
3 Gorillas – Congo
4 Barbary macaques – Atlas Mountains
5 Gibbons – South-east Asia and India
6 Lemurs – Madagascar
7 Japanese macaques – Honshu, Japan
8 Gelada baboon – Ethiopian highlands

A gripping tail

Apart from the apes, most primates have tails, but *prehensile* tails are unique to the New World monkeys. Prehensile means 'gripping' and the howler, spider and woolly monkeys have a bare pad of skin on the end of their tails that lets them grip food and small objects. The capuchin monkeys don't have this pad and only use their tail as a fifth arm when climbing. Old World monkeys only use their tails for balance.

Chimp chase

Chimps will eat almost anything. In fact, they're partial to the odd small tree-dwelling monkey. In order to catch these swifter, more nimble monkeys, the chimps get organised

Colobus monkey
Surprised by the driver, the hapless tree monkey takes to the trees to escape.

Ambusher
The money's fate is sealed, all the other chimpanzees work together to steer the prey towards this one chimpanzee who will make the grizzly kill.

Blocker
Like the chaser, the blockers prevent the monkey from taking a new route away from the waiting ambusher.

Chaser
If the monkey runs in the wrong direction, chaser monkeys will wait in the trees till it comes near and steer it back on course towards the ambusher.

Driver
A driver chimpanzee startles the monkey and gives chase.

Deforestation destroys the primates' habitat

Threats to primates

More than a third of primate species are critically endangered or vulnerable. Deforestation accounts for a lot of this, mainly through forest clearance for agriculture. But poaching is a significant problem as well. The smaller primates are captured to supply the pet trade, larger animals are hunted for traditional medicine and for their meat. In some African cities, half of all the protein eaten is 'bush meat', which includes primates. Armed conflict in the Democratic Republic of Congo has made poaching much worse because of general lawlessness. Primates reproduce much more slowly than other mammals so populations take a long time to recover.

In Madagascar, at least 15 species of primate have become extinct since humans first settled there 1,500 years ago, including a lemur larger than a gorilla.

There's a good chance his eyes are bigger than his stomach

How flying squirrels glide

Meet the rodent with its own built-in parachute

Many arboreal (tree-dwelling) animals have developed wing-like extensions called patagia, which are elastic membranes stretched between their limbs or toes. These flaps of skin are ideal for helping them glide through the air either to evade predators or to catch their own prey.

The southern flying squirrel is a nocturnal rodent capable of taking to the air and gliding from tree to tree in a single leap. The length of a single flight depends on the height at which the squirrel launches, but some can reach distances of up to 50 metres (165 feet). This form of gliding is known as volplaning.

Flying squirrels are found in North America and northern Europe, living in nests or natural cavities high in the trees. When down on the ground, however, they're a vulnerable target.

Flying squirrels are omnivorous and feast on a wide range of different food from nuts, fruit and fungi to many insects, bird eggs and even carrion from time to time. ✿

The statistics...

Southern flying squirrel

Binomial name:	Glaucomys volans
Type:	Mammal
Diet:	Omnivore
Average life span in the wild:	5 years
Weight:	15g-2kg (0.5oz-4lb)
Size:	10-90cm (4-35in)
Length of glide:	50m (165ft)

Born to fly
We break down the squirrel's flight path from takeoff to landing

Launch
The flying squirrel leaps out from a tree with its body tilted up and its arms and legs outstretched.

Stretch
After pushing off, the squirrel gains height and momentum. It then stretches its arms and legs out in front to help propel it forwards as it falls.

Patagia
Once the rodent gains altitude, it spreads its limbs to reveal a gliding membrane (the patagium) connected to the wrist and ankle on either side. These flaps fill with air, like a parachute, to create drag.

Control
The flying squirrel can dictate the direction in which it flies by steering with its legs, flattening its tail and stiffening the patagia, the two of which also act like an airfoil to generate lift.

Braking
During the descent, the creature flexes its entire body and tail upwards. Doing this enables the squirrel to change its angle of attack at the last moment by slowing its speed through the air.

Landing
Finally, as it comes in to land – typically on another tree trunk – the squirrel's body moves into a vertical position by swinging its hind legs down and forward ready to grasp on to the new tree.

Which other animals can glide?

The colugo's gliding membrane extends from its neck all the way down to its toes and tail

Colugo
Though often called the flying lemur, it's actually a species of its own. About the size of a squirrel, but with a bat-like look, the colugo has the largest patagia of all gliders.
Length of glide:
Up to 70m (230ft)

Paradise tree snake
This reptile can launch itself into the air from a height and flatten its body into a ribbon shape with a concave underside that acts like an airfoil. It still moves in the air in an 'S' shape.
Length of glide:
Up to 100m (330ft)

Flying frog
This arboreal species has giant webbed feet that act like four airfoils. Flying frogs can be very nimble in flight, capable of banking from side to side like an aeroplane.
Length of glide:
Up to 15m (50ft)

Draco lizard
One of the greatest gliders. Sometimes called flying dragons due to their airborne antics, the Draco lizard has a large semicircular wing-like flap attached to either side of its ribs.
Length of glide:
Up to 9m (30ft)

© Alamy; Getty; Thinkstock

Meerkat survival tactics

Meet the sociable critters that play to their strengths by living in tight-knit groups

Meerkats might not be the biggest animals on the African plains, nor appear to boast any particularly formidable weapons, like the rhino's horn, or impressive skills, like the cheetah's speed. Nevertheless, through a combination of hardy biology, smart tricks and a unique community spirit, these mammals have adapted perfectly to their harsh environment.

They escape the most extreme temperatures of southern Africa – as well as the vast majority of predators who'd like to make a meal of them – by living in underground burrows. Some of these subterranean networks can play host to up to 50 or so individuals, though an average colony is about half this size, with two or three families living together communally.

A type of mongoose, they are equipped with sharp, curved claws – each about two centimetres (0.8 inches) long – used for digging and self-defence, as well as acute vision, which comes in very handy for spotting any nearby danger.

In fact, when they do venture out of their burrows en masse to search for food, there will always be at least one meerkat that stands sentry – often on a rock or in a bush – primarily looking to the skies for their number-one enemy: birds of prey. As soon as any threat is detected, the lookout will give a shrill warning bark and the others will immediately make a dash for a nearby bolthole or other cover. It's thought that meerkats have dozens of different calls to signify a range of threats.

As well as hunting together over a territorial range that can cover as much as ten square kilometres (four square miles), meerkats also share childcare duties. Typically, only the colony's alpha pair will mate, but all the others pitch in to babysit, groom and feed the pups, as well as demonstrating valuable life skills, like where to find food, play-fighting and which parts of a scorpion to eat. ✿

Biology of a meerkat
They may be small, but their bodies are tough

Eyes
Binocular vision helps them detect predators like eagles from as far as 1km (0.6mi) away, while the black eye patches reduce glare. Nicitating membranes act like goggles to keep sand out while digging.

Ears
The ears are small and round and can be closed when the meerkat is digging or caught in a sandstorm.

Fur
Varies in colour from light tan to dark brown depending on the terrain, with unique stripe patterns on the back. Fur is thinner on the belly and meerkats will often sunbathe in the morning to warm up.

Tail
Almost doubling the meerkat's length, the long tail is a useful aid for balancing when standing on their hind legs.

Claws
2cm (0.8in)-long claws (four on each paw) are used to dig their burrows as well as to forage for insects and roots in the arid ground.

Are they immune to venom?

Meerkats are renowned for picking fights with creatures that even the most powerful hunters give a wide berth, like snakes and scorpions, but are they really impervious to venom? Well, to some degree this may be true, because mongooses have often demonstrated a much higher tolerance to venom than most animals due to a slightly mutated neurotransmitter, which prevents the toxins from causing muscle paralysis. However, this doesn't mean meerkats are immune – they *can* die if they get stung or bitten several times or by particularly toxic species. But to sway the odds in their favour, they've developed some clever hunting tactics, including 'mobbing', where they encircle an enemy and attack it from all angles. Or in a scorpion's case, they move with lightning-quick reflexes to bite off the stinger before it can do any harm, then rub the toxic outer layer of the exoskeleton on the ground before eating it.

One meerkat will always stand guard while the others are occupied

Meerkats live in colonies of up to 50 individuals and they rely on each other for food, defence and rearing their pups

The statistics...

Meerkat

Type: Mammal

Binomial: Suricata suricatta

Diet: Omnivore, eg insects, fruit, lizards, roots, birds

Body length: 30cm (12in)

Weight: 750g (26oz)

Average life span in the wild: 10 years

141

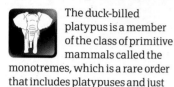

Duck-billed plat

Is it a beaver? Is it a duck? Is it a lizard? No, it's something entirely different...

The duck-billed platypus is a member of the class of primitive mammals called the monotremes, which is a rare order that includes platypuses and just four species of spiny anteater.

Monotremes are oviparous, which means they reproduce by laying eggs that develop and hatch outside the mother's body, rather than giving birth. For around ten days, the mother incubates the egg alone in her burrow by keeping it warm in a pouch between her body and her tail. When the helpless, blind baby – commonly known as a puggle – hatches it will be hungry, and while female platypuses don't have teats like other mammals, they can still suckle their young. Milk glands that are tucked away in a groove inside the pouch on her abdomen produce pools of nutritious milk. The female nurses the puggle for

several months until it can both see and swim independently.

The platypus was built for underwater activities: it has a long streamlined body, waterproof fur, paddle-like feet as well as tricks for feeling around in the dark and remaining below the surface for as long as possible. While hunting in rivers and lagoons, the platypus uses its webbed front feet to propel itself through the water and its rear feet and flat, beaverish tail to steer. The creature can remain underwater for several minutes due to the folds of skin that form watertight seals over its eyes, ears and nostrils.

Another distinguishing feature of the platypus is the fact that adult males have a poisonous spur on the hind leg, which can deliver a nasty sting. The spur is used during tussles for territory or mates and in defence against predators, making the male platypus a very nasty adversary. ✿

© Dr Philip Bethge

Platypus's lair

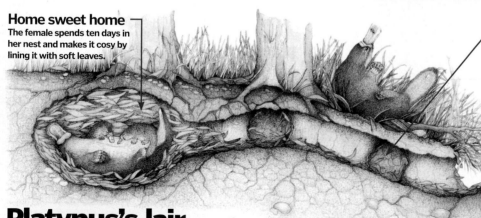

Home sweet home
The female spends ten days in her nest and makes it cosy by lining it with soft leaves.

Keep out
To prevent water from flooding the nest and to regulate humidity, Mrs Platypus builds blockages along the tunnel to her nest.

Only girls allowed
The female lays and incubates her eggs in a private nest away from the male.

Platypuses make their homes in riverbank burrows with an opening just above water level. Once the female has mated – usually between July and November – she needs a quiet place to lay and incubate her eggs away from the males, and so she tunnels deep into the riverbank creating a lair for herself and her egg. At intervals between the nest and the riverbank, she creates blockages in the tunnel – which can be as long as 18m – to prevent any rising water from inundating her hideaway. The mother lines her nest with soft leaf matter, which she drags in behind her using her versatile tail.

The Statistics
Duck-billed platypus

© Peter Scheunis

Type: Mammal
Diet: Carnivore
Life span in the wild: 10-15 years
Weight: 3lbs (1.4kg)
Size: Males up to 60cm
Females up to 50cm
Habitat: Freshwater ponds, rivers and creeks

© DK Images

HEAD2HEAD2
MAMMAL VENOM

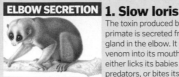

ELBOW SECRETION
1. Slow loris
The toxin produced by this primate is secreted from a gland in the elbow. It sucks the venom into its mouth and then either licks its babies to deter predators, or bites its foes.

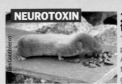

NEUROTOXIN
2. Northern short-tailed shrew
This shrew can paralyse its prey with its venomous saliva. A neurotoxin, which acts on the nerves, is secreted from a gland in the mouth.

ACID
3. Pangolin
The scaly pangolin is another mammal that can emit a noxious substance in a similar way to the skunk. The pangolin gives off a foul-smelling acid from glands near its rear end.

DID YOU KNOW? Platypuses can eat between 20 and 50 per cent of their own weight in food every day – more in winter

ypuses

Amazing platypus characteristics

Okay, so if you list the distinguishing features of our friend the platypus you have a medley of traits unique to only a few members of the animal kingdom. Take their webbed feet and rubbery bill, for instance – both examples of a duck's distinctive appearance. Or the beaver-like fur covering all but its bill and feet. And how about those legs, which protrude from the side of the body, giving the platypus a lizard's gait? Such borrowed characteristics make the platypus one of the weirdest animals waddling around the southern hemisphere. Many creatures all rolled into one quite curious mammal.

The male of the species is more deadly!

For self-defence, both sexes develop sharp calcaneus spurs on their hind legs. These growths are not fixed to the heel; they are attached to a separate bone that allows them greater freedom to move.

However, only the spurs of the males are venomous and capable of causing immobilising pain or death to small animals. The venom in the spur is unique to the platypus and is composed of special chemical proteins that can cause severe pain and swelling in the victim as well as lowering their blood pressure. The poison is produced in the crural venom gland in the upper thigh and is connected to the sharp end of the spur by way of a tiny duct. The female's spur, on the other hand, doesn't develop fully, and falls off after a year.

The duck-bill and electroreception

Since duck-billed platypuses are mainly crepuscular – that is, they're mostly active during the twilight hours of the early morning and late evening – you might assume they have excellent eyesight that enables them to hunt in these conditions.

And you'd be right; despite the fact they have very small eyes, they do have very keen eyesight. However, the platypus actually keeps its eyes shut when hunting underwater. So to stalk its prey, a platypus instead uses its highly sensitive bill. Although this may resemble the bill of a duck, it's covered with soft leathery skin that contains approximately 40,000 tiny receptors that can detect the faint electric fields produced by small animals buried in the riverbed.

By sweeping its bill from side to side, the duck-billed platypus can sense the direction of its lunch, which it will dig out of the mud.

© Rainbow66

Platypus anatomy
The body of the strongest creature on Earth!

Spurs
Male platypuses come with an added defensive feature: a poisonous spur located on the inside of the ankle on the hind legs.

Feet
A platypus's furless front paws consist of five webbed toes that act as very effective paddles for swimming gracefully through water. On land the platypus takes on a much more ungainly waddle. However, the webbing on their feet does retract to reveal a set of claws that enable it to run if needed. Platypus is Greek for flat feet.

Tiny eyes
The platypus is blind when born and even as an adult has tiny eyes located in a groove, set back from the bill. But the platypus doesn't require good eyesight to hunt for food; instead it uses that ultra-sensitive bill.

Mouth
Once the platypus has caught enough grub, it will return to the surface to feed. However, the adult platypus doesn't have any teeth; instead it has a mouthful of horny plates and gravel, which is used to grind the food. The young do have molars, but they fall out as they mature.

Nostrils
The nostrils are equipped with special flaps of skin that enable them to close not only their eyes, but also to form watertight seals over their ears and nostrils when diving.

Bill
Once the platypus has used its bill to locate and excavate its prey – that being worms, insect larvae and shellfish – it can scoop the food out of the mud and strain it through its bill. The platypus can then continue its hunt by storing food in its cheeks like a hamster.

Fur
Thick, brown, waterproof fur grows all over the platypus's body – except for the bill and feet – to trap air to insulate the animal and keep it warm.

© Rainbow66

ON THE MAP

Where the platypuses roam
Platypuses live in burrows in the freshwater creeks and lagoons the length of the eastern side of Australia and are also common throughout Tasmania.

Northern Territory
Western Australia
South Australia
Queensland
New South Wales
Tasmania

Tail
The broad, flat tail makes for an excellent rudder, enabling the platypus to twist and turn in the water. The fat reserves are also stored here.

Cloaca
Monotremes have only one cloaca, which is the external opening on the body for reproduction and excretion.

© Stefan Kraft

BIG CATS

What makes these beautiful creatures such consummate experts in the business of killing?

 The big cats aren't a single biological grouping. It's an informal term that includes the lion, tiger, jaguar and leopard (sometimes called the Great Cats), as well as the cheetah, cougar, snow leopard and clouded leopard. (The three kinds of leopard actually belong to three different genera and aren't very closely related, despite looking quite similar.) Big cats are all apex predators that hunt large mammals using their excellent camouflage to keep hidden and their powerful muscles to catch and dispatch their prey.

An antelope runs on the very tips of its feet, which allows it to have a much longer stride and means it is very fast. Cats can't do this because they have claws instead of hooves, and they need to retract them to keep them sharp. To catch hoofed animals, the big cats must run with their entire spine flexing to help elongate their effective stride. It's a very energetic technique though and cats can't run fast for long distances. This in turn pushes them to be stealthy in the approach and brutal in the attack. Where a wolf will bite and retreat as it waits for its prey to bleed to death, a cougar will leap onto the back of its prey and crunch straight through the spine with a single bite.

The roar of a big cat is a sound made by the walls of the specially elongated larynx vibrating as the cat exhales, but not all big cats can do it. The cougar, cheetah and snow leopard have no roar, but they do make a variety of other noises, including chirps, screams and growls. All of the big cats are able to climb trees. Leopards are the strongest climbers; indeed, an adult male can haul a young giraffe almost six metres (20 feet) into a tree. This skill enables big cats to protect their kills from hyenas and other pack scavengers that might steal them.

It's easy to think of animals this magnificent in terms of being 'perfectly adapted', but in fact hunting large animals is incredibly difficult and all apex predators hover perpetually close to the brink. If they were anything less than brutally fit, they simply couldn't survive at all. ⚙

Top acceleration
1 A cheetah can accelerate from 0-97km/h (0-60mph) in less than three seconds; that's faster than a Ferrari Enzo, a Lamborghini Gallardo or a Porsche 911 Turbo!

Mystery tuft
2 The lion is the only cat which features a furry tuft on its tail. This conceals a spike formed from fused bones at the end of the spine. Its anatomical function is still unknown.

Rise of the panther
3 Panthers aren't separate animals; it's actually just the term for an all-black mutation of a leopard or jaguar. In 1,500 years or so time, all leopards may have evolved to be completely black.

Long leapers
4 Snow leopards prefer to chase prey down a steep hill rather than on flat terrain. This often ends in a huge final leap of up to 14m (46ft), which is roughly the length of a bus.

Deafening roar
5 Lions have the loudest roar of any cat; a male lion's roar can be heard up to 8km (5mi) away. This helps to defend its territory against other males in the vicinity.

DID YOU KNOW? A leopard will eat anything from a dung beetle up to a 900kg (2,000lb) giant eland

Meet the cats...

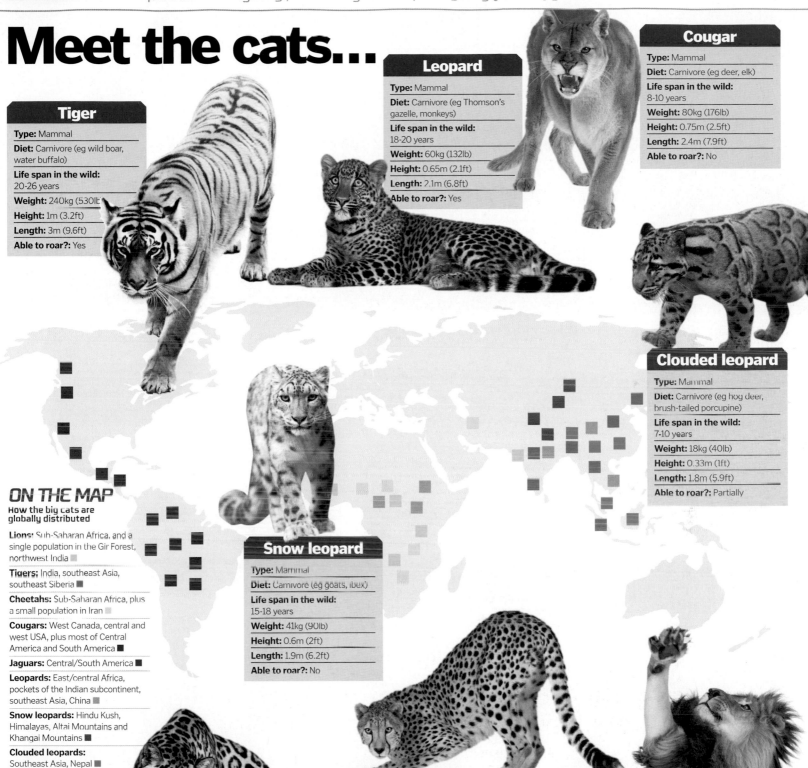

Tiger
Type: Mammal
Diet: Carnivore (eg wild boar, water buffalo)
Life span in the wild: 20-26 years
Weight: 240kg (530lb)
Height: 1m (3.2ft)
Length: 3m (9.6ft)
Able to roar?: Yes

Leopard
Type: Mammal
Diet: Carnivore (eg Thomson's gazelle, monkeys)
Life span in the wild: 18-20 years
Weight: 60kg (132lb)
Height: 0.65m (2.1ft)
Length: 2.1m (6.8ft)
Able to roar?: Yes

Cougar
Type: Mammal
Diet: Carnivore (eg deer, elk)
Life span in the wild: 8-10 years
Weight: 80kg (176lb)
Height: 0.75m (2.5ft)
Length: 2.4m (7.9ft)
Able to roar?: No

Clouded leopard
Type: Mammal
Diet: Carnivore (eg hog deer, brush-tailed porcupine)
Life span in the wild: 7-10 years
Weight: 18kg (40lb)
Height: 0.33m (1ft)
Length: 1.8m (5.9ft)
Able to roar?: Partially

Snow leopard
Type: Mammal
Diet: Carnivore (eg goats, ibex)
Life span in the wild: 15-18 years
Weight: 41kg (90lb)
Height: 0.6m (2ft)
Length: 1.9m (6.2ft)
Able to roar?: No

ON THE MAP
How the big cats are globally distributed

Lions: Sub-Saharan Africa, and a single population in the Gir Forest, northwest India ■

Tigers: India, southeast Asia, southeast Siberia ■

Cheetahs: Sub-Saharan Africa, plus a small population in Iran ■

Cougars: West Canada, central and west USA, plus most of Central America and South America ■

Jaguars: Central/South America ■

Leopards: East/central Africa, pockets of the Indian subcontinent, southeast Asia, China ■

Snow leopards: Hindu Kush, Himalayas, Altai Mountains and Khangai Mountains ■

Clouded leopards: Southeast Asia, Nepal ■

Jaguar
Type: Mammal
Diet: Carnivore (eg caimans, capybaras)
Life span in the wild: 12-15 years
Weight: 75kg (165lb)
Height: 0.7m (2.2ft)
Length: 2.2m (7.2ft)
Able to roar?: Yes

Cheetah
Type: Mammal
Diet: Carnivore (eg Thomson's gazelle, impala)
Life span in the wild: 12-14 years
Weight: 55kg (120lb)
Height: 0.8m (2.6ft)
Length: 1.3m (4.3ft)
Able to roar?: No

Lion
Type: Mammal
Diet: Carnivore (eg wildebeest, zebra)
Life span in the wild: 10-14 years
Weight: 200kg (440lb)
Height: 1.2m (3.9ft)
Length: 2.2m (7.2ft)
Able to roar?: Yes

Purr-fect predators
Want to kill something three times your size? You'll need:

Markings
Stripes, spots and a contrasting light belly help to break up the animal's outline.

Flexible spine
Acts as a spring when pouncing and increases the effective stride length by flexing when running.

Ears
Independently movable to locate prey. White spots on the back are used to signal to other cats.

Forward-facing eyes
Binocular vision for accurate distance and speed perception. Reflective tapetum lucidum layer behind the retina gives excellent night vision.

Tail
Accounts for a third of body length. Used for balance and as a rudder when changing direction at high speeds.

Vomeronasal organ
The roof of the mouth has special receptors for detecting pheromones. Cats 'grimacing' are 'smelling' with their vomeronasal, or Jacobson's, organ.

Whiskers
Whiskers swivel forwards when striking prey to provide accurate touch sensitivity when the cat is too close to see.

Incisors
These huge teeth are used to puncture skulls, sever spines and crush windpipes.

Retractable claws
Most cats pull the claws in to keep them sharp when running. Cheetahs, in contrast, leave them out for extra traction.

Threats to the big cats

Top carnivores are inherently vulnerable species. They require large home ranges and reproduce relatively slowly. Lions, leopards and cheetahs all suffer high infant mortality from other predators – indeed, up to 90 per cent of cheetah cubs are lost. Cheetahs also have very low genetic variability, possibly due to an extreme population bottleneck thousands of years ago, leading to birth defects as a result of inbreeding; captive breeding schemes have had very limited success. The biggest threats to big cats, though, are habitat loss due to human expansion and poaching. Although most cats have a wide geographic distribution, human development has fragmented these ranges into pockets, each of which may be too small for them to flourish in the long term.

Feuding families

Most big cats are solitary creatures. Female tigers, cougars, jaguars and leopards will maintain a territory of roughly 15-25 square kilometres (5.8-9.7 square miles) and raise their cubs alone. The male has a much larger territory – indeed, cougars have been reported with territories as extensive as 1,300 square kilometres (500 square miles) – but this is to control access to females, not food.

In the big cat kingdom, lions are unusually social because they hunt in the open and need to co-operate to have any chance of success. A typical pride consists of five or six females and one or two males, along with several cubs. Females do most of the hunting; males overheat too easily with their large manes. Males that join a pride will normally start by killing all the cubs. Females are very promiscuous and mate 20-40 times a day when in heat; this makes it harder for males to tell which cubs are theirs and so reduces the rate of infanticide.

A day in the life of a snow leopard

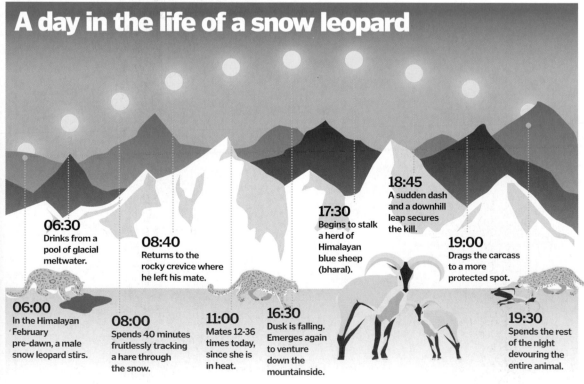

06:00
In the Himalayan February pre-dawn, a male snow leopard stirs.

06:30
Drinks from a pool of glacial meltwater.

08:00
Spends 40 minutes fruitlessly tracking a hare through the snow.

08:40
Returns to the rocky crevice where he left his mate.

11:00
Mates 12-36 times today, since she is in heat.

16:30
Dusk is falling. Emerges again to venture down the mountainside.

17:30
Begins to stalk a herd of Himalayan blue sheep (bharal).

18:45
A sudden dash and a downhill leap secures the kill.

19:00
Drags the carcass to a more protected spot.

19:30
Spends the rest of the night devouring the entire animal.

RECORD BREAKERS

CAT ALIASES

40+

ANIMAL WITH THE MOST NAMES

The cougar is the animal with the most folk names. These include catamount, ghost cat, puma, shadow cat, mountain lion, deer tiger, silver lion, devil cat and catawampus.

DID YOU KNOW? *If you shave a tiger of its fur the skin beneath will still be stripy*

Hunting techniques

Big cats generally hunt between sunset and dawn. They are ambush predators that move silently through dense undergrowth using their excellent vision and hearing to spot their prey before their prey spots them. Although they are all incredible sprinters, big cats lack stamina. A cheetah may exhaust itself so badly in a 60-second dash that it needs half an hour to recover and most cats will give up if they cannot run down their quarry in 30 seconds. Accordingly, they always attack from a position of advantage, leaping from cover or a tree branch, etc. Tigers will even launch attacks from the riverbank into the water and are strong enough swimmers to take on crocodiles.

Strangulation
The most common attack technique, used by all big cats, is to lunge at the neck and clamp down on the windpipe with powerful jaws. This cuts off the air supply and prey that is already out of breath from the chase quickly loses consciousness.

Asphyxiation
Another way to achieve the same result is to take a wide bite and clamp over the victim's mouth and nostrils, so it can't breathe. Lions and occasionally leopards will use this technique on antelope, but it isn't suitable for larger prey like zebra.

Neck breaking
The largest cats can leap on the back of an animal and bite right through its neck, severing the spine. This paralyses the victim instantly and ends the struggle, but it requires tremendous bite force. Lions, tigers and cougars all use this method.

Artery slicing
In the chaos of the final lunge, a cat may miss the windpipe of its prey and instead slice open the carotid artery. This is a slightly slower kill but it still gets the job done, as the victim will bleed to death.

The paw swipe
Lions and tigers are so strong that they can kill merely with a swipe of their paws. Tigers in particular have been witnessed swiping at adult domestic cattle with enough force to shatter the skull.

Skull piercing
The jaguar has the strongest bite of any cat – twice as powerful as the much larger lion. This may have evolved to enable them to bite through the shells of turtles, but jaguars also use it for a unique finishing move: their canine teeth can puncture an animal's skull and pierce the brain.

What's on the menu?

Hunting big game is an erratic profession. Cheetahs can generally manage a 50 per cent success rate but a tiger may only kill its prey one time in every 20 attempts. Consequently, they need to be able to make the most of each kill. Lions will eat 30 kilograms (66 pounds) of meat in one sitting, while jaguars can eat 25 kilograms (55 pounds) – a third of their body weight; that is the equivalent of you eating over a hundred Big Macs in one sitting! After a meal like that, lions, tigers, cougars and snow leopards can go for up to two weeks without eating again. Big cats are all quite opportunistic hunters. As well as their favoured prey of medium to large herd animals, they will eat monkeys, rodents, lizards, porcupines and birds' eggs. Many cats – especially the forest dwellers – will also eat insects and a small amount of fruit and vegetation.

How lions hunt

Lionesses work as a team to efficiently bring down large prey on the savannah and provide food for the entire pride

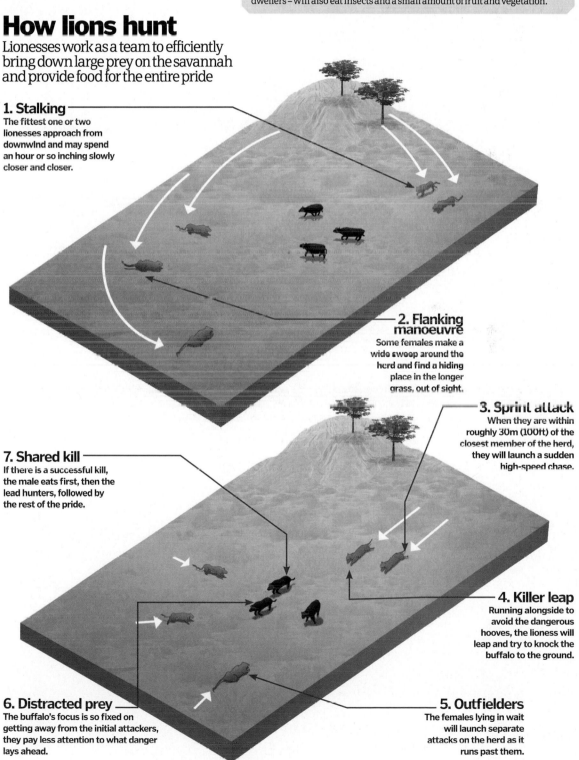

1. Stalking
The fittest one or two lionesses approach from downwind and may spend an hour or so inching slowly closer and closer.

2. Flanking manoeuvre
Some females make a wide sweep around the herd and find a hiding place in the longer grass, out of sight.

3. Sprint attack
When they are within roughly 30m (100ft) of the closest member of the herd, they will launch a sudden high-speed chase.

4. Killer leap
Running alongside to avoid the dangerous hooves, the lioness will leap and try to knock the buffalo to the ground.

5. Outfielders
The females lying in wait will launch separate attacks on the herd as it runs past them.

6. Distracted prey
The buffalo's focus is so fixed on getting away from the initial attackers, they pay less attention to what danger lays ahead.

7. Shared kill
If there is a successful kill, the male eats first, then the lead hunters, followed by the rest of the pride.

How jaguars survive

With the odds are stacked against you, how do you survive if your habitat is being wiped out?

The jaguar (Panthera onca) is the largest cat of the Americas and the third largest in the world after lions and tigers. While they can sometimes be mistaken for leopards due to their characteristic black-ringed markings, jaguars have a distinctive black spot at the centre of the rosette. Interestingly, although the base colour of most jaguar fur is pale or sandy, some jaguars are all brown or black (eg panthers), but their markings are always faintly evident. Sadly, these beautiful markings are one of the reasons these cats are persecuted by humans and poached for their pelts – as well as for their teeth, paws and several other parts.

All big cats have powerful muscles, which help them chase down prey, but are also handy for climbing trees where jaguars spend much of the day asleep. This apex predator tends to hunt and feed alone at night in the swamps, grasslands and forest of the Amazon, using stealth and ambush tactics to catch quarry.

As much of the jaguar's home has been eliminated to make way for cattle ranches and crops, these normally covert cats have been forced out into the open. Their natural prey – including peccaries and turtles – are also dwindling. As a result these cats have developed a new taste for the more abundant cattle. By venturing out of cover, the jaguars leave themselves exposed to ranchers who view these amazing animals as pests. Jaguars will also often have to cross vast distances in search of their next meal, which brings them near to other dangers like roads and traps.

To safeguard the future of this remarkable creature, a project has been set up to conserve the jaguars' safe passage from Argentina to Mexico. Called the Panthera Jaguar Corridor Initiative, it involves governments and conservation organisations as well as local communities making sure jaguars can travel from one wild region – through human-inhabited areas – to another. Activities include finding the safest and most beneficial corridor routes for the cats to take; educating local communities; and monitoring jaguar numbers as well as their prey populations. ✿

The statistics...

Jaguar

Binomial: Panthera onca

Type: Mammal

Diet: Carnivore (eg caimans, capybaras, turtles)

Life span in the wild: 12-15 years

Length: 2.2m (7.2ft)

Weight: 45-115kg (99-254lb)

Height: 0.7m (2.2ft)

There are thought to be some 2,000 jaguars living in the rainforests of Central America

What activity do jaguars like to do for fun?

A Go for a swim B Moonwalk C Hunt in packs

Answer:
Unlike most of the feline family, jaguars delight in playing and hunting in water. They are aquatic cats and appear to really enjoy stalking turtles and caimans in marshy ponds, using their paws to feel around for them in the murky water.

DID YOU KNOW? As well as spraying scent from a gland below the tail, jaguars also have scent glands in their cheeks

Along with tigers, jaguars are unusual in that they enjoy swimming – even if this one doesn't seem too happy!

Learn more

To find out more about Panthera's Jaguar Corridor Initiative, you can visit the organisations website at the address below; **www.panthera.org.**

©Thinkstock/Steve Winter, Panthera

149

Dogs

What is it that makes man's best friend tick?

Dogs evolved around 15,000 years ago in China and are descended from the Asian wolf. DNA studies have shown that 95 per cent of the dogs in the world are descended from the same three females. This is probably because those ancestral dogs showed a special trait that made them much more useful to humans. Dogs are better than any other animal at correctly recognising and interpreting human social cues; better even than our closest relative the chimpanzee, and far better than a wolf. This is true even with puppies as young as nine weeks, which shows this is an innate ability rather than something learned from close association.

Originally, dogs were kept exclusively for their hunting and defensive value but about 12,000 years ago, a mutation emerged that resulted in miniature dog breeds. Later, breeders began selecting for 'cute' features to create dogs that keep puppy characteristics into adulthood, such as floppy ears and rounder faces. At the same time, much of the pack instinct of many dog breeds was lost. Dogs became pets, rather than just weapons.

Dogs show more physical variation between breeds than any other domesticated animal. Genetically, the Tibetan Lhasa Apso and the Chinese Shih Tzu are closest to the ancestral dog but the earliest dogs would have been sight hounds, like the wolf. These are dogs that track their prey visually and rely on short bursts of speed to bring them down. They have long thin heads and long legs. Later, scent hounds emerged with shorter faces and short legs to keep their nose close to the ground. These dogs hunt game over much larger distances by following a scent trail and they use their superior endurance to exhaust an animal. ✿

Who could resist that puppy-dog look?

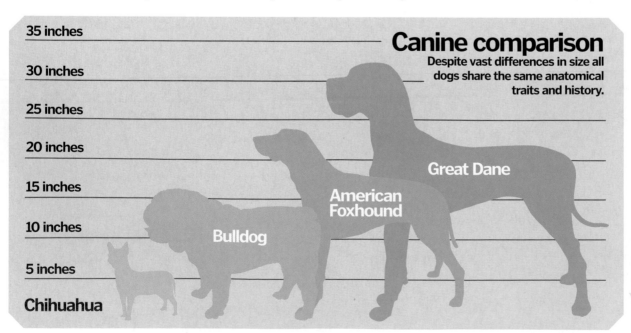

Canine comparison

Despite vast differences in size all dogs share the same anatomical traits and history.

35 inches

30 inches

25 inches

20 inches

15 inches

10 inches

5 inches

Great Dane

American Foxhound

Bulldog

Chihuahua

BIGGEST

1. Mastiff
While Irish wolfhounds may be taller, the Mastiff is the heaviest dog breed weighing as much as 155kg, or 24st 5lb. That's more than a fully grown man!

SMALLEST

2. Chihuahua
At just 15-23cm from nose to the tip of the tail, the Chihuahua is the smallest breed. It's because of their size that sadly they have become a popular Hollywood accessory.

LOUDEST

3. German Shepherd
Sentry breeds like the German Shepherd have very loud barks. The record is 108 decibels by a German Shepherd called Daz.

DID YOU KNOW? Chocolate, onions, grapes and macadamia nuts can all be poisonous for dogs to digest

Dogs can perform a number of tasks to aid humans

How do dogs smell?

Ever wondered why canine noses are so good at finding food? We sniff out the answer

Man's best friend is famous for its incredible sense of smell. In canines this consists of a nasal vestibule and olfactory epithelium. The former channels odour-rich particles to the latter, with the epithelium supporting millions of receptor cells that absorb the odour's chemical composition patterns and then transports them to the brain for interpretation. Indeed, an average dog's nose has so many olfactory receptors that its sense of smell is around 1,000 times more acute than ours so it really is no use trying to hide the biscuits. And why are dog noses wet? Well, they generally have damp snouts for two reasons. Firstly, a wet nose is better for smelling. The moisture comes from a layer of mucous that thinly covers the surface, trapping and soaking up scent particles. The dog can therefore naturally sniff in the smell as it radiates off the nose, or lick it to taste the odour. The second reason is that it is one of the few parts of the body where dogs can excrete sweat. ☼

Clever dog!

Just how bright are our four-legged friends?

The average domestic dog can exhibit social intelligence that's seldom found in the animal world, even in our closest relative the chimp. Dogs can learn, and therefore be trained, in a number of ways by reinforcement (punishment and reward) and by observation. For instance, puppies will learn behaviour more quickly if they follow the examples set by older dogs and will even learn from watching humans perform tasks.

Dogs can demonstrate a sophisticated social cognition by associating behavioural cues with an abstract meaning. In tests dogs have successfully located a treat hidden under one of two buckets from a wide range of signals including taps, nods and even looks. In fact they out-performed chimpanzees, wolves and human infants at the task.

3. Brain
Odour patterns detected by the olfactory epithelium are transported via a sub-series of cells and nerves to the nearby brain for processing.

1. Nasal vestibule
Odour particles sniffed into the nose are transported to the olfactory epithelium via the nasal vestibule.

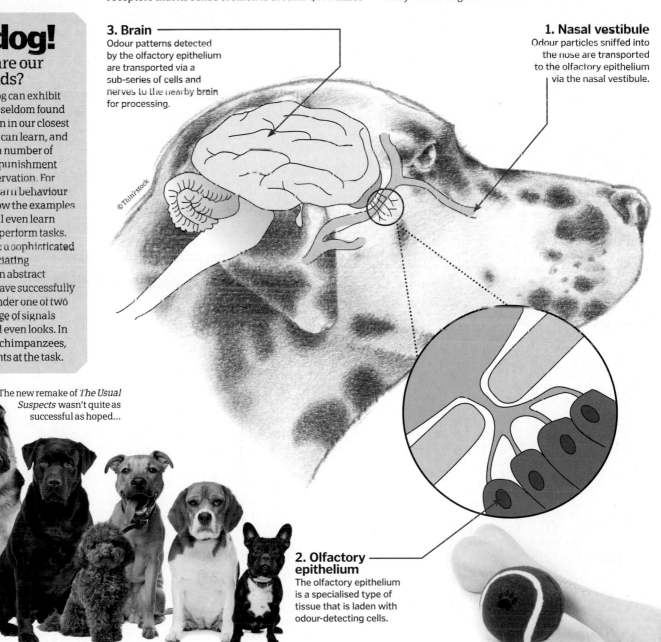

© Thinkstock

The new remake of *The Usual Suspects* wasn't quite as successful as hoped...

2. Olfactory epithelium
The olfactory epithelium is a specialised type of tissue that is laden with odour-detecting cells.

Wolves

They may be the ancestors of man's best friend but these social carnivores are totally equipped for life in the wild

Wolves evolved around 2 million years ago, at the end of the Pliocene epoch. There are 37 subspecies of canis lupus but that includes two that aren't actually wolves. That's because about 16,000 years ago wild wolves were domesticated by man and eventually became canis lupus familiaris, or the dog. In Australia, some dogs escaped to form a feral subspecies – the dingo.

The modern wolf isn't just an undomesticated dog, however. For thousands of years, domestication has acted to change the genetics of the wolf, as well as the dog. Early humans tamed the friendliest and most empathic members of the wild wolf population, so the ones that were left behind were the more suspicious and reclusive individuals. Later, when wolves were hunted because of the threat they posed to humans and

livestock, wolves were pushed to ever more remote and forbidding environments and they grew tougher as a result.

Wolf subspecies are divided into the Northern and Southern wolves. The Southern wolves live in the Middle East and South Asia and are lighter than their cousins, with smaller brains, weaker jaws and shorter fur. The Northern wolves, on the other hand, are adapted to survive in cold climates and live primarily in North America and northern Russia. The largest subspecies is the grey wolf (canis lupus lupus).

Most of the early studies of wolf social structure were based on captive animals and packs in national parks with artificially abundant food supplies. This led researchers to believe that wolves lived in large packs of 15-30 animals, with an alpha male in charge. The alpha male had priority

access to the breeding females and led the hunt. Younger males would either try and sneak food and mating opportunities without the alpha male noticing or would gradually work their way up the ranks until they were strong enough to challenge the alpha for the top job. We now know that wolves form much smaller packs in the wild, consisting of close family members and generally hunt in groups of just two to six. This is an adaptation to the harsh conditions in which they live because larger packs actually catch less food per individual than the smaller ones.

Wolves are opportunistic hunters and will eat a wide range of animals from mice and birds to hares and deer. But when they go after these small and medium-sized prey, they are competing with a lot of other predators, including eagles, lynx and wolverines. Where wolves excel is in hunting the

5 TOP FACTS
BORN SURVIVORS

Nothing wasted
1 Wolves will eat virtually every part of an animal but they start with the liver, heart and lungs. Then they move on to the muscles, followed by the skin and bone marrow.

Outrunner
2 Wolves can sustain speeds of 40km/h (25mph) for 20 minutes and sprint at up to 61km/h (38mph). One wolf is known to have chased a deer for 21 kilometres (13 miles).

Dry fur
3 Wolf fur does not collect condensation if you breathe on it. This trait means that in cold weather frost is prevented from forming around the muzzle.

Frost resistant
4 Arctic wolves can sleep outside quite comfortably in temperatures as low as -40°C (-40°F). They tuck their muzzles between their rear legs and wrap their tails over their faces.

Lifting power
5 An adult wolf is strong enough to roll a frozen horse or moose by itself. This enables it to get at the underside of the carcass, which may not be frozen solid yet.

DID YOU KNOW? A wolf's stomach can hold 9kg (20lbs) of food. That's the equivalent of 42 Big Macs!

Wolf anatomy

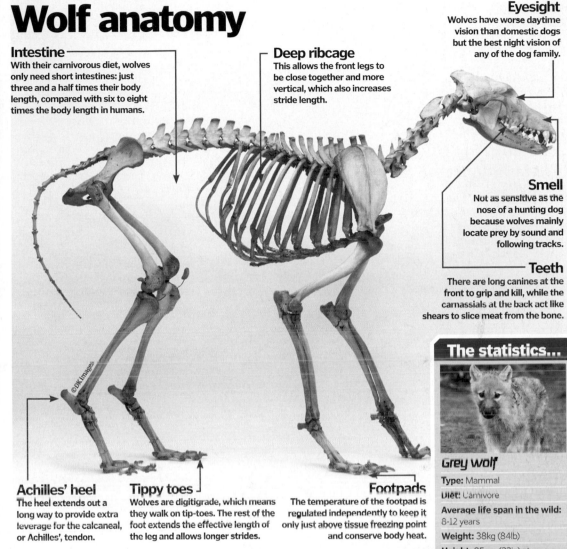

Intestine
With their carnivorous diet, wolves only need short intestines: just three and a half times their body length, compared with six to eight times the body length in humans.

Deep ribcage
This allows the front legs to be close together and more vertical, which also increases stride length.

Eyesight
Wolves have worse daytime vision than domestic dogs but the best night vision of any of the dog family.

Smell
Not as sensitive as the nose of a hunting dog because wolves mainly locate prey by sound and following tracks.

Teeth
There are long canines at the front to grip and kill, while the carnassials at the back act like shears to slice meat from the bone.

Achilles' heel
The heel extends out a long way to provide extra leverage for the calcaneal, or Achilles', tendon.

Tippy toes
Wolves are digitigrade, which means they walk on tip-toes. The rest of the foot extends the effective length of the leg and allows longer strides.

Footpads
The temperature of the footpad is regulated independently to keep it only just above tissue freezing point and conserve body heat.

© DK Images

The statistics...

Grey wolf
Type: Mammal
Diet: Carnivore
Average life span in the wild: 8-12 years
Weight: 38kg (84lb)
Height: 85cm (33in) at the shoulder

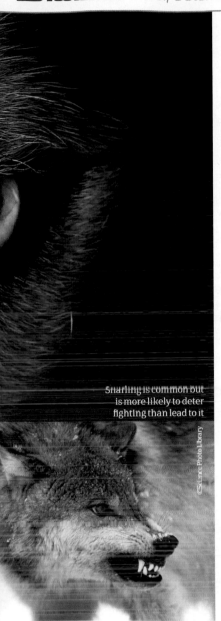

Snarling is common but is more likely to deter fighting than lead to it

©Science Photo Library

huge elk, bison and caribou. These animals may weigh 10 or 15 times as much as an individual wolf and have horns and a powerful kick to defend themselves. Hunting this kind of quarry is all about escaping injury. The elk is fighting for its life and can afford to put everything it has into the struggle; the wolf, however, is only fighting for its dinner so must be more careful. One well-aimed kick may injure him badly enough that he can't hunt and will starve to death before his wounds heal.

A pack can travel 19-80 kilometres (12-50 miles) in a day, looking for a herd. When they find one, they don't waste time stalking. Instead they will trot straight up and weave in and out among the herd, trying to spook it into running. A herd of elk or caribou is almost impregnable if it stands its ground but once it starts running, the

wolves can run alongside and weigh up which are the weakest individuals. Wolves have no problem keeping up and can bound through deep snow more easily than narrow-hoofed deer. When they pounce, they will strike for the soft tissue of the perineum; their teeth can leave a 15-centimetre (5.9-inch) wound that results in massive blood loss. Three bites can be enough to bring down a healthy adult elk. Another tactic is to jump for the nose – also a soft area that bleeds profusely.

Despite all this, only about one attack in ten results in a kill. And when they are successful, the wolves still have to defend the carcass from various other predators such as bears, coyotes, wolverines and other wolves. Large grizzly bears will often follow wolf packs and wait for them to make a kill, before stealing it. In Siberia, wolves are also directly preyed upon by tigers. Wolves used to be common throughout most of the United States, Europe and Asia but were extirpated from all

Life in a pack is centred around dominance and submission

heavily populated areas by the early 20th century. Southern wolves exist only as isolated, endangered populations but the grey wolf is still common in Canada, Alaska and Russia. ⚙

> "Once a herd starts running, the wolves can run alongside and weigh up which are the weakest individuals"

Hungry like the wolf

It's a misconception to think of wolves as pack hunters. While a few large packs of 30 or more individuals have been seen, most are small family groups. Wolves are capable of taking moose and deer on their own or in pairs. A typical wolf pack is a single breeding pair with this year's pups and the youngsters from last year's litter – between 5 and 11 animals all together.

By the age of two, most wolves will move away to start their own pack. This normally isn't long enough to learn complicated cooperative hunting techniques, although some packs will try and drive prey towards an ambush. Generally though, when hunting large prey, wolves will split one animal from the herd and then run it down and attack from behind. The breeding pair will monopolise the kill, before allowing the others to feed.

Scent marking
Urine and faeces are both used to mark a territory. Markers are placed every 240m (787ft) and renewed after two or three weeks.

Raised hackles
An aggressive wolf holds his body high and raises the long hairs on his shoulders to make his body appear larger.

Howling
Wolves howl to call the pack together or locate each other during storms and as a rallying cry when chasing prey.

Holding the pack together

©DK Images

Flattened ears
Another dominant gesture, used at kill sites to signal ownership of the carcass.

Boundary disputes
Up to 65 per cent of wolf fatalities are caused by other wolves, at the border between two territories.

Active submission
Used as a form of greeting. The submissive wolf approaches and licks the face of the dominant wolf.

Tail angle
A tail held out straight, or with the base high and a drooping tip, is an aggressive gesture. Hanging low between the legs is submissive.

Passive submission
To show submission a wolf rolls onto its back and allows the other wolf to sniff.

50-60k
Canada & Alaska (Grey wolf)

100
North Carolina (Red wolf)
100 reintroduced from a captive breeding programme.

45k
Russia (Grey wolf)

300
Yellowstone National Park, Wyoming (Grey wolf)

500
Wisconsin (Grey wolf)

1,000
Turkey (Indian wolf)

1,000
India (Indian wolf)

150
Israel (Indian wolf)

500
Ethiopia (Ethiopian wolf)

300-600
Saudi Arabia (Indian wolf)

Where to find wild wolves
Tracking the whereabouts and populations of wolves around the world

HEAD 2 HEAD
OTHER SUBSPECIES

SMALL

1. Arabian wolf
A variety of wolf that has adapted to life in the desert, it grows to about 66cm (26in) tall. It has short hair in the summer and a longer coat in winter.

BIG

2. Dingo
A little shorter than the Arabian wolf, but more powerfully built. Originally descended from domesticated dogs that escaped into the wild.

BIGGER

3. Domestic dog
Some dog breeds are tiny, but the Irish wolfhound and deerhound are bigger than most subspecies of wolf. Only the grey and tundra wolves are larger.

DID YOU KNOW? *A wolf has a bite that exerts 10MPa pressure (1,500psi) – twice as much as a German shepherd dog*

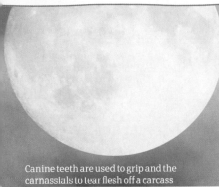

Canine teeth are used to grip and the carnassials to tear flesh off a carcass

Do wolves really howl at the moon?

No, they don't, they howl at each other. Howling is a long-range signal that allows wolves to reconnect with the pack if they become separated and to warn off rival packs. Howls have a low fundamental frequency of 150-750Hz because low frequencies carry much further, but they also layer this with up to 12 harmonic overtones to exaggerate the number of wolves in a pack. A lone wolf will not risk advertising his presence near the boundary of his territory, but a small group can keep rivals at bay by bluffing that they are more numerous.

As well as howling, wolves will bark as an alarm call, growl and snarl when staking ownership of a kill, and whine when playing or investigating one another.

How does a howl travel so far?

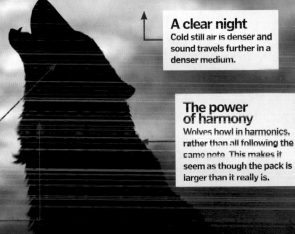

A clear night
Cold still air is denser and sound travels further in a denser medium.

Head back
The howl is projected into the air to reduce the amount of scattering from ground clutter.

The power of harmony
Wolves howl in harmonics, rather than all following the same note. This makes it seem as though the pack is larger than it really is.

Long throat
Low frequencies travel further than high ones. Straightening the throat increases the size of the resonating chamber and produces lower notes.

A wolf's coat comprises two layers: a thick furry undercoat covered by a layer of longer guard hairs

Maya is one member of the Northern Lights Wildlife Wolf Centre pack

INTERVIEW
Shelley Black

Along with her husband, Casey, Shelley has run the Northern Lights Wildlife Wolf Centre in Golden, British Columbia, for ten years. Their aim is to debunk the myths surrounding the wolf and show the critical role that these predators play within an ecosystem

What are the major threats that the wolf faces in the world today?
In Canada it's still legal for a wolf to be hunted, baited and trapped in most areas all year round; these animals are treated like vermin. Beyond the threat of hunting, they're also losing their habitat and food sources to humans [with the expansion of towns and new roads being built, and so on]. In the central Rocky Mountains, in the Banff National Park area, the number one cause of wolf mortality is humans; only five per cent die of natural causes.

How are groups like yours promoting the conservation of the wolf?
We are promoting wolf conservation by speaking to the public, from all around the world, and insisting that we have to stop eradicating wolves from the forest. We're also going into schools to promote this message. By giving hands-on experiences with wolves I think it gives the public a much better understanding of how misrepresented they are. One of the major points we try and get across is how the wolf is a 'keystone species' [one that plays a vital role in maintaining the structure of an ecosystem], as well as a bio-indicator species.

Tell us one characteristic that makes the wolf such a remarkable species.
There are far more than one! They are extremely social and intelligent animals; I'd say one of the few species that can outsmart humans. Their endurance and ability to stay alive never ceases to amaze me.

Generally, what do you find is the public perception of wolves when they first arrive at the Northern Lights Centre?
Most people think they are scary, or they are generally unsure. When they come to the Centre, we inform them that there has never been a proven vicious attack by a healthy non-habituated wolf on a human in the wild. After meeting the wolves themselves, by the time they leave, visitors take away a whole new perspective – which is why we're here.

For more info, see: **www.northernlightswildlife.com**

155

Anatomy of the pig

Often maligned in popular culture and language, hogs are much smarter and cleaner than you might at first think...

Piggy physiology

What is special about the anatomical make up of the pig?

Tail
A pig's short tail can comprise over 20 caudal vertebrae, which is around the same number found in a cow's tail.

Intestines
The cecum and colon that make up the large intestine in pigs are arranged in spiral coils.

Leg
Strong legs allow piglets to stand soon after birth. As adults they use that strength to dig for food.

It seems unfair that the English language has amassed so many derogatory sayings about pigs, because under the skin they're a lot like us. Indeed, the hearts of some breeds are similar enough in weight, internal structure and the rate at which blood is pumped through to have potential for human heart transplants. Pigs are also impressive learners. In a study published in 2009 scientists showed a reflection of food to pigs who had previously seen mirrors and compared their responses with a group that hadn't. The former were much less likely to think the food was actually behind the glass.

Pigs and other members of the Suidae family, which includes wild boars and warthogs, have a strong skeleton that allows them to be sturdy defenders of their territories and offspring. They also have a very good sense of smell that compensates for poor eyesight. A hog's snout, together with its even-toed trotters and short,

muscular limbs, is perfectly adapted for sniffing out and uncovering food buried in the soil of the forests and grasslands in which the species evolved.

Wild pigs will consume grubs, amphibians and small birds as well as forage for roots, leaves, nuts, fruit and fungi. To chew on this omnivorous diet they have canine, incisor and molar teeth, just as we do. The pig's digestive system, meanwhile, features anatomical differences from ours (a spiral colon, for example), but works the same way: food is broken down in a one-chambered stomach and intestines and then passes through to the colon for excretion.

Contrary to the myth, pigs keep bodily waste away from food and don't in fact wallow in it. They do like a mud bath because they don't perspire. Wet mud keeps them cool as heat is given off by evaporation – a technique that is also commonly used by elephants. 'Sweating like a pig' then is one saying that definitely does pigs a disservice. ✿

£64/kg

WORLD'S MOST EXPENSIVE HAM

Jamón ibérico de bellota is arguably one of the tastiest meats on Earth, but it comes at a premium. Cut from free-range, acorn-fed Spanish pigs, it is cured for two years or more before it's sold.

DID YOU KNOW? Extinct entelodonts might be nicknamed 'hell pigs' but are only distantly related to modern porkers

Spine
Projections on the strong lumbar vertebrae broaden the abdomen and are attached to muscles that support the internal organs.

Skin
Although the structure of a pig's skin is similar to our own, they have very few sweat glands. To cool down they bathe in mud; this also serves as a kind of sunscreen.

Pork's unwanted passengers

Pigs can be infected by common roundworms in the genus Trichinella. Transmission to humans can occur through eating meat that isn't cooked at a high enough temperature to kill the larvae. Ingestion results in trichinosis, with symptoms including dizziness and stomach ache. Among pig parasites, though, pork tapeworm (Taenia solium) is more concerning.

The larvae of this tapeworm also enter the human body through undercooked meat. Once the tapeworms are inside, they migrate to the tissues, causing cysticercosis. The symptoms can be minor if they infect only muscles, but can include loss of vision or weakness if larvae reach the eyes or the spine. The infection can be more serious still if worms reach the brain and form cysts, causing neurocysticercosis; in these cases, victims can fall into a coma or even die suddenly.

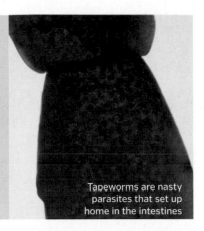
Tapeworms are nasty parasites that set up home in the intestines

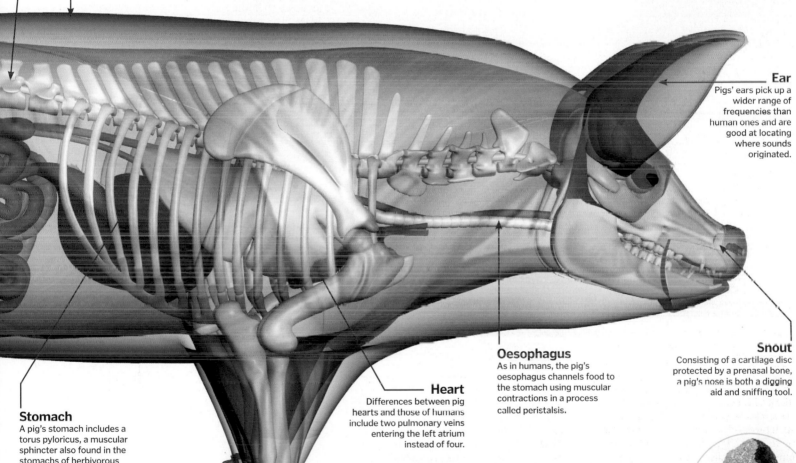

Ear
Pigs' ears pick up a wider range of frequencies than human ones and are good at locating where sounds originated.

Snout
Consisting of a cartilage disc protected by a prenasal bone, a pig's nose is both a digging aid and sniffing tool.

Oesophagus
As in humans, the pig's oesophagus channels food to the stomach using muscular contractions in a process called peristalsis.

Heart
Differences between pig hearts and those of humans include two pulmonary veins entering the left atrium instead of four.

Stomach
A pig's stomach includes a torus pyloricus, a muscular sphincter also found in the stomachs of herbivorous ruminants such as cattle.

Trotter
Pigs are even-toed ungulates, which means their weight is carried on the third and fourth toes of their cloven hooves.

Truth about truffles

Sows have long been associated with truffle hunting. Yet it isn't clear what makes them good at rooting out the subterranean fruiting bodies of these fungi. Truffles have a distinctive smell, but pigs must be attracted by more than just appreciation of the aroma.

For many years the prospect of sex was thought to tempt them. That's because some truffle species produce androstenol, a pheromone-like hormone found in the testes of boars (as well as humans). That theory, however, was undermined by French chemist Thierry Talou. He buried samples of androstenol, fresh truffles and a synthetic cocktail of aroma-causing chemicals and let some sows loose. Surprisingly, the pigs skipped the androstenol and went for the other two options. Whatever it is that attracts sows, though, is too strong for them to resist so it is difficult to stop them from easting them once they've found them. Many truffle-hunters have replaced pigs with trained dogs that don't eagerly gobble up the fungal delicacies they find.

©Alamy;Thinkstock

What's inside horse hooves?

Discover the structure of a horse's feet and why fitting horseshoes doesn't cause pain

Horse hooves are the thick horny coverings that protect the end of the horse's leg and also provide shock absorbency. Horse hooves are made of a tough protein called keratin – the same stuff our nails and hair are made of. The keratin in a horse's hoof is layered in horizontal sheets, in order to add strength and minimise the extent of any damage that could split the hoof irreparably in the event of a crack.

Horses are digitigrade – ie they walk on their tiptoes – and therefore require a spongy pad beneath the heel on which to walk. While the outer wall of the hoof

is insensitive – much like human hair and fingernails – the inner parts can feel pain. Therefore, when a farrier fits a horseshoe to the hoof, they do so by hammering the nails into only the outer wall of the hoof. Horseshoes, which are often made of steel these days, offer added shock absorbency as well as traction on the ground. These curved metal bands come with between six and eight square nail holes through which the metal pins can be slotted. One by one, the nails are hammered into the hard, nerve-free outer wall of the hoof, securely fastening the shoe to the creature's hoof. ✿

Food that is regurgitated and chewed again is known as the cud.

How does a cow's stomach work?

A complex system of sacs and guts, cows' stomachs allow seemingly indigestible foods to be broken down

A cow's stomach is a compartmental digestive system that allows normally indigestible products (grasses, for example) to be broken down repeatedly in a process of ingestion, regurgitation, rechewing and reingestion. Through this process cows can decompose the ingested product's carbohydrates, cellulose and volatile fatty acids and use them as fuel. Decomposition and breakdown is achieved by a series of bacteria and protozoa living, multiplying and dying inside the stomach's compartments. These microbes digest fibre found in pasture, hay and silage, generate proteins from nitrogen and synthesise amino acids from non-protein sources such as urea and ammonia. The microbes grant the cow additional energy, as when they die they continue to pass through the digestive compartments, breaking down and releasing protein. ✿

Horse hoof anatomy

Cannon bone
The cannon, or shin, bone is a weight-bearing structure. The front limbs in particular support around 60 per cent of a horse's total weight.

Skin
Above the coronet is regular skin featuring blood vessels and nerves.

Long pastern bone (proximal phalanx)
The joint between the cannon and the long pastern bone is the fetlock, which is a kind of ankle joint. The joint between the long and short pastern bones offers articulation and shock absorbency.

Short pastern bone (middle phalanx)
The pastern joint connects the sloping long and short pastern bones. Strong ligaments link all these bones and joints together.

Digital cushion
This structure – also known as the plantar cushion – is integral to absorbing shocks, by the transfer of blood through the venous plexuses.

Navicular bone
This bone prevents over-articulation of the coffin bone joint.

Frog
This wedge of springy tissue is the first part of the hoof to hit the ground when the horse takes a step.

Coronet
The coronet marks where the hoof meets the leg. The wall of the hoof grows out of this small bulge.

Hoof wall (crust)
This is the insensitive outer casing of the hoof, which never stops growing. The front-facing walls of the fore-hooves are slightly thicker than the rest.

Coffin bone (distal phalanx)
This is the large bone inside the hoof. Many tendons and ligaments are attached to this and a network of blood vessels run through it.

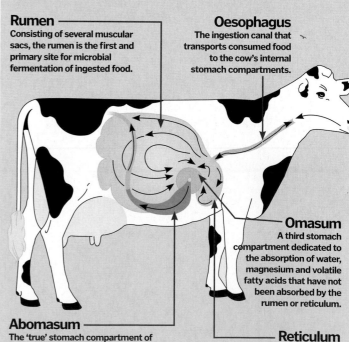

Rumen
Consisting of several muscular sacs, the rumen is the first and primary site for microbial fermentation of ingested food.

Oesophagus
The ingestion canal that transports consumed food to the cow's internal stomach compartments.

Omasum
A third stomach compartment dedicated to the absorption of water, magnesium and volatile fatty acids that have not been absorbed by the rumen or reticulum.

Abomasum
The 'true' stomach compartment of the cow, the abomasum functions similar to that of humans', with secreted enzymes and hydrochloric acid breaking down proteins.

Reticulum
The second main site for microbial fermentation, this makes up the smaller partner of the rumen.

How do vampire bats survive?

Discover how these flying mammals get by on a diet consisting solely of blood

In the realm of books and movies, vampires are big business, but the natural world can boast the real thing. Found across the tropical forests of South America through to Mexico, much like its fictional counterpart, the vampire bat sleeps during the day – usually in dark caves – and only ventures out at night to feed.

Their most common unwitting 'donors' are large herbivores like horses and cows, though human attacks are not unheard of. Most of the time, victims will rarely notice as the bats only consume about a tablespoon of blood per sitting; this said, they are often accused of spreading rabies. Contrary to popular belief, they don't actually 'suck' the blood either, but rather nip the skin with their sharp teeth and then lap at the blood that flows out.

Like all bats they use echolocation to get around, but they have also evolved some unique ways to hunt. For one thing they have special thermoreceptors on their noses, which – via infrared radiation – enable them to pinpoint where blood flows closest to the prey's skin, while an anticoagulant in their saliva stops blood clotting before they've had their fill. Vampires are also unusual within the bat family for their ability to walk, climb and even hop along the ground – ideal for stealthily approaching slumbering victims. ✹

Vampire bats live in dark caves typically in colonies of around 100

Bats' ultrasonic sonar system

We reveal how Chiroptera's supersonic hearing happens

Contrary to belief, bats (Chiroptera) do demonstrate an acute sense of vision during daylight hours. When night falls, these small mammals are more inclined to use their heightened sense of hearing when hunting prey and manoeuvring around habitats, never being at a disadvantage. This is complemented by their incredible biological sonar navigation system.

But how does this work? Well, bats are inclined to emit ultrasonic sounds, with a frequency of between 50,000 and 200,000 vibrations per second, too high-pitched for human ears to comprehend.

These sound are emitted 20 to 30 times each second with the bat listening between pulses, scanning for echoes with its head in perpetual motion. Bats separately perceive and process overlapping echo delays, arriving as little as two microseconds apart, that's an impressive two thousandths of a second. The bat's own nervous system supports this fined-tuned capability, allowing them to identify echo-reflecting points on an object the width of a pen line on paper, or objects as close together as three-tenths of a millimetre. ✹

Emitting sound
Bats emit ultrasonic sounds 20 to 30 times each second, listening between pulses for echoes.

Timing and direction
The bat then registers distance and location of prey through the timing and direction of returning sound waves.

Translating echo
The time between sending out a cry and then receiving a response is translated by the bat into distance, between itself and whatever object is in the vicinity.

Moving prey
The bat realises moving prey through delayed sound and a slightly lower or higher pitch, due to the Doppler effect.

Sourcing insects
Echoes from prey such as mosquitoes, moths and butterflies reveal fluctuations, which are caused by the flutter of their wings, easily recognised by the bat.

Stationary prey
Stationary objects are instantly recognisable, as these yield an echo that is a replica of the pulse sent out by the bat.

The statistics...

Giant anteater

Genus:
Myrmecophaga tridactyla

Class: Mammal

Length: 2m (7ft)

Tongue length: 0.6m (2ft)

Diet: Carnivore

Weight: 20-50kg (44-110lb)

Life span: 14 years (wild),
26 years (captivity)

Status: Threatened due to
habitat destruction

Fur
The anteater's fur is long, coarse and dense to help protect it from biting insects.

Eyes
Anteaters are practically blind so they make up for this with their extra-sensitive sense of smell.

Tail
The giant anteater's massive bushy tail is almost as long as its body. The tail is useful for balance if the anteater rears up to attack with its front paws. Also they sleep on the ground and use their tail to keep warm and remain hidden.

Claws
Anteater forearms are very powerful with five deadly claws on each paw, the inner three of which on the front feet are especially long and sharp. This helps them penetrate the walls of termite fortresses.

Giant anteaters

They have no teeth, walk on their knuckles and take life at their own pace, so how do they survive?

An anteater's sense of smell is so acute it can detect the species of ant or termite before breaking into a nest

As is to be expected, the giant anteater, native to the savannas of Central and South America, is the largest of its kind. This bizarre-looking mammal is designed specifically for feeding on ants and termites, and a number of anatomical features enable them to do this with great skill. Powerful forearms and long, sharp claws help the anteater to tear into anthills and termite mounds so they can insert their long, tapered snouts to get at the insects. They are always careful not to destroy the nest so as to preserve the feeding spot for another meal.

While the claws are mainly used for breaking into anthills, they can also perform a defensive role. When attacked by their main predators, which include large cats like jaguars, anteaters have been known to lash out and kill these hunters. While giant anteaters are slow, terrestrial creatures that walk around on their knuckles to protect the claws, smaller species of anteater are arboreal and spend a lot of time in trees looking for insects.

The giant anteater is a solitary creature and, aside from mothers and babies, they are rarely found in pairs or groups. Anteaters usually give birth to a single cub, who will then ride around on the mother's back for up to a year, clinging on to the thick, coarse fur. Because they live on a diet of ants, which have relatively limited nutritional value, the giant anteater does what it can to conserve energy: it has a very low metabolic rate and will sleep for up to 15 hours every day. They move around the grasslands very slowly – they cannot run – and keep their body temperature low, sometimes as cool as 32.7 degrees Celsius (90.9 degrees Fahrenheit). ⚙

1. SUPER-SLOW

Sloth
This nocturnal rainforest dweller hangs in trees by its large, powerful claws, eating vegetation. They move very slowly, and can spend a year in one tree.

2. ARMOURED

Armadillo
Another insectivore, the armadillo has hard, leathery plates on its back, head and sides. It also has the ability to hold its breath for several minutes when digging.

3. EDENTATE

Anteater
Anteaters, sloths and armadillos are all members of the xenarthra superorder. In the past, they were grouped as the edentata – meaning toothless – but only the anteater is actually toothless.

DID YOU KNOW? *Surrealist artist Salvador Dalí had a pet anteater which he used to take for walks*

Anteater anatomy

Tongue
Inside the snout is that incredibly long, ant-slurping tongue. It's covered in sticky saliva and tiny back-facing spines (filiform papillae) to help snag lots of bugs.

Snout
While anteaters only have small mouths, the elongated snout can reach lengths of 45cm (18in). Because it's hollow, the snout is the ideal shape for sucking insects into the mouth. The tip of the snout is very sensitive, helping it probe inside tiny passageways.

Eating ants

Although they have poor eyesight, anteaters have a very keen sense of smell for sniffing out insects, which include ants – of course – termites, grubs and other small insects.

Once an anthill is located the animal uses its strong claws to rip into the prey's lair, making room to insert its long snout. Because some ants can sting and bite, mealtime is a fast and furious affair and the anteater has adapted techniques for licking up ants as quickly as possible. Each feast lasts about a minute before the anteater moves on to the next location.

Inside the anteater's long snout is an even longer tongue, which can protrude up to 60cm (24in). The tongue is covered with sticky saliva produced by extra-large glands and thousands of tiny back-facing spines known as filiform papillae to ensnare the bugs. When the snout enters an anthill the tongue rapidly flicks back and forth up to 150 times per minute, searching for ants. Because it doesn't have teeth, the anteater then crushes the insects against the roof of its mouth with its powerful tongue before swallowing.

Every day an anteater can consume between 30,000 and 35,000 ants, which is necessary for them to obtain enough nutrients. While ants may contain relatively high levels of protein and low levels of fat, their nutritional value for the giant anteater is low, so in order to conserve energy they move slowly and maintain a cool body temperature.

Meet the family

While the giant anteater is terrestrial, other types are known to venture into the treetops

SILKY ANTEATER
Also known as pygmy, dwarf or two-toed anteaters, silky anteaters are the smallest and most shy species in the family. They are arboreal, which means they spend most of their time up in the trees – in fact, they're rarely ever seen on the ground. To help them get around in the treetops they have strong prehensile tails that can grip on to things; they use them to swing from branch to branch and even from tree to tree. They have much shorter snouts than the other species and soft golden fur.

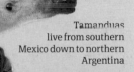

Giant anteaters can sleep for up to 15 hours a day

Tamanduas live from southern Mexico down to northern Argentina

TAMANDUA
Tamanduas are sometimes known by other names, such as collared or lesser anteaters. This species is semi-arboreal, which means they spend time up in the trees but also come down for a look around on the ground now and then. Again, when in the trees a prehensile tail comes in very handy. There are northern and southern tamanduas; the former variety is distinguishable not only by its more northerly location, but also because of the distinctive black V-shaped marking that's located on its back.

Giant pandas explained

The carnivore that thinks it's vegetarian

There he sits, the giant panda. Solitary, peaceful, resting upright on his furry haunches like a black-and-white Buddha. A born carnivore, this perplexing member of the bear family passes on the meat course almost entirely, choosing instead to persist with nature's version of a celery diet: bamboo.

A highly endangered animal (less than 2,500 exist in the wild) the panda's monotonous, nearly monovorous, diet is part of its undoing. The nutritional value of bamboo is negligible, exacerbated by the fact that the panda is genetically incapable of digesting cellulose. The result is that much of the panda's extremely high-fibre diet passes right through it, providing only minimal calories to an animal that can grow up to 136kg (300lbs) in the wild.

So there the giant panda sits, for up to 16 hours every day, tearing and grinding away at piles of this nearly indigestible plant simply to eke out enough caloric energy to wake up the next day and do it all again. That peaceful, almost Zen-like demeanour has less to do with temperament than low blood sugar. The poor panda can hardly muster the energy to mate, and when he does successfully reproduce, the female will only raise one young at a time, even though the majority of births are twins. Such a slow reproductive rate makes the giant panda population highly susceptible to outside pressures, of which there are many.

Habitat loss is the panda's greatest threat followed by poaching. Because of their singular devotion to bamboo, pandas must live where the plant is abundant. Today, the only suitable habitat is limited to 20 isolated sections of mountain forest in south-west China, all of which have thankfully been protected by the Chinese government with help from conservationist organisations like the World Wildlife Fund. ✿

A newborn panda is practically hairless

Calories from food

The amount of energy an animal obtains from food is measured in calories. The following information reveals how many calories a panda must consume per day compared with other creatures.

ANIMAL	CALORIES CONSUMED PER DAY
Elephant	40,000
Giant panda	20,000
Adult humans	2,300-2,600
Mouse	20

Giant panda anatomy

Fur
Pandas have two types of fur: long bristly hairs and a thick wool-like undercoat. The reason for their black-and-white colouring is unknown.

Teeth
A set of knife-like front teeth rip the bamboo, then the panda uses its jaw to grind down the plant with four flat molars.

Paws
A pseudo-thumb, an elongated wrist bone covered with a thick pad of skin, is used for grasping bamboo stalks.

Front legs
The panda relies on its strong, flexible front legs to pull out bamboo shoots, break them into usable pieces and to even climb trees.

Hind legs
The panda's hind legs are spread widely apart, helping it to sit comfortably for hours on end, but making it difficult to run.

Skin
The skin under a panda's black fur is grey and the skin under its white fur is pink. Newborn pandas are entirely pink and nearly hairless.

Stomach
With the stomach of a carnivore, pandas rely on microbes to help break down the abundant cellulose in bamboo. A thick layer of mucus protects against splinters.

RARE

1. Polar bears
As the polar ice caps shrink, so too do the hunting grounds of this magnificent animal, which could be extinct in the wild within the century.

RARER

2. Mountain gorilla
The WWF estimates that only 720 of these majestic gorillas remain in fragile habitats threatened by ongoing African wars.

RAREST

3. White-headed langur
Confined to Cat Ba Island off the coast of Vietnam, only 59 exist in the wild due to habitat distruction and illegal hunting for 'monkey balm'.

© Doniv79

DID YOU KNOW? A giant panda cub weighs 142g (5oz) at birth, approximately 1/900th the size of its mother

The statistics...

© Thinkstock

Giant panda

Species: Ailuropoda melanoleuca

Type: Mammal

Diet: Omnivore

Average life span in the wild: 20 years

Weight: Up to 136kg (300lbs)

Size: Up to 2m (6ft) head to tail and 1m (3ft) at the shoulders

Without opposable thumbs, the panda had to adapt to grip bamboo

© Thinkstock

The grip of a panda...

Thumb
An evolved bone pseudo-thumb helps dexterity and grip strength.

Fingers
Five strong, bulbous fingers help strip bamboo for consumption.

Pads
Toughened skinned pads have developed to increase grip friction.

ON THE MAP

Where the wild pandas are...

1 Minshan mountains: 45% of the wild panda population live in these biodiverse Chinese mountain forests.

2 Qinling mountains: 200-300 pandas live on the cool, wet southern slopes of this Chinese range.

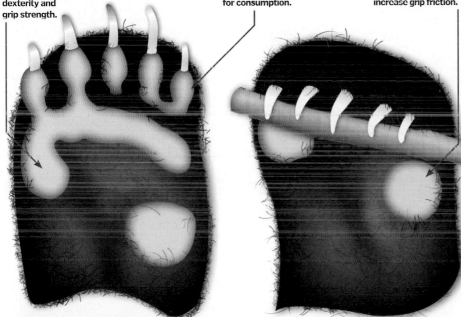

© Thinkstock

Adapting to bamboo

It's the diet they were designed for, so why do pandas shun meat?

Although giant pandas are technically carnivores, they have adapted to eating a diet of 99% bamboo, which they can barely digest. Pandas are genetically unable to turn cellulose into energy, so they must eat up to 38kg (84lbs) of the fibrous plant every day to get enough calories to survive. The task requires 12-16 hours of foraging and eating.

The panda's gut has developed a thick layer of mucus to protect against bamboo splinters. So, aside from the rare rodent or bird, why don't pandas eat meat? Clues in the recently sequenced panda genome point to a genetic mutation that may render them unable to taste flesh. Fossil studies show that the giant panda's ancestors swapped meat for bamboo somewhere between 2 and 7 million years ago – perhaps due to a major environmental event wiping out their prey. Being forced to change their diet may have caused the gene responsible for tasting savoury foods to become obsolete, and without it they might not have wanted to eat the tasteless meat even when it became plentiful.

A 'carnivorous' panda will opt for bamboo over meat, every time

© Thinkstock

The life of elephants

Elephants are big in every sense of the word, but also surprisingly sensitive. Here we unpack some of the myths and explain what makes them so special

Elephants are the largest land animals in the world, with African males averaging five tons. They have evolved to this huge size to protect themselves from predators but almost everything that makes an elephant unique is a consequence of this bulk. Large mammals don't have enough skin surface area to shed excess body heat so elephants have large flapping ears to act as radiators. A heavy head precludes a long neck so elephants have evolved a trunk, both to stretch up into branches and to be able to reach down to the ground to drink.

Most mammals stand with their leg joints half bent, which makes it easier to accelerate from a standstill. Elephants can only support their body weight by keeping the bones all in a line, like a pillar. Humans are the only other animal that does this. Elephants do not have fused ankle joints, as some people think, but it is true that they do not jump. The impact stresses would risk serious injury if they tried. This is the same reason that elephants don't gallop. Instead, they have a curious half-jogging gait where the front legs run and the hind legs walk fast.

Elephants used to be classified as pachyderms and lumped with the rhino and hippopotamus. Scientists now place them in their own order, the proboscidea, along with the extinct mammoths. There are three species of elephant living today: the African Bush elephant, African Forest elephant and the Asian elephant. All elephant species are protected but poaching is a very serious problem and current population numbers are unknown.

No stick in the mud
1 Elephant feet spread out underneath their weight but shrink again when lifted. This lets elephants break the suction when they are walking through deep mud.

Bendy knees
2 Elephants are the only animal to have four forward-facing knees. All other four-legged animals have at least one pair of legs with knees that face backwards.

Thirsty work
3 Hanging around the savannah is thirsty work and the average elephant drinks more than 200 litres of water per day. That's around two very deep bathfulls!

The daily grind
4 Elephants replace their teeth six times in their life, with new teeth moving forward from the back of the mouth. When the last set wears down, the elephant dies of starvation.

Don't try to outrun one
5 They may not look fast and although elephants take a long time to accelerate during a charge they can, in fact, reach 40km/h (25mph). Quite a speed for its size!

DID YOU KNOW? *Elephants are either right- or left-tusked. The 'master tusk' wears down quicker from extra use*

Cool it! An elephant's ears are used for cooling and communication

Anatomy of an elephant
The physical attributes of the world's largest mammal

Brain
At 5kg, their brain is the largest of any land animal. Like humans and dolphins, elephant brains have a highly convoluted neocortex, thought to be a sign of complex intelligence.

Ears
The large flapping ears are used for cooling and signalling. African elephants have ears up to three times larger than those of the Asian elephants.

Stomach
Elephants have an inefficient metabolism that doesn't properly digest cellulose. Consequently they have to eat 100-200kg of plant matter every day.

Hair
Although they look smooth-skinned, elephants actually have sparse hair all over their body, particularly on the head and back. Hair on the tail can be 1m long.

Eyes
Elephants don't see well at distances of more than 20 metres. There are no ducts to drain tears away either – they simply run down the cheeks.

Skin
Elephant skin is 2.5cm thick on the back legs and trunk, but it's surprisingly delicate and elephants frequently coat themselves in mud to escape the sun.

Tusks
Although they are useful for digging in the ground, stripping bark from trees and fighting, the ivory in the tusks is also the main reason that elephants are endangered.

© DK Images

Legs
The leg bones are very thick and a wide foot spreads the load. Even so the pressure under an elephant's foot is 3.5 times greater than a human's.

Tail
Elephants can produce 75kg of dung per day so an efficient swat to keep the flies away is essential. The tail looks small but it's over 1m long.

Trunk
Composed of 100,000 muscle units, arranged into six main groups. The trunk is a hand, nose, bucket and weapon all rolled into one.

Ears looking at you, kid

African elephants have enormous ears – 1.5 metres across for an adult. But those huge flaps aren't there to improve their hearing; they are air conditioning units. The skin covering the ears is paper-thin and richly supplied with blood vessels. By waving them back and forth, the elephant can dump body heat. Elephants have also evolved a secondary use for their ears; as a threat display. With his ears outstretched, an elephant appears even bigger, which might discourage attacks. Asian elephants have smaller ears because they generally live in cooler habitats.

Elephants hear over a much lower range of sound frequencies than we do, but this is mainly a function of their much larger size. Their sense of hearing is very acute but it isn't limited to their ears. Elephants also hear through the soles of their feet and the sides of the trunk.

Indian elephant

African elephant

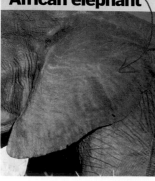

Safety in numbers

Elephants have a highly matriarchal society. The herd is an extended family group of mothers, daughters, sisters and aunts with the oldest female in charge. Males leave the herd at an early age and wander alone or in temporary all-male groups, joining a herd only to compete for, and mate with, females during their oestrus cycle.

Herd members are all very aware of the various family relationships and will often renew contact with other related herds that have split away in the past. Non-breeding females will often act as nursemaids to young calves and at night the adults will surround the calves to protect them.

The longest pregnancy

Female elephants are fertile for just two days out of every four months. When the female oestrus cycle begins, she calls to advertise the fact and the males begin competing for dominance. The winner will mate with the female up to five times a day while she is fertile. Elephant testicles are kept inside the body, near the kidneys. The elephant's penis is almost as long as his trunk and equally manoeuvrable but despite this, the normal mounting position only just allows the penis to reach the flap covering the downward-facing vagina. Instead of penetrating her, the male sprays about half a pint of semen at the entrance.

Elephants will gestate for 22 months – longer than any other animal. When the calf is born it weighs around 115kg. It will be suckled by the mother for another 22 months after that. Most females only reproduce once every four to nine years.

Junior here was nearly two years in the making

Packing a trunk

The elephant's trunk has evolved from a fused nose and upper lip. There are two nostrils that remain separate all the way up the trunk. The African elephants have two finger-like projections on the end of the trunk, which can pick berries from a tree. The Asian elephant only has one projection and is limited to using it as a scoop.

Elephants have an excellent sense of smell and will often be seen pointing their trunks around to identify the source of a scent. But at the same time, the trunk is tough enough to be used for hoovering up mud and dust to squirt over the elephant's body as a protection from the Sun. Elephants also suck up water through their trunk but it's more a syringe than a straw because they always squirt the water into their mouth before swallowing.

1ST

1. Blue whale
Not only the biggest mammal but also the biggest animal ever to have existed. In fact, whales could occupy all three spaces here.

2ND

2. Elephant
The largest land mammal, elephants would occupy both second and third place if we counted African and Indian species as separate.

3RD

3. Rhino
The horny rhino comes in as the second largest land mammal with the hippo coming in a very close third. Rhinos are native to Africa and Asia.

DID YOU KNOW? *A prehistoric elephant species that lived in Crete 2 million years ago was only the size of a pig*

Tusks

In most mammals, the largest teeth are the canines but elephant tusks are formed from the second upper incisors. Both male and female African elephants have tusks but female Asian elephants do not. The tusks grow throughout the elephant's life at a rate of about 18cm per year. The largest African elephant tusks can reach 3m long. One third of the tusk is embedded in the skull. This root is full of blood vessels and nerves that supply the growing tusk. The outer two-thirds is bony dentine covered in a layer of a mineral called apatite, which is mainly calcium phosphate. This layer is the ivory. African elephants use their tusks to dig for water and roots whereas Asian elephants use the tusks mainly for dominance displays between males.

Elephants can be left-tusked or right-tusked

ON THE MAP

Where do elephants live?
African elephants are found in scattered populations across all of sub-Saharan African (1) countries, apart from Somalia and Madagascar. The Asian elephant is found mainly in India (2), with smaller populations extending through Burma (3), Thailand (4) and Borneo (5).

Dainty steps

An elephant is essentially walking in high-heeled shoes, because the heel bones are raised right up inside the foot and rest on a thick pad of fatty cartilage. This cushions the bones and aligns them more vertically so that the vast weight of the elephant rests directly over the pillar-like legs. African elephants have four toenails at the front and three on the hind legs. Asian elephants have five at the front and four at the back. But these 'toenails' are actually just hardened skin patches that aren't attached to the toe bones at all. Buried inside, elephants have five toes on each foot.

"Does grey make my bum look big?"

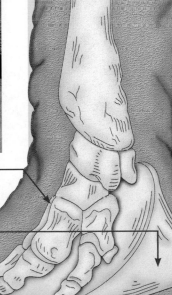

Lined up
The bones are cushioned and aligned vertically to aid weight distribution.

High heels
The heel bones are raised right up inside the foot.

Safe from harm?

One of the main reasons elephants have evolved to be so large is to protect themselves from predators. Lions and occasionally hyenas may successfully kill a young elephant, if it can be separated from the herd, but an adult elephant is virtually invulnerable.

Tusks, however, are their greatest vulnerability. The ivory in the tusks of a large African male can be worth more than £5,000 to poachers and an estimated 20,000 elephants a year are illegally killed for their ivory. Periodic legal culls and one-off sales of old ivory have made it much harder to police the illegal ivory trade. The evolutionary pressure from poaching is such that a once-rare genetic mutation, which results in tuskless elephants, is spreading rapidly. As many as ten per cent of Asian elephants in China may now be tuskless.

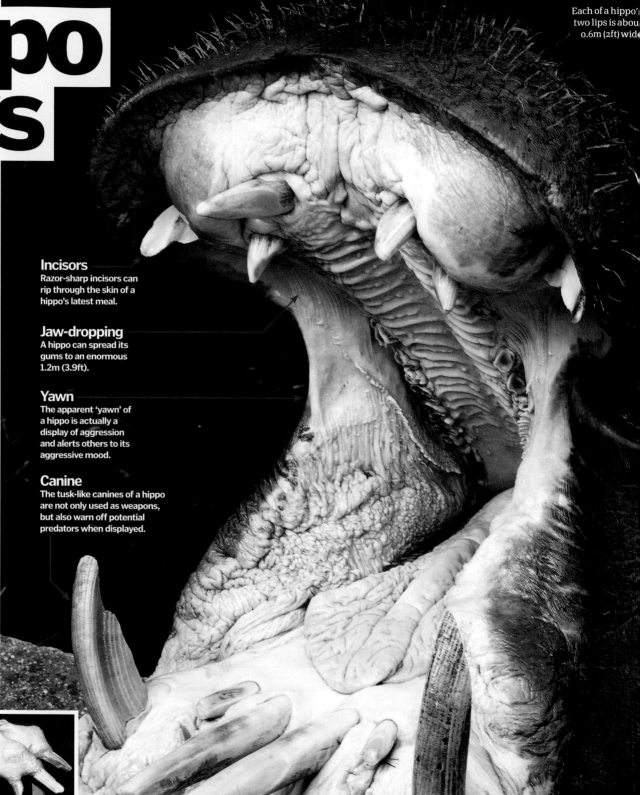

Each of a hippo's two lips is about 0.6m (2ft) wide

Hippo jaws

Why do these water-dwelling creatures open their mouths so wide?

A hippo may open its mouth wide as a sign of aggression, similar to other animals such as lions and baboons. Opening their jaws shows others their fearsome set of weaponry: their teeth.

Although hippos eat vegetation, they do not use their teeth to do so. Their giant canines and incisors are used only for killing. Instead, they use their huge lips to rip grass from the ground for consumption. A hippo is able to spread its lips through a jaw-dropping 150 degrees and up to 1.2m (3.9ft) in width. The strength of a hippo's jaw muscles – a bite force of 1,800lb – is such that it can use its fearsome teeth to bite a crocodile, human, or even a small boat in half. ✿

Incisors
Razor-sharp incisors can rip through the skin of a hippo's latest meal.

Jaw-dropping
A hippo can spread its gums to an enormous 1.2m (3.9ft).

Yawn
The apparent 'yawn' of a hippo is actually a display of aggression and alerts others to its aggressive mood.

Canine
The tusk-like canines of a hippo are not only used as weapons, but also warn off potential predators when displayed.

The skull of a hippopotamus contains tusk-like canines as long as your arm

© Raul654

Why camels have the hump

How do these 'ships of the desert' adapt to life in extreme climates?

Camels are experts at living where food and water are scarce. The reason they can survive in such arid terrain is their amazing ability to conserve the water they do take on. When a dehydrated camel finds a water source, it can lap up as much as 120 litres (32 gallons) in 15 minutes – a volume that if consumed by humans, would lead to water intoxication and undoubtedly kill us. To conserve the lifesaving H$_2$O, camels can regulate their body temperature so that they hardly sweat at all. Their kidneys can also concentrate the urine to further reduce water loss.

Not only this but these creatures also store a lot of water in their blood; the erythrocytes (red blood cells) can swell to over twice their normal size without bursting. Thanks to this tailored physiology, camels can go for weeks with little to no food or water.

However, when sustenance is in seriously short supply, they make use of a secret energy stash on their backs. The camel's hump does not store water as commonly thought; it functions as a reserve of adipose tissue (fat cells) that they are able to metabolise in order to provide emergency energy. As the fat is depleted, the hump will begin to wilt and flop to one side.

These fatty humps are also great for keeping cool too as fat conducts the Sun's heat relatively slowly, and their woolly covering provides extra insulation.

Native to the African Sahara, dromedaries have only one hump

Camel anatomy
Discover more about how camels have adapted to their environments

Eyes
Camels have very long, double layered eyelashes to protect their large eyes from sand storms and silt.

Feet
Camels are able to spread their toes very wide to increase the surface area and stop them from sinking. Their feet are also padded to protect them on rocky ground.

Coat
Camels have a thick coat which may seem strange but it insulates them from the intense desert heat, ensuring they don't overheat.

Camels have been used for thousands of years for transport and load bearing as well as for dairy and meat products.

The statistics...

Dromedary camel

Type: Mammal

Diet: Herbivore

Average life span in the wild: Up to 50 years

Weight: 726kg (1,601lb)

Height (ground to hump): 2.1m (6.9ft)

©Thinkstock

169

Why are kangaroos expert jumpers?

Discover why this antipodean animal is a natural-born long jumper

In such an expansive country such as Australia, the ability to cross vast distances in search of food and water is a key aspect to survival. And one such animal that can traverse barren lands at high speed for hours is the kangaroo.

Capable of an eight-metre (25-foot) single bound across level ground, the red kangaroo is one of the world's greatest long jumpers. Thanks to large feet and strong legs, it can also travel at over 50 kilometres (30 miles) per hour. While a kangaroo's hind legs are big and powerful, they can't work independently of each other and so kangaroos have to hop on two feet.

The hind leg tendons are strong and elastic and, with every hop, elastic energy is recaptured in the tendons ready for the next jump.

To help the bounce, kangaroos use their tails as a counterbalance. It propels the animal in a similar way to the principal of using your legs on a swing to gain momentum. When the kangaroo's back legs are fully outstretched behind it the tail is in the downward position, and when the legs are pushing forwards the tail is high in the air. ✿

Pouch
Kangaroos give birth to joeys that must continue to grow inside the pouch for around ten months.

Built to bounce
Why is this Australian marsupial so good at the long jump?

Forearms
Though the forearms are much shorter than the hind legs, a kangaroo can walk (not hop) on all fours if it leans forward and uses its tail as a fifth leg to take some of the weight.

Hind legs
Strong tendons act like tightly wound springs that store and release energy. On touching down, the spring is compressed, storing energy for the next hop.

Feet
A kangaroo's big toes are in the centre of the other toes (not to one side like ours) in line with their leg bones, which enables them to push off with force.

Tail
The long tail – up to 1m (3.3ft) – is used for both balance and as a counterweight. It swings up as the animal leaves the ground and down as the legs swing back with every bounce to help propel the kangaroo.

The statistics...
Red kangaroo

Type: Mammal	
Diet: Herbivore	
Average life span in the wild: 20 years	
Weight: 90kg (200lb)	
Size: 1-1.6m (3.3-5.3ft)	
Speed: 56km/h (35mph)	

Who can leap the farthest?

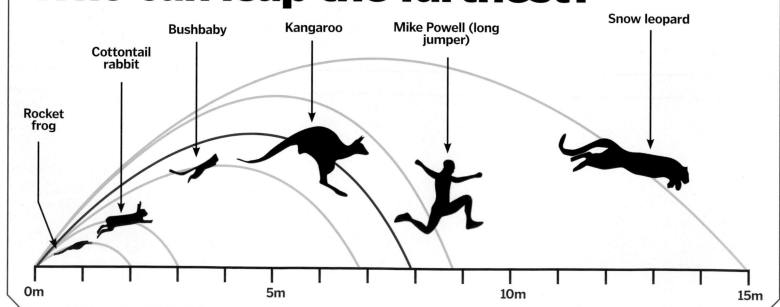

Rocket frog · Cottontail rabbit · Bushbaby · Kangaroo · Mike Powell (long jumper) · Snow leopard

0m · 5m · 10m · 15m

©Thinkstock

Ligers and tigons

When lions and tigers mate, new species are born

Ligers and tigons are two resultant species that emanate when lions and tigers cross breed. If a male lion mates with a tigress then a liger is born, if a male tiger mates with a lioness then a tigon is born. Both hybrid species are extinct in the wild as their respective habitats lead to minimal interaction, however many examples of both species can be found in captivity across the world in zoos and wildlife parks.

Ligers are now the more prevalent of the two species due to the greater probability of them living past birth, although during the early 20th Century this was not the case. The liger, as with the tigon, shares characteristics from both parent species – ligers enjoy swimming for example, a trait which is associated with tigers, however they also have spots, a characteristic gene of the lion – and tend to be bigger due to imprinted genes. Indeed, the current largest liger in the world weighs over 400 kilograms and is twice the size of its parents. Interestingly, though, tigons tend to suffer from dwarfism rather than gigantism as they always inherit the growth inhibitory genes from the lioness mother, often weighing only around 200 kilograms.

Unfortunately, due to the hybrid man-made nature of ligers and tigons, growth disorders and degenerative diseases are common, as well as shortened life spans. ✿

A male liger in Novosibirsk Zoo, Russia

Size
Ligers can grow to twice the size of their parents.

BIRDS

174
Bird feathers

© Thinkstock

Secretary bird
186

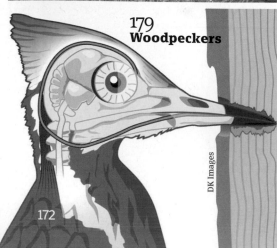

179
Woodpeckers

DK Images

172

190
Penguins

Birds

179
Parrot speech

178
Hummingbirds

180
Owls

Birds of prey
182

176
Chickens and eggs

The peacock's colourful tail feathers, or train, can make up 60 per cent of its body length

How feathers work

A bird's plumage performs many different roles – not least flight, defence, sensory reception and egg incubation

All birds have feathers – and *only* birds have feathers. In fact, some species can have over 25,000, including long flight feathers, insulating downy feathers and stiff tail feathers that act like rudders.

While they obviously facilitate flight – by forming the airfoil shape that generates lift as air flows over the wing – feathers serve a great many other roles. Birds are among the most magnificently decorated creatures on Earth and they use their handsome colours to attract mates, ward off predators and also to remain unseen by blending in with the background.

Birds display different plumage depending on their age, sex and seasonal changes. They see in colour and the plumage of a male has a dramatic effect on how attractive he is to the female, which impacts on mating success. It works both ways as the males of some species judge the health of a female by her feathers.

Most of the colours are the result of chemical pigments – eg melanin, carotenoids and porphyrins – produced in the feathers as they grow. Other colours can be caused by refraction of light due to feather structure. Spectacular colours can also be made by a combination of the two; for instance, when yellow-pigmented feathers overlay those with blue-reflecting properties, the plumage will look green.

Some birds use these colours as camouflage. Depending on the season, a bird's hormones can instruct it to shed (moult) its old feathers and grow a new set more suited to the current environment. Birds from snowy regions may be pure white in winter, but – after a moult – often regrow brighter or patterned feathers to better match the summer environment.

Birds also moult regularly in order to renew any damaged feathers because they cannot heal themselves. A moult can be total or partial during which time the damaged feather will be replaced. However if an individual feather has fallen out altogether, it will start growing a new one straight away. Growing new feathers requires a lot of the bird's energy, though, so a complete or partial moult will never coincide with demanding events in the year like breeding, nesting or migration. ✿

Long-tailed widowbird
With a 50-centimetre (20-inch)-long tail, it has been proven that when its tail feathers are docked females are less interested.

Quetzal
During mating season, the males of this species from the rainforests of Central America grow two extra tail feathers that reach up to a metre (3.3 feet) long.

Onagadori
This is a Japanese breed of chicken, the cockerel of which can grow very long tail feathers – over ten metres (32 feet) in some cases – due to a mutation.

DID YOU KNOW? By vibrating its wings twice as fast as a hummingbird the club-winged manakin makes a noise like a violin

Parts of a feather
A feather may look like a single blade but it actually comprises many important features

Central shaft
The main stem of a feather is divided into two parts: the calamus and the rachis. The outer side of the vanes is on the leading edge.

Calamus
Also called the quill, the horny calamus is the hollow part of the feather nearest the body with no vanes.

Rachis
The region at the distal end of the feather is the solid rachis, along which hundreds of tiny strands called vanes offshoot.

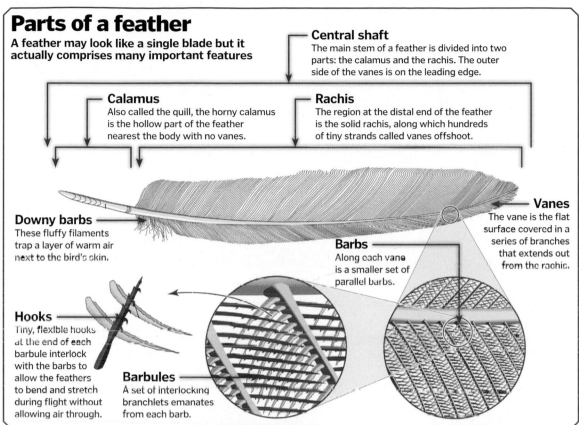

Vanes
The vane is the flat surface covered in a series of branches that extends out from the rachis.

Downy barbs
These fluffy filaments trap a layer of warm air next to the bird's skin.

Barbs
Along each vane is a smaller set of parallel barbs.

Hooks
Tiny, flexible hooks at the end of each barbule interlock with the barbs to allow the feathers to bend and stretch during flight without allowing air through.

Barbules
A set of interlocking branchlets emanates from each barb.

How does a feather grow?
Feathers are attached to the bird along regularly spaced tracts known as pterylae that cover almost the entire body; areas without feather tracts are called apteria. Growth begins beneath the surface of the skin in pimples called papillae, which capillaries supply with blood. The feather grows from a follicle – similar to hair – which forms when cells multiply in a ring shape.

Keratin cells harden the epidermis and concentrate the number of cells in the dermis. The keratinocytes continue to multiply in a ring shape, pushing old cells upwards while creating new cells at the base, until a tube pushes towards the skin's surface. A softer vane sheath, meanwhile, provides a protective barrier for the growing tube. The epidermal layer then splits into what will become the barbs. Before the feather emerges through the skin the barbs are curled around the tube. The opening at the base, where blood enters, is sealed off once the feather is fully grown.

Which feathers do what?
Discover the key types of feather on a bird that help it fly

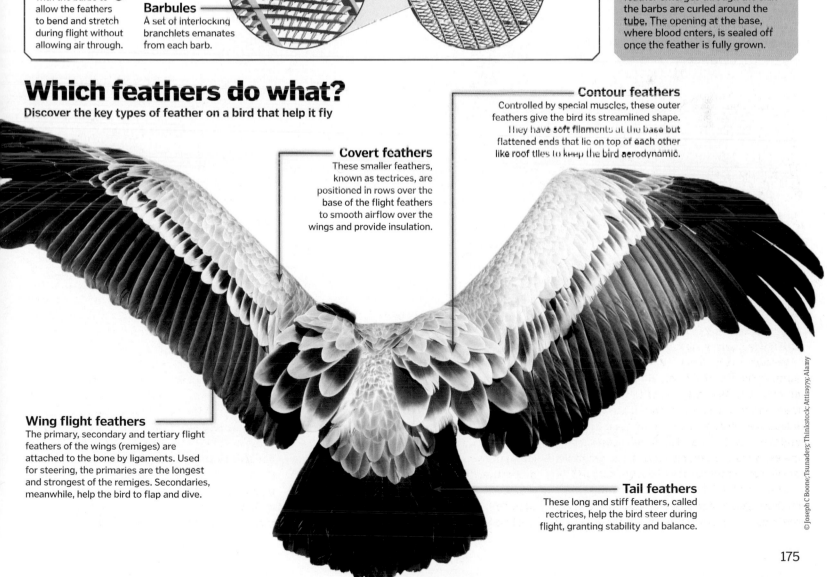

Contour feathers
Controlled by special muscles, these outer feathers give the bird its streamlined shape. They have soft filaments at the base but flattened ends that lie on top of each other like roof tiles to keep the bird aerodynamic.

Covert feathers
These smaller feathers, known as tectrices, are positioned in rows over the base of the flight feathers to smooth airflow over the wings and provide insulation.

Wing flight feathers
The primary, secondary and tertiary flight feathers of the wings (remiges) are attached to the bone by ligaments. Used for steering, the primaries are the longest and strongest of the remiges. Secondaries, meanwhile, help the bird to flap and dive.

Tail feathers
These long and stiff feathers, called rectrices, help the bird steer during flight, granting stability and balance.

© Joseph C Boone/Tsunaders; Thinkstock; Attis979; Alamy

Chicks need to rest for several minutes after hatching to regain their strength

How do chickens lay eggs?

The debate over which came first – the chicken or the egg – still rages. However, we can tell you how a chick emerges from an egg...

 Hens lay no more than one egg per day as the process of laying an egg is governed by the presence of sunlight. The lack of natural light during the winter months means that even fewer eggs are laid during this time of the year. Humans can, however, 'trick' chickens into laying despite the limited sunlight by adding artificial light (such as a light bulb) to the coop.

The laying process starts when light entering the hen's eye activates a photosensitive gland (the pineal gland) positioned nearby. Once stimulated, this gland triggers a process that leads to the release of an egg, or oocyte, from the hen's ovary. An egg can still be laid whether or not it has been fertilised by a male, but only fertilised eggs can develop into chicks.

The orifice through which the egg leaves the hen is called the vent. Though this hole also forms the outlet for waste by-products (ie urine and faeces), there is a valve called the cloaca which separates the oviduct from the intestine. ✿

Hen anatomy

Even unfertilised eggs still undergo the same initial formation process

1. Ovary
The female's egg cell, the oocyte, is released from the ovary into the oviduct – a process called ovulation.

2. Layers
As the oocyte travels along the oviduct it is covered in layers of protective substances, including albumen.

3. Shell
The final layer to cover the egg is calcite, which forms a hard, protective outer shell. Eggshell colour is determined by genetic pigment deposition inside the oviduct.

4. Embryo
A fertilised egg will now develop a chick embryo inside. Unfertilised eggs will simply get laid with yolk and albumen.

5. Contractions
When the hen is laying her egg, the intestine and inner part of the cloaca are blocked shut by the emerging egg. A series of careful muscular contractions helps the egg pass through the cloaca.

6. Cloaca
The cloaca is the section at the end of the oviduct, which turns itself inside out when the egg is released, keeping the almost sterile egg away from any faecal matter leaving the intestine.

7. Vent
This is the common opening used not only for reproduction and the release of an egg, but also for the excretion of urine and faeces. Two separate ducts lead to this orifice: one for reproduction and outgoing eggs, and the other for waste only.

1. HEATING

Fried egg
Egg white contains mainly water and protein. Heat excites the proteins and this breaks down bonds, enabling the proteins to bind with one another.

2. BEATING

Meringue
Just like heating causes bonding, so does adding air. Whisking exposes one end of the molecules to air and the other to water causing the proteins to align and fuse.

3. MIXING

Mayonnaise
Oil and water don't mix due to differing polarities. However, an emulsifier like egg yolk attaches one end of an egg's protein strand to water and the other end to the oil, binding the two.

DID YOU KNOW? The chicken is now believed to be the closest living relative of the T-rex

In a natural environment, chickens live in a flock and take a communal approach to caring for eggs

Feeling broody?

A hen will keep laying around one egg per day until she has a dozen eggs – also known as a clutch. If the eggs are collected by humans each day, however, the hen will continue to lay eggs in an effort to produce a clutch of 12. Once an egg has been laid, the hen will leave the nest, causing the embryo to cool and suspending its development. As long as the nest temperature stays warm enough, an embryo can remain suspended for up to two weeks until the hen has managed to lay a full clutch. Once she has produced a clutch of eggs the hen will stop laying and start brooding, which involves sitting on the eggs for three weeks while the embryos develop. This means the eggs should all hatch at the same time.

Inside the egg
What goes on under the shell?

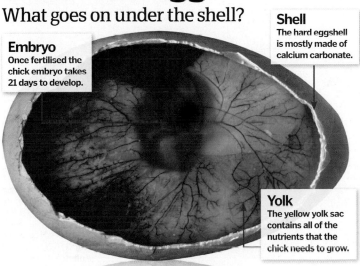

Shell
The hard eggshell is mostly made of calcium carbonate.

Embryo
Once fertilised the chick embryo takes 21 days to develop.

Yolk
The yellow yolk sac contains all of the nutrients that the chick needs to grow.

Embryo development
How a fertilised yolk transforms into a chick

The chick starts out as a single cell that divides and forms a hollow disc on the surface of the yolk. This yolk is then released into a spiralling oviduct tube. As it travels down the oviduct it builds up a number of layers, including a vitelline membrane directly surrounding the yolk, and two layers of viscous white albumen divided by a structural fibrous layer. Lower in the oviduct tube the eggshell layer develops around the yolk, protecting it and giving it form. When the egg is expelled from the body so begins the following 21-day period of embryonic development…

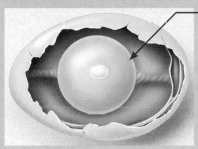

DAY 1 Yolk
The fertilised yolk contains all the nutrients needed to sustain a developing embryo – the darker the yolk the better. By the time a fertilised egg is laid, many cells have already started to divide in the germinal disc on the surface of the yolk. A structure called a chalaza made of albumen located inside the egg holds the yolk in place, anchoring it to either end of the shell and protecting it. Over time the chalaza gets twisted as the yolk moves around.

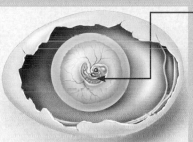

DAY 4 Heart
After a couple of days the heart will have formed and begun to beat independently. At this stage the head, eyes and even the beginnings of its legs will have begun to form, and by day four the embryo's reproductive organs will start to develop. The thin membrane separating the albumen from the eggshell grows as the contents of the egg shrinks, creating a tiny pocket of air. This air space will eventually enable the chick to start to breathe.

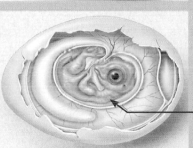

DAY 10 Skeleton
After ten days the embryo will still be featherless but it will start to draw calcium from the shell in order to grow its tiny skeleton, enabling the bones of the legs and spine to develop. The claws and beak will also begin to form.

DAY 16 Preparing to hatch
The leg and wing bones will become increasingly advanced and strong. Internal organs are now almost fully developed too. By now the beak will also be upturned towards the pocket of air inside the shell, ready to break through the soft inner membrane and take its first breath.

DAY 20 Breakthrough
Between day 16 and hatching, the chick's beak will have penetrated the inner membrane to access the air inside the shell and the lungs will have begun to function. The yolk sac has now been absorbed into the chick's body cavity. The chick pecks at the outer shell using a horny projection on its beak called the egg tooth. The second stage involves twisting its body and chipping away at the shell, until it can push the top of the shell off with its head.

3 x© SPL

Hummingbirds

Like a cross between bird and insect, the hummingbird can beat its wings up to 80 times every second, but how?

Hummingbirds are tiny fliers that can flap their wings extremely fast – so fast in fact that they can hover. Not only that, the hummingbird can also fly up, down, sideways, backwards, and even upside down. The reason they can achieve such exceptional flight patterns is that they can rotate their wings in a circle, creating power on the upstroke as well as the downstroke. Hummingbirds use their unique 'hands', which are long bones at the end of their arms that support the wing. The wing itself is flexible at the shoulder but not at the wrist, helping the bird beat them fast without any bending.

5 TOP FACTS HUMMINGBIRDS

1 Variety
There are around 330 different species of hummingbird – and most are found in central and southern America.

2 A busy day!
The average hummingbird can flit from bloom to bloom and pollinate up to 2,000 flowers in a period of 24 hours.

3 Heart of the matter
Just like humans, hummingbird hearts have four chambers, enabling very efficient oxygen transport. The hummingbird's heart can beat at 500 beats per minute (at rest!).

4 Fast flappers
Small hummingbirds can beat their wings 40-80 times per second, larger species 20-30 times and the giant hummingbird beats its wings as 'few' as ten times a second.

5 Feeling peckish?
Hummingbirds have the fastest metabolism of any other creature and so consume up to three times their own weight each day. Time between feeds can be just ten minutes.

Featherweight champion
What is it that makes this bird so special?

© Science Photo Library

Hands
These very long bones support the main wing feathers and allow the bird to beat its wings extremely quickly without having to bend the wings.

Feathers
Hummingbirds have a huge number of iridescent feathers but no down. Their tail feathers act as a paddle for steering while they're airborne.

Feet
Hummingbirds do have feet, which they use for perching and scratching, but they cannot use them for walking – they fly literally everywhere.

Wings
Hummingbirds have short 'upper arms' and their elbow and wrist joints don't move. The shoulder joint can rotate 180° and move in all directions.

Bill
Hummingbirds feed on sweet nectar that they industriously collect through their especially long tapered bills and straw-like, hairy tongues.

Flight patterns
Hummingbird anatomy enables unique flight

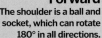

Upwards
Hummingbirds' extra large supracoracoideus muscles and pectoralis majors contain all-red fibres for sustained use.

Forward
The shoulder is a ball and socket, which can rotate 180° in all directions.

Backwards
Hummingbirds fly with their bodies held upright.

Hovering
Hummingbirds don't flap their wings, they rotate them using their unique hands.

The lyrebird's song

The bird that can replicate the noises it hears – from other birds to chainsaws felling trees

Birds get their vocal skills from the syrinx organ, the equivalent of a human's larynx. The lyrebird contains the most complicated syrinx of the songbirds (passerines), allowing it to mimic almost any sound. The syrinx, found at the base of the trachea, is surrounded by an air sac that produces the resonant sound when a lyrebird sings, while muscles move the syrinx and adjust the tension on highly elastic vibrating membranes. There are two species: the 80cm (31in) or so superb lyrebird, and the slightly shorter Albert's lyrebird, both of which are found in Australia. Male lyrebirds build a mound of dirt that acts as their amphitheatre and then mimic songs and man-made noises, like camera shutters and chainsaws, as they dance in order to draw female attention.

The all-singing all-dancing lyrebird

© Caspian Blue

Woodpeckers explained

Woodpeckers whack their heads against wood up to 20 times a second, at 1,200 times the force of gravity, without suffering concussion, detached retinas or any other symptoms of head injury. But why?

Woodpeckers' tongues have longitudinal muscles for side-to-side movement when poking around for insects

Holes
Woodpeckers excavate small rectangular holes on the sides of tree trunks, prying off wood to expose tasty beetle larvae and carpenter ants.

Skull
Woodpeckers have a thicker skull than most other birds. It's made of extremely strong yet spongy compressible bone, to help cushion the blow. The beak and skull are linked by elastic connective tissue.

Brain
Unlike human brains, which are floating about in a pool of cushioning cerebrospinal fluid, woodpecker brains are tightly enclosed in the skull with practically no cerebrospinal fluid.

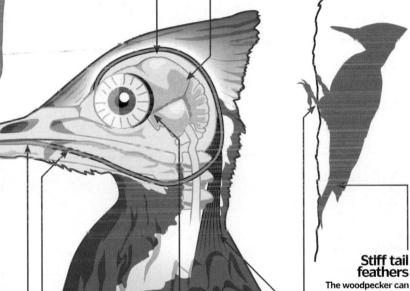

Beak
The strong bones that comprise the woodpecker's straight bill are strengthened by a horn-covered beak, which hammers into the wood and bark of a tree at something like 12,000 impacts per day in search of bugs and ants.

Hyoid apparatus
Within the long tongue is a skeletal structure called the 'hyoid apparatus'. This is a collection of small bones supported by cartilage and muscles, which fold up like an accordion and enable the woodpecker to stick its tongue out further.

Third eyelid
Woodpeckers have a thick inner eyelid, which acts as a seatbelt to ensure the bird's eyeballs don't pop out and also prevents tearing the retina. The eye is filled with blood to support the retina.

Stiff tail feathers
The woodpecker can prop itself up like a tripod, using its strong tail-feather muscles.

Zygodactyl feet
For optimum insect foraging, woodpeckers' feet are zygodactyl, which helps them cling onto vertical tree trunks. Zygodactyl means they have two front-facing toes and two back-facing toes.

Barbed tongue
Because a woodpecker probes around inside tree trunks for insects, its barbed tongue needs to be longer than its beak – sometimes up to four times longer. In some species the tongue actually forks in the throat and disappears below the base of the jaw, wrapping up and over the head before rejoining behind the eye socket or nostril.

Neck muscles
A split second before every tap, the dense muscles in the bird's neck contract and distribute the force of the impact away from the skull down through the rest of the body, like shock absorbers.

How are parrots able to talk?

Discover the physiology of this bird that enables it to mimic human speech

 While parrots do seem to make noises that sound like words, they do not create the sound in the same way that we do. For starters, birds possess neither a voicebox nor vocal cords. Instead they have a vocal organ called the syrinx lower down the throat. When air is expelled from the parrot's lungs across the syrinx, a wide range of noises can be formed. Located at the bottom of the trachea, just before the lungs, the syrinx is a bony structure whose walls vibrate as air passes through it. Parrots use the muscles around the syrinx (at the base of the trachea and the top of the bronchi) to change the shape and depth of the space, producing a multitude of different sounds. Changes in resonance come from the variations in air pressure, which is controlled by the bird's lungs.

Trachea
The trachea, or windpipe, is a tube that runs from the back of the bird's throat (pharynx) to the syrinx. Sound is created by air waves leaving the trachea.

Beak
Unlike our lips, which enable us to form shapes to create specific sounds, a parrot's beak remains open but relatively still when it is speaking.

Syrinx
The syrinx is a bird's vocal organ. This resonant hollow is found between the bronchi and trachea. A cartilaginous flap – the tympanic membrane – vibrates like the reed of a saxophone when air passes through it.

Larynx
In humans, the larynx contains the vocal cords. While birds do have a larynx, it does not have vocal cords and instead keeps food and water out of the lungs.

Lungs
Sound is produced by air passing through the syrinx from the lungs. Birds can control the air pressure in each lung individually, enabling them to adjust the resonance of the sounds they make. This also means they can make more than one noise at a time.

Bronchi
Air from the lungs travels through the two bronchi into the syrinx directly above the point where the bronchi branch off to each lung.

© DK Images

How owls hunt

Discover what makes this nocturnal bird of prey such a superior predator

 The owl has evolved a number of traits that make it a masterful sky hunter. As well as being a keen territorial predator, with an intimate knowledge of the local terrain, the owl also has a number of physical characteristics that make it a formidable aerial assassin. Features include powerful talons, a sharp, hooked beak for rending flesh from bone plus heightened senses for locating and homing in on prey from above.

Super-sensitive hearing helps the owl pick up on the gentle rustling of small-footed prey such as birds, rodents and frogs far below. The extra-large disc-like shape of an owl's face with a ridge of feathers down the middle further improves hearing as sound waves are collected and channelled outwards towards the ears.

While we humans can hear sounds on a horizontal plane – ie we have the ability to tell whether a sound came from the left or right by turning our head in a particular direction to focus on the location of a sound, owls can hear things on a vertical plane. Species like the great horned owl, for example, have lopsided ears – with the left ear positioned slightly higher than the right, enabling them to accurately detect whether a sound originated from above or below.

Unlike the majority of other bird species, whose eyes are positioned on the sides of their heads, owls have front-facing eyes, giving them binocular vision and depth perception. This helps them get a fix on their quarry. They cannot, however, move their eyes in the sockets; instead they have the ability to turn their entire head some 270 degrees. This means they do not have to move the rest of their body to see what's going on behind them, which helps the birds to stay quiet. It's the ability to remain silent that gives an owl its greatest advantage when hunting. ✿

The great grey owl lives in the taiga, a coniferous, snowy zone in the northern half of the planet that stretches from Alaska to Siberia

The statistics...

Owl

Type: Bird

Diet: Carnivore, including rodents, rabbits, snakes, fish, frogs and even other owls

Average life span in the wild: 5-15 years

Weight: 0.9-2.5kg (2-5.5lb)

Size: Body 45-65cm (18-25in), wing span 1-2m (3.2-6.4ft)

1. Surveillance
Many owls scan for their next meal from a concealed perch while others glide high over the ground until they spot a potential victim.

2. Surprise
When the owl has locked on to its prey it either dives down wings folded, opening them at the last second, or glides down keeping the animal in its line of sight.

The silent stalker

Owls use stealth and the element of surprise to execute deadly strikes from above. An owl can glide silently and swoop down on prey due to the clever engineering and arrangement of the feathers on its wings. An owl's flight feathers feature soft, serrated fringes that disrupt the turbulent flow of air over the wings. This reduces the noise produced as air flows over a smooth surface, making flight almost silent.

Dive-bombing owls

While owls remain generally out of sight during the day, there are occasional reports of them exhibiting aggressive behaviour, attacking or dive-bombing animals many times their size, including domestic dogs and even humans. Rather than attempting to kill and eat said humans, they are in fact defending their territory, mates, nests and/or chicks.

Seeing is believing

Owls have forward-facing eyes, like humans, and so this means they can see an object with both eyes at the same time. That is, their vision is binocular, as opposed to the monocular vision of most other birds whose eyes are located on the sides of their heads. As you can see from this diagram, owls have a wide field of view – around 110 degrees – but only about 70 degrees of this are binocular.

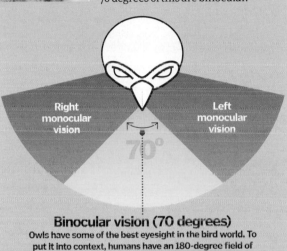

Right monocular vision
Left monocular vision

70°

Binocular vision (70 degrees)

Owls have some of the best eyesight in the bird world. To put it into context, humans have an 180-degree field of vision, 140 degrees of which are binocular.

3. Grab and go

Just before reaching its quarry, the owl pulls its head back and pushes its legs forwards with the talons open as wide as possible ready to grab its victim.

4. Quick

The sudden impact is usually enough to knock out the animal while the powerful talons complete the kill.

Pellets get rid of anything the owl can't digest

What are pellets?

You can discover a lot about what an owl eats from the pellets it spits out. These pellets contain the indigestible parts of an owl's diet. Birds of prey eat rodents and small birds. However, because they don't have teeth and cannot chew their food, they have to swallow things whole – that includes any fur, bones, feathers, claws and teeth. While other birds have a special organ called a crop, which is used for storing food for digestion later, owls do not have one of these. Instead, when an owl consumes food, it passes into the muscular gizzard called the ventriculus, a kind of secondary stomach full of small stones. The stones help to grind up the digestible food (which includes muscle, skin and organs) and digestive enzymes and acids dissolve the food so it can pass into the intestines. The leftover rubbish, which can't be broken down, is squeezed by the muscles of the gizzard and compacted into a soft pellet to be expelled from the body after many hours. The owl cannot eat again until the pellet has been coughed up, or regurgitated.

Learn more

'Hunters of the Sky', brought to Longleat Park by the Hawk Conservancy Trust, returned in 2012 with a brand new birds of prey show. This spectacular display of eagles, kites, vultures and owls fills the skies over Longleat; this is family fun at its very best! Open weekends only: 25 February-18 March. Open daily: 24 March-4 November. For more information on Longleat Safari & Adventure Park visit www.longleat.co.uk.

Interview Jimmy Robinson

Hawk Conservancy Trust curator Jimmy runs the 'Hunters of the Sky' bird of prey display at Longleat

What kinds of prey do owls usually like to eat?
Owls will eat a variety of different prey, normally depending on the size of the owl and where it lives. A barn owl mainly feeds on rodents while eagle owls will take prey like rabbits and even foxes on rare occasions.

What is the owl's most effective method or tactic for hunting down this kind of prey?
Many owls have silent flight. This is thanks to a comb-like edge to their flight feathers allowing air to pass through them; this reduces the noise of its flapping wings.

At what age is a young owl old enough to attempt its first kill?
At about four months old owls are catching prey for themselves. Some small species are fully feathered at ten weeks old. They grow up at an alarming rate and, once feathered, the race is on to be hunting as quickly and successfully as possible. In the wild it's survival of the fittest.

How and where do owls make their nests?
Owls nest in many different places. Barn owls nest in farm buildings or artificial nest boxes purposely put up to help them. Snowy owls, on the other hand, nest on the ground, while some species take over nests from other birds like crows.

What do owls do all day? How are they protected from predators?
Many owls are very well camouflaged. During the day the nocturnal owls will roost in a high tree or suitable safe place away from prying eyes.

What are the owl's main natural predators?
Other birds of prey, carnivorous mammals and reptiles like snakes will all look at owls as a suitable meal.

Do owls live up to their wise reputation?
Owls have incredibly large eyes; this enables them to see at night very well, but it does mean that the eyes take up much of the skull, leaving little room for the brain. Owls are not dim-witted, by any means, but are certainly not as wise as we're led to believe. There are many links to birds of prey and Greek deities; in fact, the little owl's Latin name links it to Athena, who was known as the goddess of wisdom.

BIRDS OF PREY

The fastest, the strongest, the most agile – meet the planet's most adept aerial assassins and learn how they survive

Some are manoeuvrable dog-fighting specialists, while others soar high above the ground like stealth bombers. They attack in the air, on the ground and in water. All of them are apex predators, adapted for life at the top of the food chain.

Birds of prey, also known as raptors, may look like feathered dinosaurs, but they aren't any more related to them than any other bird. The physical resemblance comes from their shared carnivorous lifestyle. Most belong to one of two families: the Accipitrids include eagles, hawks, buzzards, kites, harriers and true vultures, while the Falconids consist of falcons, kestrels and falconets. There are also two families of owls and a few species, such as the osprey and secretary bird, that are in families of their own.

Raptors hunt in two main ways. The large Accipitrids and ospreys float high above the ground while they scan for possible targets using their extremely acute vision. They will then dive-bomb or circle around to strike silently and suddenly. Eagles prefer to snatch prey and keep flying in order to minimise the time they spend vulnerable on the ground. Sea eagles, such as the bald eagle, use this technique to catch fish swimming close to the surface. Ospreys, which hunt in freshwater as well as the sea, can spot fish under the surface while flying as high as 40 metres (130 feet) above the water. They drop feet first, and will completely submerge in pursuit of the kill. Uniquely among raptors, ospreys have nostrils they can close to keep water out.

Falcons and hawks hunt other birds in the air. The peregrine falcon attacks pigeons and water birds from high above, dive-bombing – or stooping – from 4.8 kilometres (three miles) up so that they accelerate to over 320 kilometres (200 miles) per hour. At this speed the increased air pressure is enough to burst their lungs, but peregrines have small bones in their nostrils called tubercles that divert most of the airflow to the sides.

While the peregrine is technically the fastest animal in the world, falling isn't the same thing as flying. The fastest in level flight may be the Eurasian hobby, which actually chases down speedy swallows and swifts.

Species that can't compete in speed rely on their superior agility, like the forest falcons. These sit patiently in dense forest areas, using their extremely sensitive hearing to listen for birds flying nearby. When one passes close

EXTINCT MEGA-EAGLE
THE HAAST'S EAGLE LIVED IN NEW ZEALAND UNTIL IT WAS DRIVEN EXTINCT IN THE 15TH CENTURY. IT WEIGHED 15KG (33LB) AND HAD A 3M (9.8FT) WINGSPAN!

1. SMART

Golden eagle
Golden eagles in Israel have been known to snatch tortoises and drop them onto rocks from a height in order to crack open their shells.

2. SMARTER

Egyptian vulture
These birds can't pick up smooth ostrich eggs, so it has learnt to drops stones on them from above to shatter the shell.

3. SMARTEST

Bateleur eagle
The African bateleur eagle goes one step further and sneakily throws stones at burrows, in the process scaring animals out of their safe shelters.

DID YOU KNOW? *The feathers of a bird of prey weigh more than its entire skeleton!*

Built for the kill
All the equipment you need to deliver death from above...

LAND HUNTER
THE SECRETARY BIRD RESEMBLES AN EAGLE WITH THE LEGS OF A CRANE. IT HUNTS ON THE GROUND, OFTEN STAMPING ON SNAKES AND MICE TO KILL THEM

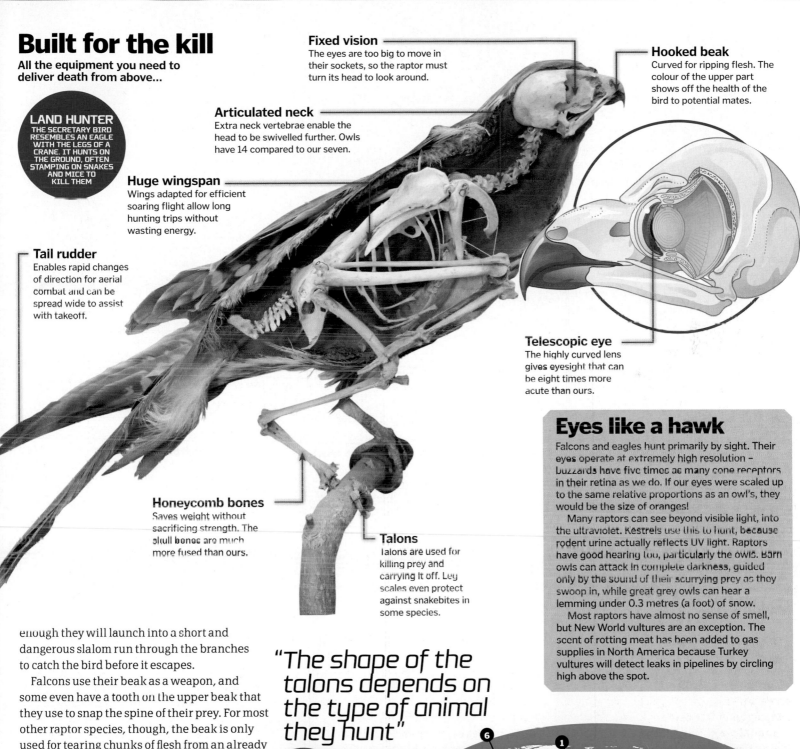

Fixed vision
The eyes are too big to move in their sockets, so the raptor must turn its head to look around.

Hooked beak
Curved for ripping flesh. The colour of the upper part shows off the health of the bird to potential mates.

Articulated neck
Extra neck vertebrae enable the head to be swivelled further. Owls have 14 compared to our seven.

Huge wingspan
Wings adapted for efficient soaring flight allow long hunting trips without wasting energy.

Tail rudder
Enables rapid changes of direction for aerial combat and can be spread wide to assist with takeoff.

Telescopic eye
The highly curved lens gives eyesight that can be eight times more acute than ours.

Honeycomb bones
Saves weight without sacrificing strength. The skull bones are much more fused than ours.

Talons
Talons are used for killing prey and carrying it off. Leg scales even protect against snakebites in some species.

Eyes like a hawk
Falcons and eagles hunt primarily by sight. Their eyes operate at extremely high resolution – buzzards have five times as many cone receptors in their retina as we do. If our eyes were scaled up to the same relative proportions as an owl's, they would be the size of oranges!

Many raptors can see beyond visible light, into the ultraviolet. Kestrels use this to hunt, because rodent urine actually reflects UV light. Raptors have good hearing too, particularly the owls. Barn owls can attack in complete darkness, guided only by the sound of their scurrying prey as they swoop in, while great grey owls can hear a lemming under 0.3 metres (a foot) of snow.

Most raptors have almost no sense of smell, but New World vultures are an exception. The scent of rotting meat has been added to gas supplies in North America because Turkey vultures will detect leaks in pipelines by circling high above the spot.

enough they will launch into a short and dangerous slalom run through the branches to catch the bird before it escapes.

Falcons use their beak as a weapon, and some even have a tooth on the upper beak that they use to snap the spine of their prey. For most other raptor species, though, the beak is only used for tearing chunks of flesh from an already downed victim. To kill, they rely on their talons. The exact shape of these depends on the type of animal they hunt: owls have short, heavily muscled toes to squeeze the breath from mice and small mammals, with thin, straight talons to hold them still; while eagles and buzzards have longer, curved talons on the backwards-facing toe and the first forward-facing toe for a powerful pincer grip. The osprey can even rotate its talons so that two toes face forward and two back to hold on to wriggling fish.

"The shape of the talons depends on the type of animal they hunt"

ON THE MAP

Famous birds of prey around the world
1. Golden eagle
2. Madagascar fish eagle
3. Galápagos hawk
4. Philippine hawk-eagle
5. Bald eagle
6. Great grey owl

Vultures and condors have the weakest talons of any raptor, because their diet consists almost entirely of carrion. Vultures have bald heads to make it easy for them to plunge their entire head into the carcass of a large animal without the blood getting on their feathers.

Judging which is the biggest bird of prey isn't easy. The Andean condor has the largest wingspan at up to 3.5 metres (11.5 feet) and the Philippine eagle the longest body at over one metre (three feet), while the heaviest is Steller's sea eagle in north-east Asia, which can weigh up to nine kilograms (20 pounds).

Because they have no predators, raptors tend to live a long time. Golden eagles last for 25 years in the wild and up to 46 years in captivity, and the Philippine eagle can survive for up to 60 years in the wild! But a long lifespan goes hand-in-hand with a slow rate of reproduction. Bald eagles take four to five years to reach sexual maturity, and usually lay only one or two eggs per season. Even when more than one egg hatches, in many raptor species the strongest chick will kill the others in the nest. This makes many raptors very vulnerable to population crashes from hunting or habitat loss. Around 120,000 Amur falcons are illegally killed by hunters every year in India as they migrate from eastern Asia to South Africa, for example.

There are success stories too though. Red kites have been reintroduced to the UK and Ireland, and peregrine falcons are no longer endangered in Britain now that organochlorine pesticides have been banned. ✻

Home sweet home

Falcons take over abandoned nests of other birds rather than building their own, but other raptors build wide platforms called eyries, or aeries. These are normally high up with a commanding view of the countryside. A golden eagle can see a hare from a mile away, and a sheep from 4.8 kilometres (three miles), so it can search a wide area without ever leaving its nest. Raptors add to their nest each breeding season and can become very big. A bald eagle's nest is strong enough to support a man and can weigh two tons!

On the hunt
How to catch a rabbit from hundreds of metres up

On the lookout
Large raptors need huge ranges to find enough food. A golden eagle can patrol an area of 200km² (77mi²).

SUSHI SPECIALIST
OSPREYS ARE THE ONLY RAPTORS THAT LIVE EXCLUSIVELY ON FISH. BACKWARDS-FACING SCALES ON THEIR TALONS ACT AS BARBS TO HELP GRIP THEIR SLIPPERY CATCH

Stealth mode
Light plumage on their underside makes them hard to see against the bright sky.

VEGGIE RAPTOR
THE PALM-NUT VULTURE GETS MOST OF ITS FOOD FROM THE FRUIT OF THE OIL PALM. IT WILL ALSO OCCASIONALLY EAT CRABS AND INSECTS, THOUGH

Eye protection
As it strikes, the raptor closes its third eyelid – or nictitating membrane – to protect the eyes.

Dust off
Staying on the ground is dangerous. Raptors will immediately carry off anything that weighs less than them.

Claws of death
Small prey die by asphyxiation – squeezed so tightly they cannot breathe. Raptors often start eating before their prey is dead.

Soaring
Large raptors need to stay aloft for long periods while they search for prey. To save energy, they make use of natural updrafts. In wide-open areas, the Sun heats the ground, which warms the air next to it. Hot air rises, creating a thermal. Another source of lift comes from cliffs and peaks, where the wind is deflected upwards.

Gliding run
The raptor glides from one updraft to another, always scanning the terrain for movement.

Divebomber
Eagles and buzzards make their attack run from downwind and swoop in at a shallow angle. This minimises the speed lost if they miss their target and allows them to gain altitude again easily. Smaller hawks and falcons aim for maximum speed, with their wings tucked back to increase their freefall speed to over 240km/h (150mph).

Hovering
Kites and buzzards prefer to hover low, near to gaps in ground cover, and drop on anything that moves.

© Ian Jackson; Thinkstock; SPL

How did the secretary bird get its name?

This bizarre bird looks like a cross between an eagle and a crane, so how did it come to be called the secretary?

 The origins of the secretary bird's name are much debated. One theory is that the feathers jutting out behind the bird's head reminded 19th-Century Europeans of the quill pens that secretaries tucked behind their ears, while its grey and black body was reminiscent of their tailcoats. A more recent theory is that the name derives from the Arabic 'saqr-et-tair', or 'hunter bird'. The secretary bird is a large bird of prey found in grasslands and savannah across Sub-Saharan Africa. It is one of only two birds of prey preferring to hunt on foot as opposed to in the air like falcons and eagles (the other being the caracara). At 1.2 metres (four feet) tall, its height allows it to spot insects, lizards, snakes and rats in the tall grass. *

Secretary birds are related to raptors, but while they can fly, they spend much of their time on the ground

What is the cassowary's crown for?

There are many theories about the purpose of this appendage, but which is right?

 Cassowaries are large flightless birds, only slightly smaller than an ostrich or emu, that live in the forests of New Guinea and north-east Australia. Their most distinctive characteristic is the large crest, or crown, on the top of their head. The outside is hard like a horn, but the inner part has a honeycomb-like structure to keep the weight down.

There are lots of theories for the purpose of the crown such as the suggestion that it may have originally evolved to protect the bird's head. Cassowaries eat fallen fruit and the wedge-shaped crest would help deflect any fruit/seeds tumbling from the treetops. Cassowaries can also run at 48 kilometres (30 miles) per hour, and as they career through the forest they lower their heads to help them to push through the undergrowth. But the honeycomb interior does more than just save weight – it also acts as an amplifier for sounds. Cassowaries have the deepest call of any bird. The note is so low it is only just audible to humans, but the crown acts as a resonating chamber that allows this sound to carry through the dense forest. Besides these useful qualities, the cassowary's crown may play a decorative role as well. Like the peacock's tail, size matters when it comes to attracting a mate. *

The Cassowary is usually very shy but when provoked, is capable of inflicting fatal injuries

© Richard Bartz 07; Thinkstock

UGLY

1. King vulture
This bird lives in Central and South America and is popular in Mayan folklore. The yellow and red fleshy caruncle on its beak is used in mating displays.

© Pieta Karstedt, 2005

UGLIER

2. Red-headed vulture
Found in Nepal and India, this species is endangered because of the drug Diclofenac, which is given to cattle but is toxic to birds.

© Vishal Subharwal, 2007

UGLIEST

3. Hooded vulture
This vulture has benefited from human association and can be found in huge flocks around waste tips in Sub-Saharan Africa.

DID YOU KNOW? *Vultures can projectile-vomit as a defensive weapon. The acid is strong enough to burn skin!*

How vultures eat

They may be the ultimate scavengers but do they deserve their reputation as freeloaders?

Vultures live in ecosystems mainly comprising large grazers. That presents a problem for a carnivore because a 2kg bird cannot take down a 500kg buffalo. Their solution is to let other animals do it for them or to wait for their lunch to die of natural causes. This requires patience; vultures have large wingspans, adapted for soaring in thermals, so they can scan a huge area of grassland at once, looking for a dead or dying beast. Vultures do not strictly hunt but if they come across a weakened animal they will have no objection to tucking in straight away, hastening the demise of their meal. After they have gorged themselves, vultures will perch sleepily on rocks or in trees, digesting and waiting for a big enough thermal to help them launch aloft once more.

Although the vultures found in the Old World and the New World look quite similar, this is because they have evolved to tackle the same evolutionary niche. New World vultures include the condors and aren't genetically very closely related to the Old World species.

Vultures feed by plunging their heads into the body cavities of large animals. A feathery head would become impossibly matted with blood and juices, interfering with the vulture's vision and risking an infection that could lead to death. A side effect of evolving a bald head is that a vulture can use its neck to regulate its body temperature, extending and hunching to adjust the amount of heat that is lost through the exposed skin.

A strong stomach

Vultures eat animals that may have died naturally weeks ago. This putrid flesh is often so riddled with bacteria that it would be lethal to any other animal. Vultures protect themselves against this in two ways. First their stomach acid is almost ten times as concentrated as ours. This kills bacteria so effectively that vulture droppings are more hygienic than their food.

The toxins that have already been produced by the time the vulture feeds are absorbed into the lining of its throat and neutralised by antibodies in the blood.

Voice
Vultures don't have a syrinx – the voice box found in other birds – so the only noises they can make are grunts and hisses.

Vision
Old World vultures locate dead animals exclusively by sight, homing in on animals lying still, away from the herd.

Beak
The hooked beak allows them to rip off chunks of meat. The name "vulture" comes from the Latin word for "tearer".

Smell
New World vultures are unusual birds of prey because they have an excellent sense of smell. They can detect the ethyl mercaptan gas given off by dead animals, from a mile away.

Legs
Vultures deliberately urinate down their legs. The uric acid kills the bacteria that they pick up from walking through carcasses.

Primary feathers
The gaps between the primary flight feathers (known as emargination) reduce turbulence and increase lift in soaring flight.

This thermograph shows the increased temperature of the vulture's exposed head

© Science Photo Library

The statistics...

Vultures

Type: Bird	
Diet: Carnivore	
Average life span in the wild: 16 years	
Weight: 2kg	
Wingspan: 180cm	

ON THE MAP

Where to find vultures
1 Southern Europe and North Africa
2 Sub-Saharan Africa
3 Middle East
4 Indian subcontinent
5 USA
6 Central and South America

How do ostriches sprint?

Find out why the largest bird on Earth is also the Usain Bolt of the avian kingdom

 A member of the ratite group of birds who have weak wing muscles and so cannot fly, the ostrich is the biggest bird on the planet today. Found mainly in the semi-arid regions of central and southern Africa, where lions, leopards and hyenas are constantly on the prowl, ostriches have had to learn how to outrun their enemies.

Ostriches have the speed to evade most African predators, and when frightened they can sprint away from danger at up to 72.5 kilometres (45 miles) per hour. They can also run over longer periods of time at slower speeds – say, for 20 minutes at 48 kilometres (30 miles) per hour. While speed is clearly an ostrich's main advantage, when trapped they are not entirely defenceless as they can use their strong legs to land a mighty blow on a would-be attacker. And their two-toed feet feature a pretty nasty ten-centimetre (four-inch) claw that can also inflict a lot of damage.

So what enables this nomadic, social bird to take off at such impressive speeds? Those unique toes we mentioned are also key to the creature's agility as – together with their strong leg muscles – they maximise speed by ensuring minimal contact is made with the ground. The ostrich is the only bird with two toes and it's the inner of the two that is the most important. This digit is longer, which assists the bird in pushing off with its feet, and it also features that potentially lethal claw. This foot layout is also helpful in providing support for the weight of this hefty bird.

An ostrich's long, powerful legs are also bare, ensuring they remain as streamlined as possible – much like athletes who shave their legs or wear tight clothing to reduce the potential for drag. ✿

Burying the myth for good

While being tall and leggy might enable an ostrich to outrun most predators, it also makes it hard to be inconspicuous. Almost half of an ostrich's total height is made up by its neck and so that's the most obvious body part to hide from view. However, while a young ostrich will often lie down with its neck flat on the ground to avoid detection, the birds also get down on the floor to rearrange their eggs that are buried in the dust. The idea that they foolishly bury their heads in the sand at the first sign of imminent danger, however, is actually a complete myth.

Anatomy of an avian sprinter

What characteristics ensure an ostrich stays ahead of the pack on the African plain?

Wing
Though their wings are very weak, they are still quite large for a bird of this size – indeed, the wings can span up to 2m (6.5ft). They aren't totally useless as when outstretched they make for great rudders for steering.

Head
The ostrich has the largest eyeballs of any of today's birds, and its small head is also covered in downy feathers.

Neck
The neck accounts for nearly half of an ostrich's great height, which makes it well equipped for spotting potential danger early.

Torso
Despite their impressive speed on land, ostriches are pretty heavy birds. The males are slightly larger and have black plumage with white edges, while the hens' feathers are brown.

Leg
Long, muscular, featherless legs make the ostrich a consummate sprinter with a massive stride of 4.6m (15ft).

Foot
The two-toed feet aid traction on the ground and help the ostrich kick off at speed. The inner of the two toes packs a lethal claw for self-defence.

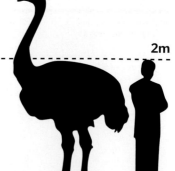

3m

2m

The statistics...

Ostrich

Binomial: Struthio camelus

Type: Bird

Diet: Omnivore (though primarily a herbivore, they are known to eat carrion and insects too)

Average life span in the wild: Up to 40 years

Weight: 90-150kg (200-330lb)

Height: 2.75m (9ft)

Top speed: 72.5km/h (45mph)

Habitat: Dry and sandy regions of Sub-Saharan Africa

The flippers are key to the penguin's swimming abilities

How do penguins swim?

Revealing the secret of the penguin's underwater prowess

Don't hold the awful jokes against the bird, blame McVitie's

Though ungainly on land, the flightless penguin has physical characteristics perfect for swimming through water – fortunate, as some species are known to be at sea for up to 75 per cent of their lives. Spending so much time in the water puts penguins at risk from predators, so swimming skills are essential. While their long, streamlined bodies and short legs give them a clumsy gait when waddling on land, penguins' wings have a unique characteristic that gives them surprising agility in water.

While penguins' wings are not suitable for aerial flight – mainly because, unlike the delicate lightweight bones of other birds, penguin bones are solid – they are perfect for soaring through water, with the Gentoo penguin reaching speeds up to 22mph. Referred to as flippers, the penguin's stiff wings act as the perfect natural paddle. What's most interesting, however, is the recent discovery that as well as being able to flap their flippers up and down like wings, penguins can also twist them in a corkscrewing motion.

The joint attaching the flipper to the body is similar to that of a human shoulder, enabling the bird to better control its movements and speed. A swimming penguin can rotate one flipper in one direction and the other in another, enabling it to turn instantly or stop suddenly. Twisting causes a greater surface area of the wing to move over the water, which generates a greater thrusting force so the penguin can increase its speed without the need for more flapping.

Another technique the penguin uses for moving through water is porpoising. Whenever it needs to breathe, the penguin will periodically swim fast under the water and then use its flippers to leap from the water in an arc. The momentum of porpoising helps penguins when they need to flee quickly from predators.

The humble penguin is one of the planet's best-equipped swimmers and the 'twisting flipper' motion is currently being applied by scientists who are looking to develop robot technology that helps to improve the efficiency and performance of underwater vehicles.

Penguins in motion

1. P-p-propel like a penguin
And it's not just the flippers that make the penguin such an able swimmer; the rest of its anatomy is also primed for underwater activity.

2. Body
A long fusiform, or torpedo-shaped, body helps the penguin glide gracefully through the water.

3. Flippers
The stiff yet flexible flippers are shorter than the wings of other birds, making them powerful oars.

4. Feathers
For every square inch of flesh a penguin can have up to 70 overlapping short, shiny feathers to keep water away from the skin and help insulate the bird.

5. Colouring
A penguin's striking colouration is essential for helping to keep it safe from predators in the water. If a killer whale looks up, it will not see the penguin because the light ventral underside blends in with the light from above. A predator looking down on a penguin, meanwhile, shouldn't spot the creature because the dark dorsal side blends in with the murky depths below.

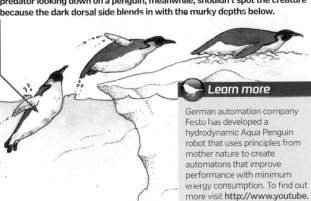

Learn more

German automation company Festo has developed a hydrodynamic Aqua Penguin robot that uses principles from mother nature to create automatons that improve performance with minimum energy consumption. To find out more visit http://www.youtube.com/watch?v=L5JHMpLIq04.

© DK Images; Thinkstock; Getty; Nicor

How do penguins survive?

They can endure freezing temperatures, 100mph winds and go without food for months, but what makes these birds so tough?

Known for being a sociable, loyal and really rather tough little creatures, the penguin is a resilient member of the flightless bird club. 18 species of penguin can be located throughout the southern hemisphere, ranging from as far south as the coast of Antarctica and as far north as the Galapagos Islands in the Pacific. The smallest species is the appropriately named fairy penguin, which makes its home in the coastal waters of Australia. The biggest member of the family, meanwhile, is the emperor penguin, which lives a somewhat more treacherous life on the perilous frozen continent of Antarctica.

When it comes to breeding, most penguin species (the emperor penguins do things differently; see 'Emperor penguin role reversal', opposite) care for usually one or two eggs in nests built from stones and vegetation. The parents take it in turns to fetch food and protect the eggs for the duration of incubation, which can be anything from 30-60 days. Then, once the chick is born, parents continue to share childcare duties for 2-13 months depending on the species.

Baby penguins won't be going anywhere near the ocean for around six months, or at least until their downy coats have been replaced with insulating, waterproof feathers. The adults therefore have to find and fetch food, which they regurgitate for the chicks. There are three main ways a penguin can bring food back for its young. Because they sometimes have to travel great distances to source fish and crustaceans, the penguin parents have developed a rather nifty way of consuming food out at sea and storing it in their stomachs in special enzymes that prevent it from being digested. Alternatively, they can also partly digest the food into a soft mush. Finally, penguins that have been feeding for weeks can fully digest the food but then secrete a nutritious oil for their young.

The penguin has a number of different predators, including leopard seals, killer whales, giant petrels, sharks and humans among others. Large scavenger seabirds called skuas will even work in teams to swipe untended eggs and unprotected chicks in the blink of an eye. One skua will provide a distraction, luring the adult penguins away from their helpless young, while another strikes, stealing eggs and newborns. ✽

The statistics...

Emperor penguin

Type: Bird
Diet: Krill, shrimp and fish
Average life span in the wild: 10-20 years
Weight: Up to 40kg (90lb)
Size: Up to 1.2m (4ft)

Once the chick has hatched, both parents must work tirelessly to rear the young bird

A hungry leopard seal will prowl for penguins at the edge of the ice

5 TOP FACTS
PENGUINS

Bowing
1 When a male and female penguin bow their heads together it is part of an elaborate courting ritual of head movements and calls that helps establish a strong bond.

Born to swim
2 Penguins have a fusiform (torpedo-shaped) body, which helps them tear through the water at high speed. Emperors are thought to be able to reach speeds of 14km/h (9mph).

Safety in numbers
3 As the ocean is teeming with predators, these birds swim in groups – adélie penguins even engage in a spot of synchronised swimming to look like one large creature.

The big moult
4 When a penguin is moulting, it can't go in the water so it may have to fast for up to a month while its feathers grow back. In preparation for this, the bird will eat as much as possible.

Counter-shading
5 A penguin's colouring is useful for both hunting and avoiding predators when at sea. The black dorsal side blends in with the dark ocean depths, while the white belly blends with the sky.

DID YOU KNOW? *Penguins can sleep lying down or standing up with their head or beak tucked under a wing*

A male emperor penguin incubates its egg, shielding it from the worst of the cold

Emperor penguin role reversal

Emperor penguins, native to the barren plains of Antarctica, must endure some of the planet's most extreme conditions on a continent known for its freezing temperatures and relentless high winds. So how do these hardcore birds breed in such bleak conditions? Well, emperors do things a bit differently.

The female will lay a single egg in early winter and instead of taking it in turns to look after the egg, like other penguins, the male emperor stays behind to incubate it while the female heads out across the ice for two months to find food. Huddling is essential for these penguins in order to overcome the elements. Once the emperor chick is born the huddling continues in the form of crèches – not only to keep warm but also as protection against predators. The babies come together in a large group with the adults around the edge.

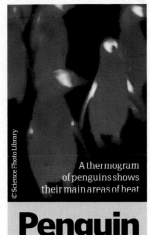

© Science Photo Library

A thermogram of penguins shows their main areas of heat

Penguin central heating

Penguins are endothermic, ie warm blooded, and regulate their temperature to both conserve energy and avoid freezing in a number of clever ways.

Penguin feathers are very numerous and very tightly packed, making them a bit like fur. At the base of each individual feather is a lot of downy fluff which traps air close to the penguin's thick skin. Not only that, but penguin feathers are also coated in a waterproof oil produced in a gland near the tail. Their thick skin has an extra layer of fat where energy is stored too. And penguins also work together to stay warm. Tens of thousands of penguins will huddle together in a huge colony to conserve their body heat, taking it in turns to shelter in the middle.

Penguins can adjust the amount of body heat they conserve and release too. To stay warm, heat from blood flowing to the feet is transferred to blood returning to the heart, which explains why penguins' feet don't freeze. Conversely, to cool down, blood vessels in the skin can dilate and move heat to the surface where it can be released.

Penguin anatomy

Beak
Expert fish catchers, penguins have hooked bills with sharp edges. Because they swallow their live prey whole their tongues and mouths are lined with backwards-pointing spines to stop the slippery quarry from sliding out.

Eyes
As well as featuring extra blood vessels to prevent the eyeballs from freezing, a penguin's eyes also have unusually shaped corneas, which help them focus both above and below water.

Flippers
Penguin wings are more like powerful oars with broad flat bones that are almost fused together.

Bones
In order to dive as deep as possible, penguin bones are not hollow like other birds - instead they are solid and heavy. Penguins can hold their breath underwater for some 15 minutes.

Legs
Penguins have very short legs, but they do in fact possess a femur, knee, tibia and fibula. That's right, penguins have knees!

Feet
Penguins have large webbed feet, which help them to swim and also stay upright. Because the feet are set back from the rest of the body they can stay balanced enough to walk upright on land.

Feathers (not shown)
As well as having more feathers per square inch than any flying bird, the penguin also produces oil from the uropygial gland near the tail, which keeps the feathers waterproof. An annual moult gets rid of any worn out feathers.

Salt gland
Penguins inadvertently ingest a lot of seawater when slurping up prey underwater. To filter the excess salt from the bloodstream, there is a salt gland above each eye.

© DK Images

Do the locomotion

Penguins prefer swimming over flying, which is just as well because unlike airborne birds whose bones are hollow, penguins have dense skeletons; great for diving but not flying. Slick and streamlined in the water they may be, but when getting around on land penguins are undeniably inelegant. They traipse across land on foot using a unique combination of an awkward side-to-side waddle and a two-footed jump for navigating rocks and uneven surfaces. Antarctic penguins are known to travel up to 80 kilometres (50 miles) in search of food. Despite their short legs, they can scurry quite quickly. However, to save energy, penguins have a third method of travel: whenever the opportunity arises they will slide downhill on their bellies, using their wings to steer and their feet to propel themselves. This is known as tobogganing.

Special trial offer

Enjoyed this book?

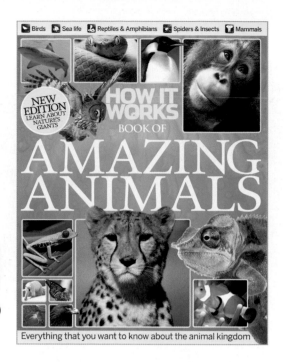

Exclusive offer for new

Try 3 issues for just £5*

* This offer entitles new UK Direct Debit subscribers to receive their first 3 issues for £5. After these issues, subscribers will then pay £17.95 every 6 issues. Subscribers can cancel this subscription at any time. New subscriptions will start from the next available issue. Offer code ZGGZINE must be quoted to receive this special subscriptions price. Direct Debit guarantee available on request. This offer will expire 30 April 2015.

** This is a US subscription offer. The USA issue rate is based on an annual subscription price of £50 for 13 issues, which is equivalent to $78 at the time of writing compared with the newsstand price of $9.50 for 13 issues being $123.50. Your subscription will start from the next available issue. This offer expires 30 April 2015.

About the mag

The magazine that feeds minds

Full-colour illustrations
Jam-packed with amazing visuals to really get you excited about science and technology

Expert writers
We commission a pool of highly intelligent and talented experts to write every article

Join the community
Link up with other readers with a passion for knowledge at **www.howitworksdaily.com**

subscribers to…
HOW IT WORKS

SCIENCE ✦ ENVIRONMENT ⚡ TECHNOLOGY ✦ TRANSPORT ◆ HISTORY ✦ SPACE

Try 3 issues for £5 in the UK*
or just $6 per issue in the USA**
(saving 37% off the newsstand price)

For amazing offers please visit
www.imaginesubs.co.uk/hiw
Quote code ZGGZINE

Or telephone UK 0844 815 5944 overseas +44 (0)1795 418 680

Everything you need to know

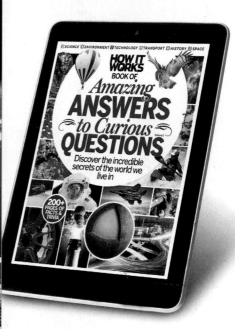

HOW IT WORKS

BUY YOUR COPY TODAY

Print edition available at www.imagineshop.co.uk

Digital edition available at www.greatdigitalmags.com

Available on the following platforms

 Print Tablet Phone Desktop

 facebook.com/ImagineBookazines   twitter.com/Books_Imagine